The Battle of Poictiers
From the painting by H Dupray
(*See page 52*)

THE HARVARD CLASSICS
EDITED BY CHARLES W ELIOT LLD

CHRONICLE AND ROMANCE
FROISSART · MALORY · HOLINSHED

WITH INTRODUCTIONS AND NOTES

VOLUME 35

P F COLLIER & SON COMPANY
NEW YORK

Designed, Printed, and Bound at
The Collier Press, New York

CONTENTS

INTRODUCTORY NOTE

JEAN FROISSART, *the most representative of the chroniclers of the later Middle Ages, was born at Valenciennes in 1337. The Chronicle which, more than his poetry, has kept his fame alive, was undertaken when he was only twenty; the first book was written in its earliest form by 1369; and he kept revising and enlarging the work to the end of his life. In 1361 he went to England, entered the Church, and attached himself to Queen Philippa of Hainault, the wife of Edward III, who made him her secretary and clerk of her chapel. Much of his life was spent in travel. He went to France with the Black Prince, and to Italy with the Duke of Clarence. He saw fighting on the Scottish border, visited Holland, Savoy, and Provence, returning at intervals to Paris and London. He was Vicar of Estinnes-au-Mont, Canon of Chimay, and chaplain to the Comte de Blois; but the Church to him was rather a source of revenue than a religious calling. He finally settled down in his native town, where he died about 1410.*

Froissart's wandering life points to one of the most prominent of his characteristics as a historian. Uncritical and often inconsistent as he is, his mistakes are not due to partizanship, for he is extraordinarily cosmopolitan. The Germans he dislikes as unchivalrous; but though his life lay in the period of the Hundred Years' War between England and France, and though he describes many of the events of that war, he is as friendly to England as to France.

By birth Froissart belonged to the bourgeoisie, but his tastes and associations made him an aristocrat. Glimpses of the sufferings which the lower classes underwent in the wars of his time appear in his pages, but they are given incidentally and without sympathy. His interests are all in the somewhat degenerate chivalry of his age, in the splendor of courts, the pomp and circumstance of war, in tourneys, and in pageantry. Full of the love of adventure, he would travel across half of Europe to see a gallant feat of arms, a coronation, a royal marriage. Strength and courage and loyalty were the virtues he loved; cowardice and petty greed he hated. Cruelty and injustice could not dim for him the brilliance of the careers of those brigand lords who were his friends and patrons.

The material for the earlier part of his Chronicles he took largely from his predecessor and model, Jean Lebel; the later books are filled with narratives of what he saw with his own eyes, or gathered from the lips of men who had themselves been part of what they told. This fact, along with his mastery of a style which is always vivacious if sometimes diffuse, accounts for the vividness and picturesqueness of his work. The pageant of medieval life in court and camp dazzled and delighted him, and it is as a pageant that we see the Middle Ages in his book.

Froissart holds a distinguished place among the poets as well as the historians of his century. He wrote chiefly in the allegorical style then in vogue; and his poems, though cast in a mold no longer in fashion, are fresh and full of color, and were found worthy of imitation by Geoffrey Chaucer.

But it is as the supreme chronicler of the later age of chivalry that he lives. "God has been gracious enough," he writes, " to permit me to visit the courts and palaces of kings, . . . and all the nobles, kings, dukes, counts, barons, and knights, belonging to all nations, have been kind to me, have listened to me, willingly received me, and proved very useful to me. . . . Wherever I went I enquired of old knights and squires who had shared in deeds of arms, and could speak with authority concerning them, and also spoke with heralds in order to verify and corroborate all that was told me. In this way I gathered noble facts for my history, and as long as I live, I shall, by the grace of God, continue to do this, for the more I labour at this the more pleasure I have, and I trust that the gentle knight who loves arms will be nourished on such noble fare, and accomplish still more."

THE CAMPAIGN OF CRECY

THE king of England, who had heard how his men were sore constrained in the castle of Aiguillon, then he thought to go over the sea into Gascoyne with a great army. There he made his provision and sent for men all about his realm and in other places, where he thought to speed for his money. In the same season the lord Godfrey of Harcourt came into England, who was banished out of France: he was well received with the king and retained to be about him, and had fair lands assigned him in England to maintain his degree. Then the king caused a great navy of ships to be ready in the haven of Hampton, and caused all manner of men of war to draw thither. About the feast of Saint John Baptist the year of our Lord God MCCCXLVI., the king departed from the queen and left her in the guiding of the earl of Kent his cousin; and he stablished the lord Percy and the lord Nevill to be wardens of his realm with [the archbishop of Canterbury,] the archbishop of York, the bishop of Lincoln and the bishop of Durham; for he never voided his realm but that he left ever enough at home to keep and defend the realm, if need were. Then the king rode to Hampton and there tarried for wind: then he entered into his ship and the prince of Wales with him, and the lord Godfrey of Harcourt, and all other lords, earls, barons and knights, with all their companies. They were in number a four thousand men of arms and ten thousand archers, beside Irishmen and Welshmen that followed the host afoot.

Now I shall name you certain of the lords that went over with king Edward in that journey. First, Edward his eldest son, prince of Wales, who as then was of the age of thirteen years or thereabout,[1] the earls of Hereford, Northampton, Arundel, Cornwall, Warwick, Huntingdon, Suffolk, and Oxford; and of barons the lord Mortimer, who was after earl of March, the lords John, Louis and Roger of Beauchamp, and the lord Raynold Cobham; of lords the lord of Mowbray, Ros, Lucy, Felton, Bradestan, Multon, Delaware, Manne,[2] Basset, Berkeley, and Willoughby, with divers other lords; and of bachelors there was John Chandos, Fitz-Warin, Peter and James Audley, Roger of Wetenhale, Bartholomew of Burghersh, and Richard of Pembridge, with divers other that I cannot name. Few there were of strangers: there was the earl Hainault,[3] sir Wulfart of Ghistelles, and five or six other knights of Almaine, and many other that I cannot name.

Thus they sailed forth that day in the name of God. They were well onward on their way toward Gascoyne, but on the third day there rose a contrary wind and drave them on the marches of Cornwall, and there they lay at anchor six days. In that space the king had other counsel by the means of sir Godfrey Harcourt: he counselled the king not to go into Gascoyne, but rather to set aland in Normandy, and said to the king: 'Sir, the country of Normandy is one of the plenteous countries of the world: sir, on jeopardy of my head, if ye will land there, there is none that shall resist you; the people of Normandy have not been used to the war, and all the knights and squires of the country are now at the siege before Aiguillon with the duke. And, sir, there ye shall find great towns that be not walled, whereby your men shall have such winning, that they shall be the better thereby twenty year after; and, sir, ye may follow with your army till ye come to Caen in Normandy: sir, I require you to believe me in this voyage.'

The king, who was as then but in the flower of his youth, desiring nothing so much as to have deeds of arms, inclined greatly to the saying of the lord Harcourt, whom he called cousin. Then he commanded the mariners to set their course to Normandy, and he took into his ship the token of

---

[1] He was in fact sixteen; born 15th June 1330.
[2] Probably 'Mohun.'
[3] The usual confusion between 'comté' and 'comte.' It means, 'of the county of Hainault there was sir Wulfart of Ghistelles,' etc.

the admiral the earl of Warwick, and said how he would be admiral for that viage, and so sailed on before as governour of that navy, and they had wind at will. Then the king arrived in the isle of Cotentin, at a port called Hogue Saint-Vaast.[4]

Tidings anon spread abroad how the Englishmen were aland: the towns of Cotentin sent word thereof to Paris to king Philip. He had well heard before how the king of England was on the sea with a great army, but he wist not what way he would draw, other into Normandy, Bretayne or Gascoyne. As soon as he knew that the king of England was aland in Normandy, he sent his constable the earl of Guines, and the earl of Tancarville, who were but newly come to him from his son from the siege at Aiguillon, to the town of Caen, commanding them to keep that town against the Englishmen. They said they would do their best: they departed from Paris with a good number of men of war, and daily there came more to them by the way, and so came to the town of Caen, where they were received with great joy of men of the town and of the country thereabout, that were drawn thither for surety. These lords took heed for the provision of the town, the which as then was not walled. The king thus was arrived at the port Hogue Saint-Vaast near to Saint-Saviour the Viscount[5] the right heritage to the lord Godfrey of Harcourt, who as then was there with the king of England.

HOW THE KING OF ENGLAND RODE IN THREE BATTLES THROUGH NORMANDY

WHEN the king of England arrived in the Hogue Saint-Vaast, the king issued out of his ship, and the first foot that he set on the ground, he fell so rudely, that the blood brast out of his nose. The knights that were about him took him up and said: ' Sir, for God's sake enter again into your ship, and come not aland this day, for this is but an evil sign for us.' Then the king answered quickly and said: ' Wherefore? This is a good token for me, for the land desireth to have me.' Of the which answer all his men were right joy-

---

[4] Saint-Vaast-de la Hogue.   [5] Saint-Sauveur-le-Vicomte.

ful. So that day and night the king lodged on the sands, and in the meantime discharged the ships of their horses and other baggages: there the king made two marshals of his host, the one the lord Godfrey of Harcourt and the other the earl of Warwick, and the earl of Arundel constable. And he ordained that the earl of Huntingdon should keep the fleet of ships with a hundred men of arms and four hundred archers: and also he ordained three battles, one to go on his right hand, closing to the sea-side, and the other on his left hand, and the king himself in the midst, and every night to lodge all in one field.

Thus they set forth as they were ordained, and they that went by the sea took all the ships that they found in their ways: and so long they went forth, what by sea and what by land, that they came to a good port and to a good town called Barfleur, the which incontinent was won, for they within gave up for fear of death. Howbeit, for all that, the town was robbed, and much gold and silver there found, and rich jewels: there was found so much riches, that the boys and villains of the host set nothing by good furred gowns: they made all the men of the town to issue out and to go into the ships, because they would not suffer them to be behind them for fear of rebelling again. After the town of Barfleur was thus taken and robbed without brenning, then they spread abroad in the country and did what they list, for there was not to resist them. At last they came to a great and a rich town called Cherbourg: the town they won and robbed it, and brent part thereof, but into the castle they could not come, it was so strong and well furnished with men of war. Then they passed forth and came to Montebourg, and took it and robbed and brent it clean. In this manner they brent many other towns in that country and won so much riches, that it was marvel to reckon it. Then they came to a great town well closed called Carentan, where there was also a strong castle and many soldiers within to keep it. Then the lords came out of their ships and fiercely made assault: the burgesses of the town were in great fear of their lives, wives and children: they suffered the Englishmen to enter into the town against the will of all the soldiers that were there; they put all their goods to the Englishmen's pleasures, they thought that most advantage. When the soldiers within saw that, they went into the castle: the Englishmen went into the town, and two days together they made sore assaults, so that when they within saw no succour, they yielded up, their lives and goods saved, and so departed. The Englishmen had their pleasure of that good town and castle, and when they saw they might not maintain to keep it, they set fire therein and brent it, and made the burgesses of the town to enter into their ships, as they had done with them of Barfleur, Cherbourg and Montebourg, and of other towns that they had won on the sea-side. All this was done by the battle that went by the sea-side, and by them on the sea together.[1]

Now let us speak of the king's battle. When he had sent his first battle along by the sea-side, as ye have heard, whereof one of his marshals, the earl of Warwick, was captain, and the lord Cobham with him, then he made his other marshal to lead his host on his left hand, for he knew the issues and entries of Normandy better than any other did there. The lord Godfrey as marshal rode forth with five hundred men of arms, and rode off from the king's battle as six or seven leagues, in brenning and exiling the country, the which was plentiful of everything—the granges full of corn, the houses full of all riches, rich burgesses, carts and chariots, horse, swine, muttons and other beasts: they took what them list and brought into the king's host; but the soldiers made no count to the king nor to none of his officers of the gold and silver that they did get; they kept that to themselves. Thus sir Godfrey of Harcourt rode every day off from the king's host, and for most part every night resorted to the king's field. The king took his way to Saint-Lo in Cotentin, but or he came there he lodged by a river, abiding for his men that rode along by the sea-side; and when they were come, they set forth their carriage, and the earl of Warwick, the earl of Suffolk, sir Thomas Holland and sir Raynold Cobham, and their

[1] Froissart is mistaken in supposing that a division of the land army went to these towns: Barfleur and Cherbourg were visited only by the fleet. According to Michael of Northburgh, who accompanied the expedition, Edward disembarked 12th July and remained at Saint-Vaast till the 18th, and meanwhile the fleet went to Barfleur and Cherbourg. The army arrived at Caen on the 26th.

company rode out on the one side and wasted and exiled
the country, as the lord Harcourt had done; and the king
ever rode between these battles, and every night they
lodged together.

OF THE GREAT ASSEMBLY THAT THE FRENCH KING MADE TO RESIST THE KING OF ENGLAND

THUS by the Englishmen was brent, exiled, robbed, wasted
and pilled the good, plentiful country of Normandy. Then
the French king sent for the lord John of Hainault, who
came to him with a great number: also the king sent for other
men of arms, dukes, earls, barons, knights and squires, and
assembled together the greatest number of people that had
been seen in France a hundred year before. He sent for men
into so far countries, that it was long or they came together,
wherefore the king of England did what him list in the mean
season. The French king heard well what he did, and sware
and said how they should never return again unfought
withal, and that such hurts and damages as they had done
should be dearly revenged; wherefore he had sent letters to
his friends in the Empire, to such as were farthest off, and
also to the gentle king of Bohemia and to the lord Charles
his son, who from thenceforth was called king of Almaine;
he was made king by the aid of his father and the French
king, and had taken on him the arms of the Empire: the
French king desired them to come to him with all their
powers, to the intent to fight with the king of England, who
brent and wasted his country. These princes and lords made
them ready with great number of men of arms, of Almains,
Bohemians and Luxemburgers, and so came to the French
king. Also king Philip sent to the duke of Lorraine, who
came to serve him with three hundred spears: also there
came the earl [of] Salm in Saumois, the earl of Sarrebruck,
the earl of Flanders, the earl William of Namur, every
man with a fair company.

Ye have heard herebefore of the order of the Englishmen,
how they went in three battles, the marshals on the right
hand and on the left, the king and the prince of Wales his
son in the midst. They rode but small journeys and every

day took their lodgings between noon and three of the clock, and found the country so fruitful, that they needed not to make no provision for their host, but all only for wine; and yet they found reasonably sufficient thereof.[1] It was no marvel though they of the country were afraid, for before that time they had never seen men of war, nor they wist not what war or battle meant. They fled away as far as they might hear speaking of the Englishmen,[2] and left their houses well stuffed, and granges full of corn, they wist not how to save and keep it. The king of England and the prince had in their battle a three thousand men of arms and six thousand archers and a ten thousand men afoot, beside them that rode with the marshals.

Thus as ye have heard, the king rode forth, wasting and brenning the country without breaking of his order. He left the city of Coutances[3] and went to a great town called Saint-Lo, a rich town of drapery and many rich burgesses. In that town there were dwelling an eight or nine score burgesses, crafty men. When the king came there, he took his lodging without, for he would never lodge in the town for fear of fire: but he sent his men before and anon the town was taken and clean robbed. It was hard to think the great riches that there was won, in clothes specially; cloth would there have been sold good cheap, if there had been any buyers.

Then the king went toward Caen, the which was a greater town and full of drapery and other merchandise, and rich burgesses, noble ladies and damosels, and fair churches, and specially two great and rich abbeys, one of the Trinity, another of Saint Stephen; and on the one side of the town one of the fairest castles of all Normandy, and captain therein was Robert of Wargny, with three hundred Genoways, and in the town was the earl of Eu and of Guines, constable of France, and the earl of Tancarville, with a

---

[1] Or rather, 'thus they found reasonably sufficient provisions.'

[2] That is, they fled as soon as they heard their coming spoken of.

[3] That is, he did not turn aside to go to it. Froissart says, 'He did not turn aside to the city of Coutances, but went on toward the great town of Saint-Lo in Cotentin, which at that time was very rich and of great merchandise and three times as great as the city of Coutances.' Michael of Northburgh says that Barfleur was about equal in importance to Sandwich and Carentan to Leicester, Saint-Lo greater than Lincoln, and Caen greater than any city in England except London.

good number of men of war. The king of England rode that day in good order and lodged all his battles together that night, a two leagues from Caen, in a town with a little haven called Austrehem, and thither came also all his navy of ships with the earl of Huntingdon, who was governour of them.

The constable and other lords of France that night watched well the town of Caen, and in the morning armed them with all them of the town: then the constable ordained that none should issue out, but keep their defences on the walls, gate, bridge and river, and left the suburbs void, because they were not closed; for they thought they should have enough to do to defend the town, because it was not closed but with the river. They of the town said how they would issue out, for they were strong enough to fight with the king of England. When the constable saw their good wills, he said: 'In the name of God be it, ye shall not fight without me.' Then they issued out in good order and made good face to fight and to defend them and to put their lives in adventure.

OF THE BATTLE OF CAEN, AND HOW THE ENGLISHMEN TOOK THE TOWN

THE same day the Englishmen rose early and apparelled them ready to go to Caen.[1] The king heard mass before the sun-rising and then took his horse, and the prince his son, with sir Godfrey of Harcourt marshal and leader of the host, whose counsel the king much followed. Then they drew toward Caen with their battles in good array, and so approached the good town of Caen. When they of the town, who were ready in the field, saw these three battles coming in good order, with their banners and standards waving in the wind, and the archers, the which they had not been accustomed to see, they were sore afraid and fled away toward the town without any order or good array, for all that the constable could do: then the Englishmen pursued them eagerly. When the constable and the earl Tancarville

[1] This was 26th July. Edward arrived at Poissy on 12th August: Philip of Valois left Paris on the 14th: the English crossed the Seine at Poissy on the 16th, and the Somme at Blanche-taque on the 24th.

saw that, they took a gate at the entry and saved themselves[2] and certain with them, for the Englishmen were entered into the town. Some of the knights and squires of France, such as knew the way to the castle, went thither, and the captain there received them all, for the castle was large. The Englishmen in the chase slew many, for they took none to mercy.

Then the constable and the earl of Tancarville, being in the little tower at the bridge foot, looked along the street and saw their men slain without mercy: they doubted to fall in their hands. At last they saw an English knight with one eye called sir Thomas Holland, and a five or six other knights with him: they knew them, for they had seen them before in Pruce, in Granade, and in other viages. Then they called to sir Thomas and said how they would yield themselves prisoners. Then sir Thomas came thither with his company and mounted up into the gate, and there found the said lords with twenty-five knights with them, who yielded them to sir Thomas, and he took them for his prisoners and left company to keep them, and then mounted again on his horse and rode into the streets, and saved many lives of ladies, damosels, and cloisterers from defoiling, for the soldiers were without mercy. It fell so well the same season for the Englishmen, that the river, which was able to bear ships, at that time was so low, that men went in and out beside the bridge. They of the town were entered into their houses, and cast down into the street stones, timber and iron, and slew and hurt more than five hundred Englishmen, wherewith the king was sore displeased. At night when he heard thereof, he commanded that the next day all should be put to the sword and the town brent; but then sir Godfrey of Harcourt said: 'Dear sir, for God's sake assuage somewhat your courage, and let it suffice you that ye have done. Ye have yet a great voyage to do or ye come before Calais, whither ye purpose to go; and, sir, in this town there is much people who will defend their houses, and it will cost many of your men their lives, or ye have all at your will; whereby peradventure ye shall not keep your purpose to Calais, the which should redound to your rack. Sir, save

[2] ' Set themselves for safety in a gate at the entry of the bridge.'

your people, for ye shall have need of them or this month pass; for I think verily your adversary king Philip will meet with you to fight, and ye shall find many straight passages and rencounters; wherefore your men, an ye had more, shall stand you in good stead: and, sir, without any further slaying ye shall be lord of this town; men and women will put all that they have to your pleasure.' Then the king said: 'Sir Godfrey, you are our marshal, ordain everything as ye will.' Then sir Godfrey with his banner rode from street to street, and commanded in the king's name none to be so hardy to put fire in any house, to slay any person, nor to violate any woman. When they of the town heard that cry, they received the Englishmen into their houses and made them good cheer, and some opened their coffers and bade them take what them list, so they might be assured of their lives; howbeit there were done in the town many evil deeds, murders and robberies. Thus the Englishmen were lords of the town three days and won great riches, the which they sent by barks and barges to Saint-Saviour by the river of Austrehem,[3] a two leagues thence, whereas all their navy lay. Then the king sent the earl of Huntingdon with two hundred men of arms and four hundred archers, with his navy and prisoners and riches that they had got, back again into England. And the king bought of sir Thomas Holland the constable of France and the earl of Tancarville, and paid for them twenty thousand nobles.

HOW SIR GODFREY OF HARCOURT FOUGHT WITH THEM OF AMIENS BEFORE PARIS.

Thus the king of England ordered his business, being in the town of Caen, and sent into England his navy of ships charged with clothes, jewels, vessels of gold and silver, and of other riches, and of prisoners more than sixty knights and three hundred burgesses. Then he departed from the town of Caen and rode in the same order as he did before, brenning and exiling the country, and took the way to

---

[3] Froissart says that they sent their booty in barges and boats 'on the river as far as Austrehem, a two leagues from thence, where their great navy lay.' He makes no mention of Saint-Sauveur here. The river in question is the Orne, at the mouth of which Austrehem is situated.

Evreux and so passed by it; and from thence they rode to a great town called Louviers: it was the chief town of all Normandy of drapery, riches, and full of merchandise. The Englishmen soon entered therein, for as then it was not closed; it was overrun, spoiled and robbed without mercy: there was won great riches. Then they entered into the country of Evreux and brent and pilled all the country except the good towns closed and castles, to the which the king made none assault, because of the sparing of his people and his artillery.

On the river of Seine near to Rouen there was the earl of Harcourt, brother to sir Godfrey of Harcourt, but he was on the French party, and the earl of Dreux with him, with a good number of men of war: but the Englishmen left Rouen and went to Gisors, where was a strong castle: they brent the town and then they brent Vernon and all the country about Rouen and Pont-de-l'Arche and came to Mantes and to Meulan, and wasted all the country about, and passed by the strong castle of Rolleboise; and in every place along the river of Seine they found the bridges broken. At last they came to Poissy, and found the bridge broken, but the arches and joists lay in the river: the king lay there a five days: in the mean season the bridge was made, to pass the host without peril. The English marshals ran abroad just to Paris, and brent Saint-Germain in Laye and Mont-joie, and Saint-Cloud, and petty Boulogne by Paris, and the Queen's Bourg:[1] they of Paris were not well assured of themselves, for it was not as then closed.

Then king Philip removed to Saint-Denis, and or he went caused all the pentices in Paris to be pulled down; and at Saint-Denis were ready come the king of Bohemia, the lord John of Hainault, the duke of Lorraine, the earl of Flanders, the earl of Blois, and many other great lords and knights, ready to serve the French king. When the people of Paris saw their king depart, they came to him and kneeled down and said: 'Ah, sir and noble king, what will ye do? leave thus this noble city of Paris?' The king said: 'My good people, doubt ye not: the Englishmen will approach you no nearer than they be.' 'Why so, sir?' quoth they; 'they

---

[1] Bourg-la-Reine.

be within these two leagues, and as soon as they know of your departing, they will come and assail us; and we not able to defend them: sir, tarry here still and help to defend your good city of Paris.' 'Speak no more,' quoth the king, 'for I will go to Saint-Denis to my men of war: for I will encounter the Englishmen and fight against them, whatsoever fall thereof.'

The king of England was at Poissy, and lay in the nunnery there, and kept there the feast of our Lady in August and sat in his robes of scarlet furred with ermines; and after that feast he went forth in order as they were before. The lord Godfrey of Harcourt rode out on the one side with five hundred men of arms and thirteen[2] hundred archers; and by adventure he encountered a great number of burgesses of Amiens a-horseback, who were riding by the king's commandment to Paris. They were quickly assailed and they defended themselves valiantly, for they were a great number and well armed: there were four knights of Amiens their captains. This skirmish dured long: at the first meeting many were overthrown on both parts; but finally the burgesses were taken and nigh all slain, and the Englishmen took all their carriages and harness. They were well stuffed, for they were going to the French king well appointed, because they had not seen him a great season before. There were slain in the field a twelve hundred.

Then the king of England entered into the country of Beauvoisis, brenning and exiling the plain country, and lodged at a fair abbey and a rich called Saint-Messien[3] near to Beauvais: there the king tarried a night and in the morning departed. And when he was on his way he looked behind him and saw the abbey a-fire: he caused incontinent twenty of them to be hanged that set the fire there, for he had commanded before on pain of death none to violate any church nor to bren any abbey. Then the king passed by the city of Beauvais without any assault giving, for because he would not trouble his people nor waste his artillery. And so that day he took his lodging betime in a little town called Milly. The two marshals came so near to Beauvais, that

[2] A better reading is 'twelve.'
[3] Commonly called Saint-Lucien, but Saint-Maximianus (Messien) is also associated with the place.

they made assault and skirmish at the barriers in three places, the which assault endured a long space; but the town within was so well defended by the means of the bishop, who was there within, that finally the Englishmen departed, and brent clean hard to the gates all the suburbs, and then at night they came into the king's field.

The next day the king departed, brenning and wasting all before him, and at night lodged in a good village called Grandvilliers. The next day the king passed by Dargies: there was none to defend the castle, wherefore it was soon taken and brent. Then they went forth destroying the country all about, and so came to the castle of Poix, where there was a good town and two castles. There was nobody in them but two fair damosels, daughters to the lord of Poix; they were soon taken, and had been violated, an two English knights had not been, sir John Chandos and sir Basset; they defended them and brought them to the king, who for his honour made them good cheer and demanded of them whither they would fainest go. They said, 'To Corbie,' and the king caused them to be brought thither without peril. That night the king lodged in the town of Poix. They of the town and of the castles spake that night with the marshals of the host, to save them and their town from brenning, and they to pay a certain sum of florins the next day as soon as the host was departed. This was granted them, and in the morning the king departed with all his host except a certain that were left there to receive the money that they of the town had promised to pay. When they of the town saw the host depart and but a few left behind, then they said they would pay never a penny, and so ran out and set on the Englishmen, who defended themselves as well as they might and sent after the host for succour. When sir Raynold Cobham and sir Thomas Holland, who had the rule of the rearguard, heard thereof, they returned and cried, 'Treason, treason!' and so came again to Poix-ward and found their companions still fighting with them of the town. Then anon they of the town were nigh all slain, and the town brent, and the two castles beaten down. Then they returned to the king's host, who was as then at Airaines and there lodged, and had commanded all manner of men on pain of death to do no hurt to no town of Arsyn,[4] for there the king was minded to lie a day or two to take advice how he might pass the river of Somme; for it was necessary for him to pass the river, as ye shall hear after.

HOW THE FRENCH KING FOLLOWED THE KING OF ENGLAND IN BEAUVOISINOIS

Now let us speak of King Philip, who was at Sant-Denis and his people about him, and daily increased. Then on a day he departed and rode so long that he came to Coppegueule, a three leagues from Amiens, and there he tarried. The king of England being at Airaines wist not where for to pass the river of Somme, the which was large and deep, and all bridges were broken and the passages well kept. Then at the king's commandment his two marshals with a thousand men of arms and two thousand archers went along the river to find some passage, and passed by Longpré, and came to the bridge of Remy,[1] the which was well kept with a great number of knights and squires and men of the country. The Englishmen alighted afoot and assailed the Frenchmen from the morning till it was noon; but the bridge was so well fortified and defended, that the Englishmen departed without winning of anything. Then they went to a great town called Fountains on the river of Somme, the which was clean robbed and brent, for it was not closed. Then they went to another town called Long-en-Ponthieu; they could not win the bridge, it was so well kept and defended. Then they departed and went to Picquigny, and found the town, the bridge, and the castle so well fortified, that it was not likely to pass there: the French king had so well defended the passages, to the intent that the king of England should not pass the river of Somme, to fight with him at his advantage or else to famish him there.

When these two marshals had assayed in all places to find passage and could find none, they returned again to

---

[4] A mistranslation. The original is '[il avoit] deffendu sus le hart que nuls ne fourfesist rien à le ville d'arsin ne d'autre cose,' 'he had commanded all on pain of hanging to do no hurt to the town by burning or otherwise.' The translator has taken 'arsin' for a proper name.

[1] Pont-à-Remy, corrupted here into 'bridge of Athyne.'

the king, and shewed how they could find no passage in no place. The same night the French king came to Amiens with more than a hundred thousand men. The king of England was right pensive, and the next morning heard mass before the sun-rising and then dislodged; and every man followed the marshals' banners and so rode in the country of Vimeu approaching to the good town of Abbeville, and found a town thereby, whereunto was come much people of the country in trust of a little defence that was there; but the Englishmen anon won it, and all they that were within slain, and many taken of the town and of the country. The king took his lodging in a great hospital[2] that was there. The same day the French king departed from Amiens and came to Airaines about noon; and the Englishmen were departed thence in the morning. The Frenchmen found there great provision that the Englishmen had left behind them, because they departed in haste. There they found flesh ready on the broaches, bread and pasties in the ovens, wine in tuns and barrels, and the tables ready laid. There the French king lodged and tarried for his lords.

That night the king of England was lodged at Oisemont. At night when the two marshals were returned, who had that day overrun the country to the gates of Abbeville and to Saint-Valery and made a great skirmish there, then the king assembled together his council and made to be brought before him certain prisoners of the country of Ponthieu and of Vimeu. The king right courteously demanded of them, if there were any among them that knew any passage beneath Abbeville, that he and his host might pass over the river of Somme: if he would shew him thereof, he should be quit of his ransom, and twenty of his company for his love. There was a varlet called Gobin Agace who stepped forth and said to the king: 'Sir, I promise you on the jeopardy of my head I shall bring you to such a place, whereas ye and all your host shall pass the river of Somme without peril. There be certain places in the passage that ye shall pass twelve men afront two times between day and night: ye shall not go in the water to the knees. But when the flood cometh, the river then waxeth so great, that no

[2] That is, a house of the knights of Saint John.

man can pass; but when the flood is gone, the which is two times between day and night, then the river is so low, that it may be passed without danger both a-horseback and afoot. The passage is hard in the bottom with white stones, so that all your carriage may go surely; therefore the passage is called Blanche-taque. An ye make ready to depart betimes, ye may be there by the sun-rising.' The king said: 'If this be true that ye say, I quit thee thy ransom and all thy company, and moreover shall give thee a hundred nobles.' Then the king commanded every man to be ready at the sound of the trumpet to depart.

OF THE BATTLE OF BLANCHE-TAQUE BETWEEN THE KING OF ENGLAND AND SIR GODEMAR DU FAY

THE king of England slept not much that night, for at midnight he arose and sowned his trumpet: then incontinent they made ready carriages and all things, and at the breaking of the day they departed from the town of Oisemont and rode after the guiding of Gobin Agace, so that they came by the sun-rising to Blanche-taque; but as then the flood was up, so that they might not pass: so the king tarried there till it was prime; then the ebb came.

The French king had his currours in the country, who brought him word of the demeanour of the Englishmen. Then he thought to close the king of England between Abbeville and the river of Somme, and so to fight with him at his pleasure. And when he was at Amiens he had ordained a great baron of Normandy, called sir Godemar du Fay, to go and keep the passage of Blanche-taque, where the Englishmen must pass or else in none other place. He had with him a thousand men of arms and six thousand afoot, with the Genoways: so they went by Saint-Riquier in Ponthieu and from thence to Crotoy, whereas the passage lay; and also he had with him a great number of men of the country, and also a great number of them of Montreuil, so that they were a twelve thousand men one and other.

When the English host was come thither, sir Godemar du Fay arranged all his company to defend the passage. The king of England let not for all that; but when the flood was gone, he commanded his marshals to enter into the water in the name of God and Saint George. Then they that were hardy and courageous entered on both parties, and many a man reversed. There were some of the Frenchmen of Artois and Picardy that were as glad to joust in the water as on the dry land.

The Frenchmen defended so well the passage at the issuing out of the water, that they had much to do. The Genoways did them great trouble with their cross-bows: on the other side the archers of England shot so wholly together, that the Frenchmen were fain to give place to the Englishmen. There was a sore battle, and many a noble feat of arms done on both sides. Finally the Englishmen passed over and assembled together in the field. The king and the prince passed, and all the lords; then the Frenchmen kept none array, but departed, he that might best. When sir Godemar saw that discomfiture, he fled and saved himself: some fled to Abbeville and some to Saint-Riquiers. They that were there afoot could not flee, so that there were slain a great number of them of Abbeville, Montreuil, Rue and of Saint-Riquiers: the chase endured more than a great league. And as yet all the Englishmen were not passed the river, and certain currours of the king of Bohemia and of sir John of Hainault came on them that were behind and took certain horses and carriages and slew divers, or they could take the passage.

The French king the same morning was departed from Airaines, trusting to have found the Englishmen between him and the river of Somme: but when he heard how that sir Godemar du Fay and his company were discomfited, he tarried in the field and demanded of his marshals what was best to do. They said, 'Sir, ye cannot pass the river but at the bridge of Abbeville, for the flood is come in at Blanche-taque': then he returned and lodged at Abbeville.

The king of England when he was past the river, he thanked God and so rode forth in like manner as he did before. Then he called Gobin Agace and did quit him his ransom and all his company, and gave him a hundred nobles and a good horse. And so the king rode forth fair and

easily, and thought to have lodged in a great town called
Noyelles; but when he knew that the town pertained to
the countess d'Aumale, sister to the lord Robert of Artois,[1]
the king assured the town and country as much as pertained to her, and so went forth; and his marshals rode to
Crotoy on the sea-side and brent the town, and found in
the haven many ships and barks charged with wines of
Poitou, pertaining to the merchants of Saintonge and of
Rochelle: they brought the best thereof to the king's host.
Then one of the marshals rode to the gates of Abbeville and
from thence to Saint-Riquiers, and after to the town of
Rue-Saint-Esprit. This was on a Friday, and both battles
of the marshals returned to the king's host about noon and so
lodged all together near to Cressy in Ponthieu.

The king of England was well informed how the French
king followed after him to fight. Then he said to his company: 'Let us take here some plot of ground, for we will
go no farther till we have seen our enemies. I have good
cause here to abide them, for I am on the right heritage of
the queen my mother, the which land was given at her marriage: I will challenge it of mine adversary Philip of
Valois.' And because that he had not the eighth part in
number of men as the French king had, therefore he commanded his marshals to chose a plot of ground somewhat
for his advantage: and so they did, and thither the king
and his host went. Then he sent his currours to Abbeville,
to see if the French king drew that day into the field or
not. They went forth and returned again, and said how
they could see none appearance of his coming: then every
man took their lodging for that day, and to be ready in
the morning at the sound of the trumpet in the same place.
This Friday the French king tarried still in Abbeville abiding for his company, and sent his two marshals to ride out
to see the dealing of the Englishmen, and at night they
returned, and said how the Englishmen were lodged in the
fields. That night the French king made a supper to all
the chief lords that were there with him, and after supper
the king desired them to be friends each to other. The
king looked for the earl of Savoy, who should come to

[1] She was in fact his daughter.

him with a thousand spears, for he had received wages for a three months of them at Troyes in Champagne.

OF THE ORDER OF THE ENGLISHMEN AT CRESSY, AND HOW THEY MADE THREE BATTLES AFOOT

ON the Friday, as I said before, the king of England lay in the fields, for the country was plentiful of wines and other victual, and if need had been, they had provision following in carts and other carriages. That night the king made a supper to all his chief lords of his host and made them good cheer; and when they were all departed to take their rest, then the king entered into his oratory and kneeled down before the altar, praying God devoutly, that if he fought the next day, that he might achieve the journey to his honour: then about midnight he laid him down to rest, and in the morning he rose betimes and heard mass, and the prince his son with him, and the most part of his company were confessed and houselled; and after the mass said, he commanded every man to be armed and to draw to the field to the same place before appointed. Then the king caused a park to be made by the wood side behind his host, and there was set all carts and carriages, and within the park were all their horses, for every man was afoot; and into this park there was but one entry. Then he ordained three battles: in the first was the young prince of Wales, with him the earl of Warwick and Oxford, the lord Godfrey of Harcourt, sir Raynold Cobham, sir Thomas Holland, the lord Stafford, the lord of Mohun, the lord Delaware, sir John Chandos, sir Bartholomew de Burghersh, sir Robert Nevill, the lord Thomas Clifford, the lord Bourchier, the lord de Latimer, and divers other knights and squires that I cannot name: they were an eight hundred men of arms and two thousand archers, and a thousand of other with the Welshmen: every lord drew to the field appointed under his own banner and pennon. In the second battle was the earl of Northampton, the earl of Arundel, the lord Ros, the lord Lucy, the lord Willoughby, the lord Basset, the lord of Saint-Aubin, sir Louis Tufton, the lord of Multon, the lord Lascelles and divers other, about an eight hundred men of arms and twelve hundred archers. The third battle had the king: he had seven hundred men of arms and two thousand archers. Then the king leapt on a hobby,[1] with a white rod in his hand, one of his marshals on the one hand and the other on the other hand: he rode from rank to rank desiring every man to take heed that day to his right and honour. He spake it so sweetly and with so good countenance and merry cheer, that all such as were discomfited took courage in the seeing and hearing of him. And when he had thus visited all his battles, it was then nine of the day: then he caused every man to eat and drink a little, and so they did at their leisure. And afterward they ordered again their battles: then every man lay down on the earth and by him his salet and bow, to be the more fresher when their enemies should come.

THE ORDER OF THE FRENCHMEN AT CRESSY, AND HOW THEY BEHELD THE DEMEANOUR OF THE ENGLISHMEN

THIS Saturday the French king rose betimes and heard mass in Abbeville in his lodging in the abbey of Saint Peter, and he departed after the sun-rising. When he was out of the town two leagues, approaching toward his enemies, some of his lords said to him: 'Sir, it were good that ye ordered your battles, and let all your footmen pass somewhat on before, that they be not troubled with the horsemen.' Then the king sent four knights, the Moine [of] Bazeilles, the lord of Noyers, the lord of Beaujeu and the lord d'Aubigny to ride to aview the English host; and so they rode so near that they might well see part of their dealing. The Englishmen saw them well and knew well how they were come thither to aview them: they let them alone and made no countenance toward them, and let them return as they came. And when the French king saw these four knights return again, he tarried till they came to him and said: 'Sirs, what tidings?' These four knights each of them looked on other, for there was none would speak before his companion; finally the king said to [the] Moine, who pertained to the king of Bohemia and had done in his

[1] 'Un petit palefroi.'

days so much, that he was reputed for one of the valiantest knights of the world: 'Sir, speak you.' Then he said: 'Sir, I shall speak, sith it pleaseth you, under the correction of my fellows. Sir, we have ridden and seen the behaving of your enemies: know ye for truth they are rested in three battles abiding for you. Sir, I will counsel you as for my part, saving your displeasure, that you and all your company rest here and lodge for this night: for or they that be behind of your company be come hither, and or your battles be set in good order, it will be very late, and your people be weary and out of array, and ye shall find your enemies fresh and ready to receive you. Early in the morning ye may order your battles at more leisure and advise your enemies at more deliberation, and to regard well what way ye will assail them; for, sir, surely they will abide you.'

Then the king commanded that it should be so done. Then his two marshals one rode before, another behind, saying to every banner: 'Tarry and abide here in the name of God and Saint Denis.' They that were foremost tarried, but they that were behind would not tarry, but rode forth, and said how they would in no wise abide till they were as far forward as the foremost: and when they before saw them come on behind, then they rode forward again, so that the king nor his marshals could not rule them. So they rode without order or good array, till they came in sight of their enemies: and as soon as the foremost saw them, they reculed then aback without good array, whereof they behind had marvel and were abashed, and thought that the foremost company had been fighting. Then they might have had leisure and room to have gone forward, if they had list: some went forth and some abode still. The commons, of whom all the ways between Abbeville and Cressy were full, when they saw that they were near to their enemies, they took their swords and cried: 'Down with them! let us slay them all.' There is no man, though he were present at the journey, that could imagine or shew the truth of the evil order that was among the French party, and yet they were a marvellous great number. That I write in this book I learned it specially of the Englishmen, who well beheld their dealing; and also certain knights of sir John of Hainault's, who was always about king Philip, shewed me as they knew.

OF THE BATTLE OF CRESSY BETWEEN THE KING OF ENGLAND AND THE FRENCH KING

THE Englishmen, who were in three battles lying on the ground to rest them, as soon as they saw the Frenchmen approach, they rose upon their feet fair and easily without any haste and arranged their battles. The first, which was the prince's battle, the archers there stood in manner of a herse and the men of arms in the bottom of the battle. The earl of Northampton and the earl of Arundel with the second battle were on a wing in good order, ready to comfort the prince's battle, if need were.

The lords and knights of France came not to the assembly together in good order, for some came before and some came after in such haste and evil order, that one of them did trouble another. When the French king saw the Englishmen, his blood changed, and said to his marshals: ' Make the Genoways go on before and begin the battle in the name of God and Saint Denis.' There were of the Genoways cross-bows about a fifteen thousand,[1] but they were so weary of going afoot that day a six leagues armed with their cross-bows, that they said to their constables: ' We be not well ordered to fight this day, for we be not in the case to do any great deed of arms: we have more need of rest.' These words came to the earl of Alençon, who said: ' A man is well at ease to be charged with such a sort of rascals, to be faint and fail now at most need.' Also the same season there fell a great rain and a clipse[2] with a terrible thunder, and before the rain there came flying over both battles a great number of crows for fear of the tempest coming. Then anon the air began to wax clear, and the sun to shine fair and bright, the which was right in the Frenchmen's eyen and on the Englishmen's backs. When

---

[1] Villani, a very good authority on the subject, says 6000, brought from the ships at Harfleur.

[2] A mistranslation of ' une esclistre,' ' a flash of lightning.'

the Genoways were assembled together and began to approach, they made a great leap [3] and cry to abash the Englishmen, but they stood still and stirred not for all that: then the Genoways again the second time made another leap and a fell cry, and stept forward a little, and the Englishmen removed not one foot: thirdly, again they leapt and cried, and went forth till they came within shot; then they shot fiercely with their cross-bows. Then the English archers stept forth one pace and let fly their arrows so wholly [together] and so thick, that it seemed snow. When the Genoways felt the arrows piercing through heads, arms and breasts, many of them cast down their cross-bows and did cut their strings and returned discomfited. When the French king saw them fly away, he said: 'Slay these rascals, for they shall let and trouble us without reason.' Then ye should have seen the men of arms dash in among them and killed a great number of them: and ever still the Englishmen shot whereas they saw thickest press; the sharp arrows ran into the men of arms and into their horses, and many fell, horse and men, among the Genoways, and when they were down, they could not relieve [4] again, the press was so thick that one overthrew another. And also among the Englishmen there were certain rascals that went afoot with great knives, and they went in among the men of arms, and slew and murdered many as they lay on the ground, both earls, barons, knights and squires, whereof the king of England was after displeased, for he had rather they had been taken prisoners.

The valiant king of Bohemia called Charles of Luxembourg, son to the noble emperor Henry of Luxembourg, for all that he was nigh blind, when he understood the order of the battle, he said to them about him: 'Where is the lord Charles my son?' His men said: 'Sir, we cannot tell; we think he be fighting.' Then he said: 'Sirs, ye are my

[3] These 'leaps' of the Genoese are invented by the translator, and have passed from him into several respectable English text-books, sometimes in company with the eclipse above mentioned. Froissart says: 'Il commencièrent à juper moult epouvantablement'; that is, 'to utter cries.' Another text makes mention of the English cannons at this point: 'The English remained still and let off some cannons that they had, to frighten the Genoese.'

[4] The translator's word 'relieve' (relyuue) represents 'relever,' for 'se relever.'

men, my companions and friends in this journey: I require you bring me so far forward, that I may strike one stroke with my sword.' They said they would do his commandment, and to the intent that they should not lose him in the press, they tied all their reins of their bridles each to other and set the king before to accomplish his desire, and so they went on their enemies. The lord Charles of Bohemia his son, who wrote himself king of Almaine and bare the arms, he came in good order to the battle; but when he saw that the matter went awry on their party, he departed, I cannot tell you which way. The king his father was so far forward that he strake a stroke with his sword, yea and more than four, and fought valiantly and so did his company; and they adventured themselves so forward, that they were there all slain, and the next day they were found in the place about the king, and all their horses tied each to other.

The earl of Alençon came to the battle right ordinately and fought with the Englishmen, and the earl of Flanders also on his part. These two lords with their companies coasted the English archers and came to the prince's battle, and there fought valiantly long. The French king would fain have come thither, when he saw their banners, but there was a great hedge of archers before him. The same day the French king had given a great black courser to sir John of Hainault, and he made the lord Tierry of Senzeille to ride on him and to bear his banner. The same horse took the bridle in the teeth and brought him through all the currours of the Englishmen, and as he would have returned again, he fell in a great dike and was sore hurt, and had been there dead, an his page had not been, who followed him through all the battles and saw where his master lay in the dike, and had none other let but for his horse, for the Englishmen would not issue out of their battle for taking of any prisoner. Then the page alighted and relieved his master: then he went not back again the same way that they came, there was too many in his way.

This battle between Broye and Cressy this Saturday was right cruel and fell, and many a feat of arms done that came not to my knowledge. In the night[5] divers knights and squires lost their masters, and sometime came on the Englishmen, who received them in such wise that they were ever nigh slain; for there was none taken to mercy nor to ransom, for so the Englishmen were determined.

In the morning[6] the day of the battle certain Frenchmen and Almains perforce opened the archers of the prince's battle and came and fought with the men of arms hand to hand. Then the second battle of the Englishmen came to succour the prince's battle, the which was time, for they had as then much ado; and they with the prince sent a messenger to the king, who was on a little windmill hill. Then the knight said to the king: ' Sir, the earl of Warwick and the earl of Oxford, sir Raynold Cobham and other, such as be about the prince your son, are fiercely fought withal and are sore handled; wherefore they desire you that you and your battle will come and aid them; for if the Frenchmen increase, as they doubt they will, your son and they shall have much ado.' Then the king said: ' Is my son dead or hurt or on the earth felled?' ' No, sir,' quoth the knight, ' but he is hardly matched; wherefore he hath need of your aid.' ' Well,' said the king, ' return to him and to them that sent you hither, and say to them that they send no more to me for any adventure that falleth, as long as my son is alive: and also say to them that they suffer him this day to win his spurs;[7] for if God be pleased, I will this journey be his and the honour thereof, and to them that be about him.' Then the knight returned again to them and shewed the king's words, the which greatly encouraged them, and repoined[8] in that they had sent to the king as they did.

Sir Godfrey of Harcourt would gladly that the earl of Harcourt his brother might have been saved; for he heard say by them that saw his banner how that he was there in the field on the French party: but sir Godfrey could not

5 ' Sus le nuit,' ' towards nightfall.'
6 The text has suffered by omissions. What Froissart says is that if the battle had begun in the morning, it might have gone better for the French, and then he instances the exploits of those who broke through the archers. The battle did not begin till four o'clock in the afternoon.
7 ' Que il laissent à l'enfant gaegnier ses esperons.'
8 i. e. ' they repoined ': Fr. ' se reprisent.'

come to him betimes, for he was slain or he could come at him, and so was also the earl of Aumale his nephew. In another place the earl of Alençon and the earl of Flanders fought valiantly, every lord under his own banner; but finally they could not resist against the puissance of the Englishmen, and so there they were also slain, and divers other knights and squires. Also the earl Louis of Blois, nephew to the French king, and the duke of Lorraine fought under their banners, but at last they were closed in among a company of Englishmen and Welshmen, and there were slain for all their prowess. Also there was slain the earl of Auxerre, the earl of Saint-Pol and many other.

In the evening the French king, who had left about him no more than a three-score persons, one and other, whereof sir John of Hainault was one, who had remounted once the king, for his horse was slain with an arrow, then he said to the king: 'Sir, depart hence, for it is time; lose not yourself wilfully: if ye have loss at this time, ye shall recover it again another season.' And so he took the king's horse by the bridle and led him away in a manner perforce. Then the king rode till he came to the castle of Broye. The gate was closed, because it was by that time dark: then the king called the captain, who came to the walls and said: Who is that calleth there this time of night?' Then the king said: 'Open your gate quickly, for this is the fortune of France.'[9] The captain knew then it was the king, and opened the gate and let down the bridge. Then the king entered, and he had with him but five barons, sir John of Hainault, sir Charles of Montmorency, the lord of Beaujeu, the lord d'Aubigny and the lord of Montsault. The king would not tarry there, but drank and departed thence about midnight, and so rode by such guides as knew the country till he came in the morning to Amiens, and there he rested.

This Saturday the Englishmen never departed from their battles for chasing of any man, but kept still their field, and ever defended themselves against all such as came to assail them. This battle ended about evensong time.

[9] ' C'est la fortune de France': but the better MSS. have ' c'est li in-fortunés rois de France.'

HOW THE NEXT DAY AFTER THE BATTLE THE ENGLISHMEN
DISCOMFITED DIVERS FRENCHMEN

ON this Saturday, when the night was come and that the
Englishmen heard no more noise of the Frenchmen, then
they reputed themselves to have the victory, and the Frenchmen to be discomfited, slain and fled away. Then they made
great fires and lighted up torches and candles, because it
was very dark. Then the king avaled down from the little
hill whereas he stood; and of all that day till then his helm
came never on his head. Then he went with all his battle
to his son the prince and enbraced him in his arms and
kissed him, and said: 'Fair son, God give you good per-
severance; ye are my good son, thus ye have acquitted you
nobly: ye are worthy to keep a realm.' The prince inclined
himself to the earth, honouring the king his father.

This night they thanked God for their good adventure
and made no boast thereof, for the king would that no man
should be proud or make boast, but every man humbly to
thank God. On the Sunday in the morning there was
such a mist, that a man might not see the breadth of an acre
of land from him. Then there departed from the host by
the commandment of the king and marshals five hundred
spears and two thousand archers, to see if they might see
any Frenchmen gathered again together in any place. The
same morning out of Abbeville and Saint-Riquiers in Ponthieu the commons of Rouen and of Beauvais issued out
of their towns, not knowing of the discomfiture of the day
before. They met with the Englishmen weening they had
been Frenchmen, and when the Englishmen saw them, they
set on them freshly, and there was a sore battle; but at last
the Frenchmen fled and kept none array. There were slain
in the ways and in hedges and bushes more than seven
thousand, and if the day had been clear there had never
a one escaped. Anon after, another company of Frenchmen
were met by the Englishmen, the archbishop of Rouen and
the great prior of France, who also knew nothing of the discomfiture the day before; for they heard that the French
king should have fought the same Sunday, and they were go-

ing thitherward. When they met with the Englishmen, there
was a great battle, for they were a great number, but they
could not endure against the Englishmen; for they were
nigh all slain, few escaped; the two lords were slain.
This morning the Englishmen met with divers Frenchmen
that had lost their way on the Saturday and had lain all
night in the fields, and wist not where the king was nor the
captains. They were all slain, as many as were met with;
and it was shewed me that of the commons and men afoot
of the cities and good towns of France there was slain four
times as many as were slain the Saturday in the great
battle.

HOW THE NEXT DAY AFTER THE BATTLE OF CRESSY THEY THAT WERE DEAD WERE NUMBERED BY THE ENGLISHMEN

THE same Sunday, as the king of England came from mass,
such as had been sent forth returned and shewed the king
what they had seen and done, and said: 'Sir, we think
surely there is now no more appearance of any of our
enemies.' Then the king sent to search how many were
slain and what they were. Sir Raynold Cobham and sir
Richard Stafford with three heralds went to search the
field and country: they visited all them that were slain and
rode all day in the fields, and returned again to the host as
the king was going to supper. They made just report of that
they had seen, and said how there were eleven great princes
dead, fourscore banners, twelve hundred knights, and more
than thirty thousand other.[1] The Englishmen kept still
their field all that night: on the Monday in the morning the
king prepared to depart: the king caused the dead bodies
of the great lords to be taken up and conveyed to Montreuil, and there buried in holy ground, and made a cry in
the country to grant truce for three days, to the intent

[1] Another text makes the loss of persons below the rank of knight 15,000
or 16,000, including the men of the towns. Both estimates must be greatly
exaggerated. Michael of Northburgh says that 1542 were killed in the
battle and about 2000 on the next day. The great princes killed were the
king of Bohemia, the duke of Lorraine, the earls of Alençon, Flanders,
Blois, Auxerre, Harcourt, Saint-Pol, Aumale, the grand prior of France
and the archbishop of Rouen.

that they of the country might search the field of Cressy to bury the dead bodies.

Then the king went forth and came before the town of Montreuil-by-the-sea, and his marshals ran toward Hesdin and brent Waben and Serain, but they did nothing to the castle, it was so strong and so well kept. They lodged that night on the river of Hesdin towards Blangy. The next day they rode toward Boulogne and came to the town of Wissant: there the king and the prince lodged, and tarried there a day to refresh his men, and on the Wednesday the king came before the strong town of Calais.

THE BATTLE OF POITIERS

OF THE GREAT HOST THAT THE FRENCH KING BROUGHT
TO THE BATTLE OF POITIERS

AFTER the taking of the castle of Romorantin and of them that were therein, the prince then and his company rode as they did before, destroying the country, approaching to Anjou and to Touraine. The French king, who was at Chartres, departed and came to Blois and there tarried two days, and then to Amboise and the next day to Loches: and then he heard how that the prince was at Touraine[1] and how that he was returning by Poitou: ever the Englishmen were coasted by certain expert knights of France, who alway made report to the king what the Englishmen did. Then the king came to the Haye in Touraine and his men had passed the river of Loire, some at the bridge of Orleans and some at Meung, at Saumur, at Blois, and at Tours and whereas they might: they were in number a twenty thousand men of arms beside other; there were a twenty-six dukes and earls and more than sixscore banners, and the four sons of the king, who were but young, the duke Charles of Normandy, the lord Louis, that was from thenceforth duke of Anjou, and the lord John duke of Berry, and the lord Philip, who was after duke of Burgoyne. The same season, pope Innocent the sixth sent the lord Bertrand, cardinal of Perigord, and the lord Nicholas, cardinal of Urgel, into France, to treat for a peace between the French king and all his enemies, first between him and the king of Navarre, who was in prison: and these cardinals oftentimes spake to the king for his deliverance during the siege at Bretuel, but they could do nothing in that behalf. Then the cardinal of Perigord went to Tours, and there he heard

[1] 'En Touraine.'

34

how the French king hasted sore to find the Englishmen:
then he rode to Poitiers, for he heard how both the hosts
drew thitherward.

The French king heard how the prince hasted greatly to
return, and the king feared that he should scape him and
so departed from Haye in Touraine, and all his company,
and rode to Chauvigny, where he tarried that Thursday in
the town and without along by the river of Creuse, and the
next day the king passed the river at the bridge there, weening that the Englishmen had been before him, but they were
not. Howbeit they pursued after and passed the bridge that
day more than threescore thousand horses, and divers other
passed at Chatelleraut, and ever as they passed they took
the way to Poitiers.

On the other side the prince wist not truly where the
Frenchmen were; but they supposed that they were not far
off, for they could not find no more forage, whereby they
had great fault in their host of victual, and some of them
repented that they had destroyed so much as they had done
before when they were in Berry, Anjou and Touraine, and
in that they had made no better provision. The same Friday
three great lords of France, the lord of Craon, the lord
Raoul of Coucy and the earl of Joigny, tarried all day in
the town of Chauvigny, and part of their companies. The
Saturday they passed the bridge and followed the king, who
was then a three leagues before, and took the way among
bushes without a wood side to go to Poitiers.

The same Saturday the prince and his company dislodged
from a little village thereby, and sent before him certain
currours to see if they might find any adventure and to hear
where the Frenchmen were. They were in number a threescore men of arms well horsed, and with them was the lord
Eustace d'Aubrecicourt and the lord John of Ghistelles, and
by adventure the Englishmen and Frenchmen met together
by the foresaid wood side. The Frenchmen knew anon how
they were their enemies; then in haste they did on their
helmets and displayed their banners and came a great pace
towards the Englishmen: they were in number a two hundred men of arms. When the Englishmen saw them, and
that they were so great a number, then they determined to

fly and let the Frenchmen chase them, for they knew well
the prince with his host was not far behind. Then they
turned their horses and took the corner of the wood, and
the Frenchmen after them crying their cries and made great
noise. And as they chased, they came on the prince's battle
or they were ware thereof themselves; the prince tarried
there to have word again from them that he sent forth.
The lord Raoul de Coucy with his banner went so far forward that he was under the prince's banner: there was a
sore battle and the knight fought valiantly; howbeit he
was there taken, and the earl of Joigny, the viscount of
Brosse, the lord of Chauvigny and all the other taken or
slain, but a few that scaped. And by the prisoners the
prince knew how the French king followed him in such wise
that he could not eschew the battle:[2] then he assembled
together all his men and commanded that no man should go
before the marshals' banners. Thus the prince rode that
Saturday from the morning till it was against night, so that
he came within two little leagues of Poitiers. Then the
captal de Buch, sir Aymenion of Pommiers, the lord Bartholomew of Burghersh and the lord Eustace d'Aubrecicourt,
all these the prince sent forth to see if they might know
what the Frenchmen did. These knights departed with two
hundred men of arms well horsed: they rode so far that they
saw the great battle of the king's, they saw all the fields
covered with men of arms. These Englishmen could not
forbear, but set on the tail of the French host and cast down
many to the earth and took divers prisoners, so that the
host began to stir, and tidings thereof came to the French
king as he was entering into the city of Poitiers. Then he
returned again and made all his host do the same, so that
Saturday it was very late or he was lodged in the field.
The English currours returned again to the prince and
shewed him all that they saw and knew, and said how the
French host was a great number of people. 'Well,' said the
prince, 'in the name of God let us now study how we shall
fight with them at our advantage.' That night the Englishmen lodged in a strong place among hedges, vines and

---

[2] Or rather, 'that the French king had gone in front of them (les avoit
advancez) and that he could in no way depart without being fought with.'

bushes, and their host well watched, and so was the French host.

OF THE ORDER OF THE FRENCHMEN BEFORE THE BATTLE OF POITIERS

ON the Sunday in the morning the French king, who had great desire to fight with the Englishmen, heard his mass in his pavilion and was houselled, and his four sons with him. After mass there came to him the duke of Orleans, the duke of Bourbon, the earl of Ponthieu, the lord Jaques of Bourbon,[1] the duke of Athens, constable of France, the earl of Tancarville, the earl of Sarrebruck, the earl of Dammartin, the earl of Ventadour, and divers other great barons of France and of other neighbours holding of France, as the lord Clermont, the lord Arnold d'Audrehem, marshal of France, the lord of Saint-Venant, the lord John of Landas, the lord Eustace Ribemont, the lord Fiennes, the lord Geoffrey of Charny, the lord Chatillon, the lord of Sully, the lord of Nesle, sir Robert Duras and divers other; all these with the king went to counsel. Then finally it was ordained that all manner of men should draw into the field, and every lord to display his banner and to set forth in the name of God and Saint Denis: then trumpets blew up through the host and every man mounted on horseback and went into the field, where they saw the king's banner wave with the wind. There might a been seen great nobless of fair harness and rich armoury of banners and pennons; for there was all the flower of France, there was none durst abide at home without he would be shamed for ever. Then it was ordained by the advice of the constable and marshals to be made three battles, and in each ward sixteen thousand men of arms all mustered and passed for men of arms. The first battle the duke of Orleans to govern, with thirty-six banners and twice as many pennons, the second the duke of Normandy and his two brethren the lord Louis and the lord John, the third the king himself: and while that these battles were setting in array, the king called to him the lord Eustace Ribemont, the lord John of Landas and the lord

[1] That is, Jaques de Bourbon, earl of la Marche and Ponthieu.

Richard of Beaujeu, and said to them: 'Sirs, ride on before to see the dealing of the Englishmen and advise well what number they be and by what means we may fight with them, other afoot or a-horseback.' These three knights rode forth and the king was on a white courser and said a-high to his men: 'Sirs, among you, when ye be at Paris, at Chartres, at Orleans, then ye do threat the Englishmen and desire to be in arms out against them. Now ye be come thereto: I shall now shew you them: now shew forth your evil will that ye bear them and revenge your displeasures and damages that they have done you, for without doubt we shall fight with them.' Such as heard him said: 'Sir, in God's name so be it; that would we see [2] gladly.'

Therewith the three knights returned again to the king, who demanded of them tidings. Then sir Eustace of Ribemont answered for all and said: 'Sir, we have seen the Englishmen: by estimation they be two thousand men of arms and four thousand archers and a fifteen hundred of other. Howbeit they be in a strong place, and as far as we can imagine they are in one battle; howbeit they be wisely ordered, and along the way they have fortified strongly the hedges and bushes: one part of their archers are along by the hedge, so that none can go nor ride that way, but must pass by them, and that way must ye go an ye purpose to fight with them. In this hedge there is but one entry and one issue by likelihood that four horsemen may ride afront. At the end of this hedge, whereas no man can go nor ride, there be men of arms afoot and archers afore them in manner of a herse, so that they will not be lightly discomfited.' [3] 'Well,' said the king, 'what will ye then counsel us to do?' Sir Eustace said: 'Sir, let us all be afoot,

<hr />

[2] 'Verrons': but a better reading is 'ferons,' 'that will we do gladly.'
[3] The translation of this passage is unsatisfactory. It should be: ' Howbeit they have ordered it wisely, and have taken post along the road, which is fortified strongly with hedges and thickets, and they have beset this hedge on one side (*or according to another text,* on one side and on the other) with their archers, so that one cannot enter nor ride along their road except by them, and that way must he go who purposes to fight with them. In this hedge there is but one entry and one issue, where by likelihood four men of arms, as on the road, might ride a-front. At the end of this hedge among vines and thorn-bushes, where no man can go nor ride, are their men of arms all afoot, and they have set in front of them their archers in manner of a harrow, whom it would not be easy to discomfit.

except three hundred men of arms, well horsed, of the best in your host and most hardiest, to the intent they somewhat to break and to open the archers, and then your battles to follow on quickly afoot and so to fight with their men of arms hand to hand. This is the best advice that I can give you: if any other think any other way better, let him speak.'

The king said: 'Thus shall it be done': then the two marshals rode from battle to battle and chose out a three hundred knights and squires of the most expert men of arms of all the host, every man well armed and horsed. Also it was ordained that the battles of Almains should abide still on horseback to comfort the marshals, if need were, whereof the earl of Sarrebruck, the earl of Nidau and the earl of Nassau were captains. King John of France was there armed, and twenty other in his apparel; and he did put the guiding of his eldest son to the lord of Saint-Venant, the lord of Landas and the lord Thibault of Vaude-nay; and the lord Arnold of Cervolles, called the archpriest,[4] was armed in the armour of the young earl of Alençon.

HOW THE CARDINAL OF PERIGORD TREATED TO MAKE AGREEMENT BETWEEN THE FRENCH KING AND THE PRINCE BEFORE THE BATTLE OF POITIERS

WHEN the French king's battles was ordered and every lord under his banner among their own men, then it was commanded that every man should cut their spears to a five foot long and every man to put off their spurs. Thus as they were ready to approach, the cardinal of Perigord[1] came in great haste to the king. He came the same morning from Poitiers; he kneeled down to the king and held up his hands and desired him for God's sake a little to abstain setting forward till he had spoken with him: then he said: 'Sir, ye have here all the flower of your realm against a handful of Englishmen as to regard your company,[2] and, sir, if ye

---

[4] Arnaud de Cervolles, one of the most celebrated adventurers of the 14th century, called the archpriest because though a layman he possessed the ecclesiastical fief of Vélines.

[1] Talleyrand de Périgord.

[2] The meaning is, ' Ye have here all the flower of your realm against a handful of people, for so the Englishmen are as compared with your company.'

may have them accorded to you without battle, it shall be more profitable and honourable to have them by that manner rather than to adventure so noble chivalry as ye have here present. Sir, I require you in the name of God and humility that I may ride to the prince and shew him what danger ye have him in.' The king said: 'It pleaseth me well, but return again shortly.' The cardinal departed and diligently he rode to the prince, who was among his men afoot: then the cardinal alighted and came to the prince, who received him courteously. Then the cardinal after his salutation made he said: 'Certainly, fair son, if you and your council advise justly the puissance of the French king, ye will suffer me to treat to make a peace between you, an I may.' The prince, who was young and lusty, said: 'Sir, the honour of me and of my people saved, I would gladly fall to any reasonable way.' Then the cardinal said: 'Sir, ye say well, and I shall accord you, an I can; for it should be great pity if so many noblemen and other as be here on both parties should come together by battle.' Then the cardinal rode again to the king and said: 'Sir, ye need not to make any great haste to fight with your enemies, for they cannot fly from you though they would, they be in such a ground: wherefore, sir, I require you forbear for this day till tomorrow the sun-rising.' The king was loath to agree thereto, for some of his council would not consent to it; but finally the cardinal shewed such reasons, that the king accorded that respite: and in the same place there was pight up a pavilion of red silk fresh and rich, and gave leave for that day every man to draw to their lodgings except the constable's and marshals' battles.

That Sunday all the day the cardinal travailed in riding from the one host to the other gladly to agree them: but the French king would not agree without he might have four of the principallest of the Englishmen at his pleasure, and the prince and all the other to yield themselves simply: howbeit there were many great offers made. The prince offered to render into the king's hands all that ever he had won in that voyage, towns and castles, and to quit all prisoners that he or any of his men had taken in that season, and also to swear not to be armed against the French king in seven year after; but the king and his council would none thereof: the uttermost that he would do was, that the prince and a hundred of his knights should yield themselves into the king's prison; otherwise he would not: the which the prince would in no wise agree unto.

In the mean season that the cardinal rode thus between the hosts in trust to do some good, certain knights of France and of England both rode forth the same Sunday, because it was truce for that day, to coast the hosts and to behold the dealing of their enemies. So it fortuned that the lord John Chandos rode the same day coasting the French host, and in like manner the lord of Clermont, one of the French marshals, had ridden forth and aviewed the state of the English host; and as these two knights returned towards their hosts, they met together: each of them bare one manner of device, a blue lady embroidered in a sunbeam above on their apparel. Then the lord Clermont said: ' Chandos, how long have ye taken on you to bear my device?' ' Nay, ye bear mine,' said Chandos, ' for it is as well mine as yours.' ' I deny that,' said Clermont, ' but an it were not for the truce this day between us, I should make it good on you incontinent that ye have no right to bear my device.' ' Ah, sir,' said Chandos, ' ye shall find me to-morrow ready to defend you and to prove by feat of arms that it is as well mine as yours.' Then Clermont said: ' Chandos, these be well the words of you Englishmen, for ye can devise nothing of new, but all that ye see is good and fair.' So they departed without any more doing, and each of them returned to their host.

The cardinal of Perigord could in no wise that Sunday make any agreement between the parties, and when it was near night he returned to Poitiers. That night the Frenchmen took their ease; they had provision enough, and the Englishmen had great default; they could get no forage, nor they could not depart thence without danger of their enemies. That Sunday the Englishmen made great dikes and hedges about their archers, to be the more stronger; and on the Monday in the morning the prince and his company were ready apparelled as they were before, and about the sun-rising in like manner were the Frenchmen. The same morning betimes the cardinal came again to the French host and thought by his preaching to pacify the parties; but then the Frenchmen said to him: 'Return whither ye will: bring hither no more words of treaty nor peace: and ye love yourself depart shortly.' When the cardinal saw that he travailed in vain, he took leave of the king and then he went to the prince and said: 'Sir, do what ye can: there is no remedy but to abide the battle, for I can find none accord in the French king.' Then the prince said: 'The same is our intent and all our people: God help the right!' So the cardinal returned to Poitiers. In his company there were certain knights and squires, men of arms, who were more favourable to the French king than to the prince: and when they saw that the parties should fight, they stale from their masters and went to the French host; and they made their captain the chatelain of Amposte,[3] who was as then there with the cardinal, who knew nothing thereof till he was come to Poitiers.

The certainty of the order of the Englishmen was shewed to the French king, except they had ordained three hundred men a-horseback and as many archers a-horseback to coast under covert of the mountain and to strike into the battle of the duke of Normandy, who was under the mountain afoot. This ordinance they had made of new, that the Frenchmen knew not of. The prince was with his battle down among the vines and had closed in the weakest part with their carriages.

Now will I name some of the principal lords and knights that were there with the prince: the earl of Warwick, the earl of Suffolk, the earl of Salisbury, the earl of Oxford, the lord Raynold Cobham, the lord Spencer, the lord James Audley, the lord Peter his brother, the lord Berkeley, the lord Bassett, the lord Warin, the lord Delaware, the lord Manne, the lord Willoughby, the lord Bartholomew de Burghersh, the lord of Felton, the lord Richard of Pembroke, the lord Stephen of Cosington, the lord Bradetane and other Englishmen; and of Gascon there was the lord of Pommiers, the lord of Languiran, the captal of Buch, the lord John of Caumont, the lord de Lesparre, the lord of

---

[3] Amposta, a fortress in Catalonia.

Rauzan, the lord of Condon, the lord of Montferrand, the lord of Landiras, the lord soudic of Latrau and other that I cannot name; and of Hainowes the lord Eustace d'Aubrecicourt, the lord John of Ghistelles, and two other strangers, the lord Daniel Pasele and the lord Denis of Morbeke: all the prince's company passed not an eight thousand men one and other, and the Frenchmen were a sixty thousand fighting men, whereof there were more than three thousand knights.

OF THE BATTLE OF POITIERS BETWEEN THE PRINCE OF WALES AND THE FRENCH KING

WHEN the prince saw that he should have battle and that the cardinal was gone without any peace or truce making, and saw that the French king did set but little store by him, he said then to his men: 'Now, sirs, though we be but a small company as in regard to the puissance of our enemies, let us not be abashed therefor; for the victory lieth not in the multitude of people, but whereas God will send it. If it fortune that the journey be ours, we shall be the most honoured people of all the world; and if we die in our right quarrel, I have the king my father and brethren, and also ye have good friends and kinsmen; these shall revenge us. Therefore, sirs, for God's sake I require you do your devoirs this day; for if God be pleased and Saint George, this day ye shall see me a good knight.' These words and such other that the prince spake comforted all his people. The lord sir John Chandos that day never went from the prince, nor also the lord James Audley of a great season; but when he saw that they should needs fight, he said to the prince: 'Sir, I have served always truly my lord your father and you also, and shall do as long as I live. I say this because I made once a vow that the first battle that other the king your father or any of his children should be at, how that I would be one of the first setters on,[1] or else to die in the pain: therefore I require your grace, as in reward for any service that ever I did to the king your father or to you, that you will give me licence to depart from you and to set myself

[1] 'The first setter-on and the best combatant.'

thereas I may accomplish my vow.' The prince accorded to his desire and said, ' Sir James, God give you this day that grace to be the best knight of all other,' and so took him by the hand. Then the knight departed from the prince and went to the foremost front of all the battles, all only accompanied with four squires, who promised not to fail him. This lord James was a right sage and a valiant knight, and by him was much of the host ordained and governed the day before. Thus sir James was in front of the battle ready to fight with the battle of the marshals of France. In like wise the lord Eustace d'Aubrecicourt did his pain to be one of the foremost to set on. When sir James Audley began to set forward to his enemies, it fortuned to sir Eustace d'Aubrecicourt as ye shall hear after. Ye have heard before how the Almains in the French host were appointed to be still a-horseback. Sir Eustace being a-horseback laid his spear in the rest and ran into the French battle, and then a knight of Almaine, called the lord Louis of Recombes, who bare a shield silver, five roses gules, and sir Eustace bare ermines, two branches of gules,[2]—when this Almain saw the lord Eustace come from his company, he rode against him and they met so rudely, that both knights fell to the earth. The Almain was hurt in the shoulder, therefore he rose not so quickly as did sir Eustace, who when he was up and had taken his breath, he came to the other knight as he lay on the ground; but then five other knights of Almaine came on him all at once and bare him to the earth, and so perforce there he was taken prisoner and brought to the earl of Nassau, who as then took no heed of him; and I cannot say whether they sware him prisoner or no, but they tied him to a chare and there let him stand.[3]

Then the battle began on all parts, and the battles of the marshals of France approached, and they set forth that were appointed to break the array of the archers. They entered a-horseback into the way where the great hedges were on both sides set full of archers. As soon as the men of arms entered, the archers began to shoot on both sides and did slay and hurt horses and knights, so that the horses when

[2] That is, two hamedes gules on a field ermine.
[3] 'They tied him on to a cart with their harness.'

they felt the sharp arrows they would in no wise go forward, but drew aback and flang and took on so fiercely, that many of them fell on their masters, so that for press they could not rise again; insomuch that the marshals' battle could never come at the prince. Certain knights and squires that were well horsed passed through the archers and thought to approach to the prince, but they could not. The lord James Audley with his four squires was in the front of that battle and there did marvels in arms, and by great prowess he came and fought with sir Arnold d'Audrehem under his own banner, and there they fought long together and sir Arnold was there sore handled. The battle of the marshals began to disorder by reason of the shot of the archers with the aid of the men of arms, who came in among them and slew of them and did what they list, and there was the lord Arnold d'Audrehem taken prisoner by other men than by sir James Audley or by his four squires; for that day he never took prisoner, but always fought and went on his enemies.

Also on the French party the lord John Clermont fought under his own banner as long as he could endure: but there he was beaten down and could not be relieved nor ransomed, but was slain without mercy: some said it was because of the words that he had the day before to sir John Chandos. So within a short space the marshals' battles were discomfited, for they fell one upon another and could not go forth;[4] and the Frenchmen that were behind and could not get forward reculed back and came on the battle of the duke of Normandy, the which was great and thick and were afoot, but anon they began to open behind;[5] for when they knew that the marshals' battle was discomfited, they took their horses and departed, he that might best. Also they saw a rout of Englishmen coming down a little mountain a-horseback, and many archers with them, who brake in on the side of the duke's battle. True to say, the archers did their company that day great advantage; for they shot so thick that the Frenchmen wist not on what side to take heed, and little and little the Englishmen won ground on them.

4 ' Ne pooient aler avant.'
5 ' Which was great and thick in front (pardevant), but anon it became open and thin behind.'

And when the men of arms of England saw that the marshals' battle was discomfited and that the duke's battle began to disorder and open, they leapt then on their horses, the which they had ready by them: then they assembled together and cried, 'Saint George! Guyenne!' and the lord Chandos said to the prince: 'Sir, take your horse and ride forth; this journey is yours: God is this day in your hands: get us to the French king's battle, for their lieth all the sore of the matter. I think verily by his valiantness he will not fly: I trust we shall have him by the grace of God and Saint George, so he be well fought withal: and, sir, I heard you say that this day I should see you a good knight.' The prince said, 'Let us go forth; ye shall not see me this day return back,' and said, 'Advance, banner, in the name of God and of Saint George.' The knight that bare it did his commandment: there was then a sore battle and a perilous, and many a man overthrown, and he that was once down could not be relieved again without great succour and aid. As the prince rode and entered in among his enemies, he saw on his right hand in a little bush lying dead the lord Robert of Duras and his banner by him,[6] and a ten or twelve of his men about him. Then the prince said to two of his squires and to three archers: 'Sirs, take the body of this knight on a targe and bear him to Poitiers, and present him from me to the cardinal of Perigord, and say how I salute him by that token.' And this was done. The prince was informed that the cardinal's men were on the field against him, the which was not pertaining to the right order of arms, for men of the church that cometh and goeth for treaty of peace ought not by reason to bear harness nor to fight for neither of the parties; they ought to be indifferent: and because these men had done so, the prince was displeased with the cardinal, and therefore he sent unto him his nephew the lord Robert of Duras dead: and the chatelain of Amposte was taken, and the prince would have had his head stricken off, because he was pertaining to the cardinal, but then the lord Chandos said: 'Sir, suffer for a season: intend to a greater matter: and peradventure the cardinal will make such excuse that ye shall be content.'

[6] The original adds, 'qui estoit de France au sentoir (sautoir) de gueulles.'

Then the prince and his company dressed them on the
battle of the duke of Athens, constable of France. There
was many a man slain and cast to the earth. As the Frenchmen fought in companies, they cried, 'Mountjoy! Saint
Denis!' and the Englishmen, 'Saint George! Guyenne!'
Anon the prince with his company met with the battle of
Almains, whereof the earl of Sarrebruck, the earl Nassau
and the earl Nidau were captains, but in a short space they
were put to flight: the archers shot so wholly together that
none durst come in their dangers: they slew many a man
that could not come to no ransom: these three earls was
there slain, and divers other knights and squires of their
company, and there was the lord d'Aubrecicourt rescued
by his own men and set on horseback, and after he did that
day many feats of arms and took good prisoners. When the
duke of Normandy's battle saw the prince approach, they
thought to save themselves, and so the duke and the king's
children, the earl of Poitiers and the earl of Touraine,
who were right young, believed their governours and so departed from the field, and with them more than eight hundred spears, that strake no stroke that day. Howbeit the
lord Guichard d'Angle and the lord John of Saintré, who
were with the earl of Poitiers, would not fly, but entered
into the thickest press of the battle. The king's three sons
took the way to Chauvigny, and the lord John of Landas
and the lord Thibauld of Vaudenay, who were set to await
on the duke of Normandy, when they had brought the duke
a long league from the battle, then they took leave of the
duke and desired the lord of Saint-Venant that he should
not leave the duke, but to bring him in safeguard, whereby
he should win more thank of the king than to abide still
in the field. Then they met also the duke of Orleans and a
great company with him, who were also departed from the
field with clear hands: there were many good knights and
squires, though that their masters departed from the field,
yet they had rather a died than to have had any reproach.

Then the king's battle came on the Englishmen: there was
a sore fight and many a great stroke given and received.
The king and his youngest son met with the battle of the
English marshals, the earl of Warwick and the earl of

Suffolk, and with them of Gascons the captal of Buch, the lord of Pommiers, the lord Amery of Tastes, the lord of Mussidan, the lord of Languiran and the lord de Latrau. To the French party there came time enough the lord John of Landas and the lord of Vaudenay; they alighted afoot and went into the king's battle, and a little beside fought the duke of Athens, constable of France, and a little above him the duke of Bourbon and many good nights of Bourbonnais and of Picardy with him, and a little on the one side there were the Poitevins, the lord de Pons, the lord of Partenay, the lord of Dammartin, the lord of Tannay-Bouton, the lord of Surgieres, the lord John Saintré, the lord Guichard d'Angle, the lord Argenton, the lord of Linieres, the lord of Montendre and divers other, also the viscount of Roche-chouart and the earl of Aunay;[7] and of Burgoyne the lord James of Beaujeu, the lord de Chateau-Vilain and other: in another part there was the earl of Ventadour and of Montpensier, the lord James of Bourbon, the lord John d'Artois and also the lord James his brother, the lord Arnold of Cervolles, called the archpriest, armed for the young earl of Alençon; and of Auvergne there was the lord of Mer-cœur, the lord de la Tour, the lord of Chalençon, the lord of Montaigu, the lord of Rochfort, the lord d'Acier, the lord d'Acon; and of Limousin there was the lord de Melval, the lord of Mareuil, the lord of Pierrebuffiere; and of Picardy there was the lord William of Nesle, the lord Arnold of Ray-neval, the lord Geoffrey of Saint-Dizier, the lord of Chauny, the lord of Helly, the lord of Montsault, the lord of Hangest and divers other: and also in the king's battle there was the earl Douglas of Scotland, who fought a season right valiantly, but when he saw the discomfiture, he departed and saved himself; for in no wise he would be taken of the Englishmen, he had rather been there slain. On the English part the lord James Audley with the aid of his four squires fought always in the chief of the battle: he was sore hurt in the body and in the visage: as long as his breath served him he fought; at last at the end of the battle his four squires took and brought him out of the field and laid him under a hedge side for to refresh him; and they unarmed

---

[7] 'Le conte d'Aulnoy,' but it should be 'visconte.'

him and bound up his wounds as well as they could. On the French party king John was that day a full right good knight: if the fourth part of his men had done their devoirs as well as he did, the journey had been his by all likelihood. Howbeit they were all slain and taken that were there, except a few that saved themselves, that were with the king.[8] There was slain the duke Peter of Bourbon, the lord Guichard of Beaujeu, the lord of Landas, and the duke of Athens, constable of France, the bishop of Chalons in Champagne, the lord William of Nesle, the lord Eustace of Ribemont, the lord de la Tour, the lord William of Montaigu, sir Grismouton of Chambly, sir Baudrin de la Heuse, and many other, as they fought by companies; and there were taken prisoners the lord of Vaudenay, the lord of Pompadour, and the archpriest, sore hurt, the earl of Vaudimont, the earl of Mons, the earl of Joinville, the earl of Vendome, sir Louis of Melval, the lord Pierrebuffiere and the lord of Serignac: there were at that brunt, slain and taken more than two hundred knights.[9]

OF TWO FRENCHMEN THAT FLED FROM THE BATTLE OF POITIERS AND TWO ENGLISHMEN THAT FOLLOWED THEM

Among the battles, recounterings, chases and pursuits that were made that day in the field, it fortuned so to sir Oudart of Renty that when he departed from the field because he saw the field was lost without recovery, he thought not to abide the danger of the Englishmen; wherefore he fled all alone and was gone out of the field a league, and an English knight pursued him and ever cried to him and said, 'Return again, sir knight, it is a shame to fly away thus.'

[8] 'Howbeit they that stayed acquitted them as well as they might, so that they were all slain or taken. Few escaped of those that set themselves with the king': or according to the fuller text: 'Few escaped of those that alighted down on the sand by the side of the king their lord.'

[9] The translator has chosen to rearrange the above list of killed, wounded or taken, which the French text gives in order as they fought, saying that in one part there fell the duke of Bourbon, sir Guichard of Beaujeu and sir John of Landas, and there were severely wounded or taken the archpriest, sir Thibaud of Vodenay and sir Baudouin d'Annequin; in another there were slain the duke of Athens and the bishop of Chalons, and taken the earl of Vaudemont and Joinville and the earl of Vendome: a little above this there were slain sir William de Nesle, sir Eustace de Ribemont and others, and taken sir Louis de Melval, the lord of Pierrebufière and the lord of Seregnach.

Then the knight turned, and the English knight thought to
have stricken him with his spear in the targe, but he failed,
for sir Oudart swerved aside from the stroke, but he failed
not the English knight, for he strake him such a stroke on
the helm with his sword, that he was astonied and fell from
his horse to the earth and lay still. Then sir Oudart alighted
and came to him or he could rise, and said, 'Yield you,
rescue or no rescue, or else I shall slay you.' The Englishman yielded and went with him, and afterward was ransomed. Also it fortuned that another squire of Picardy
called John de Hellenes was fled from the battle and met
with his page, who delivered him a new fresh horse, whereon
he rode away alone. The same season there was in the
field the lord Berkeley of England, a young lusty knight,
who the same day reared his banner, and he all alone
pursued the said John of Hellenes. And when he had
followed the space of a league, the said John turned again
and laid his sword in the rest instead of a spear, and so
came running toward the lord Berkeley, who lift up his
sword to have stricken the squire; but when he saw the
stroke come, he turned from it, so that the Englishman
lost his stroke and John strake him as he passed on the
arm, that the lord Berkeley's sword fell into the field.
When he saw his sword down, he lighted suddenly off
his horse and came to the place where his sword lay,
and as he stooped down to take up his sword, the French
squire did pike his sword at him, and by hap strake him
through both the thighs, so that the knight fell to the earth
and could not help himself. And John alighted off his
horse and took the knight's sword that lay on the ground,
and came to him and demanded if he would yield him or
not. The knight then demanded his name. 'Sir,' said he,
'I hight John of Hellenes; but what is your name?' 'Certainly,' said the knight, 'my name is Thomas and am lord
of Berkeley, a fair castle on the river of Severn in the
marches of Wales.' 'Well, sir,' quoth the squire, 'then ye
shall be my prisoner, and I shall bring you in safe-guard
and I shall see that you shall be healed of your hurt.' 'Well,'
said the knight, 'I am content to be your prisoner, for ye
have by law of arms won me.' There he sware to be his

prisoner, rescue or no rescue. Then the squire drew forth the sword out of the knight's thighs and the wound was open: then he wrapped and bound the wound and set him on his horse and so brought him fair and easily to Chatel- leraut, and there tarried more than fifteen days for his sake and did get him remedy for his hurt: and when he was somewhat amended, then he gat him a litter and so brought him at his ease to his house in Picardy. There he was more than a year till he was perfectly whole; and when he de- parted he paid for his ransom six thousand nobles, and so this squire was made a knight by reason of the profit that he had of the lord Berkeley.

HOW KING JOHN WAS TAKEN PRISONER AT THE BATTLE OF POITIERS

OFTENTIMES the adventures of amours and of war are more fortunate and marvellous than any man can think or wish. Truly this battle, the which was near to Poitiers in the fields of Beauvoir and Maupertuis, was right great and perilous, and many deeds of arms there was done the which all came not to knowledge. The fighters on both sides en- dured much pain: king John with his own hands did that day marvels in arms: he had an axe in his hands wherewith he defended himself and fought in the breaking of the press. Near to the king there was taken the earl of Tancarville, sir Jaques of Bourbon earl of Ponthieu, and the lord John of Artois earl of Eu, and a little above that under the ban- ner of the captal of Buch was taken sir Charles of Artois and divers other knights and squires. The chase endured to the gates of Poitiers: there were many slain and beaten down, horse and man, for they of Poitiers closed their gates and would suffer none to enter; wherefore in the street before the gate was horrible murder, men hurt and beaten down. The Frenchmen yielded themselves as far off as they might know an Englishman: there were divers En- glish archers that had four, five or six prisoners: the lord of Pons, a great baron of Poitou, was there slain, and many other knights and squires; and there was taken the earl of Rochechouart, the lord of Dammartin, the lord of Partenay, and of Saintonge the lord of Montendre and the lord John of Saintré, but he was so sore hurt that he had never health after: he was reputed for one of the best knights in France. And there was left for dead among other dead men the lord Guichard d'Angle, who fought that day by the king right valiantly, and so did the lord of Charny, on whom was great press, because he bare the sovereign banner of the king's: his own banner was also in the field, the which was of gules, three scutcheons silver. So many Englishmen and Gascons come to that part, that perforce they opened the king's battle, so that the Frenchmen were so mingled among their enemies that sometime there was five men upon one gentleman. There was taken the lord of Pompadour and[1] the lord Bartholomew de Burghersh, and there was slain sir Geoffrey of Charny with the king's banner in his hands: also the lord Raynold Cobham slew the earl of Dammartin. Then there was a great press to take the king, and such as knew him cried, ' Sir, yield you, or else ye are but dead.' There was a knight of Saint-Omer's, retained in wages with the king of England, called sir Denis Morbeke, who had served the Englishmen five year before, because in his youth he had forfeited the realm of France for a murder that he did at Saint-Omer's. It happened so well for him, that he was next to the king when they were about to take him: he stept forth into the press, and by strength of his body and arms he came to the French king and said in good French, ' Sir, yield you.' The king beheld the knight and said: ' To whom shall I yield me? Where is my cousin the prince of Wales? If I might see him, I would speak with him.' Denis answered and said: ' Sir, he is not here; but yield you to me and I shall bring you to him.' ' Who be you? ' quoth the king. ' Sir,' quoth he, ' I am Denis of Morbeke, a knight of Artois; but I serve the king of England because I am banished the realm of France and I have forfeited all that I had there.' Then the king gave him his right gauntlet, saying, ' I yield me to you.' There was a great press about the king, for every man enforced him to say,[2] ' I have taken him,' so that the king

---

[1] This ' and ' should be ' by,' but the French text is responsible for the mistake.   [2] ' S'efforçoit de dire.'

could not go forward with his young son the lord Philip with him because of the press.

The prince of Wales, who was courageous and cruel as a lion, took that day great pleasure to fight and to chase his enemies. The lord John Chandos, who was with him, of all that day never left him nor never took heed of taking of any prisoner: then at the end of the battle he said to the prince: ' Sir, it were good that you rested here and set your banner a-high in this bush, that your people may draw hither, for they be sore spread abroad, nor I can see no more banners nor pennons of the French party; wherefore, sir, rest and refresh you, for ye be sore chafed.' Then the prince's banner was set up a-high on a bush, and trumpets and clarions began to sown. Then the prince did off his bassenet, and the knights for his body and they of his chamber were ready about him, and a red pavilion pight up, and then drink was brought forth to the prince and for such lords as were about him, the which still increased as they came from the chase: there they tarried and their prisoners with them. And when the two marshals were come to the prince, he demanded of them if they knew any tiding of the French king. They answered and said: ' Sir, we hear none of certainty, but we think verily he is other dead or taken, for he is not gone out of the battles.' Then the prince said to the earl of Warwick and to sir Raynold Cobham: ' Sirs, I require you go forth and see what ye can know, that at your return ye may shew me the truth.' These two lords took their horses and departed from the prince and rode up a little hill to look about them: then they perceived a flock of men of arms coming together right wearily:[a] there was the French king afoot in great peril, for Englishmen and Gascons were his masters; they had taken him from sir Denis Morbeke perforce, and such as were most of force said, ' I have taken him.' ' Nay,' quoth another, ' I have taken him': so they strave which should have him. Then the French king, to eschew that peril, said: 'Sirs, strive not: lead me courteously, and my son, to my cousin the prince, and strive not for my taking, for I am so great a lord to make you all rich.' The king's words somewhat ap-

[a] 'Lentement.'

peased them; howbeit ever as they went they made riot and brawled for the taking of the king. When the two foresaid lords saw and heard that noise and strife among them, they came to them and said: 'Sirs, what is the matter that ye strive for?' 'Sirs,' said one of them, 'it is for the French king, who is here taken prisoner, and there be more than ten knights and squires that challengeth the taking of him and of his son.' Then the two lords entered into the press and caused every man to draw aback, and commanded them in the prince's name on pain of their heads to make no more noise nor to approach the king no nearer, without they were commanded. Then every man gave room to the lords, and they alighted and did their reverence to the king, and so brought him and his son in peace and rest to the prince of Wales.

OF THE GIFT THAT THE PRINCE GAVE TO THE LORD AUDLEY AFTER THE BATTLE OF POITIERS

As soon as the earl of Warwick and the lord Cobham were departed from the prince, as ye have heard before, then the prince demanded of the knights that were about him for the lord Audley, if any knew anything of him. Some knights that were there answered and said: 'Sir, he is sore hurt and lieth in a litter here beside.' 'By my faith,' said the prince, 'of his hurts I am right sorry: go and know if he may be brought hither, or else I will go and see him thereas he is.' Then two knights came to the lord Audley and said: 'Sir, the prince desireth greatly to see you, other ye must go to him or else he will come to you.' 'Ah, sir,' said the knight, 'I thank the prince when he thinketh on so poor a knight as I am.' Then he called eight of his servants and caused them to bear him in his litter to the place whereas the prince was. Then the prince took him in his arms and kissed him and made him great cheer and said: 'Sir James, I ought greatly to honour you, for by your valiance ye have this day achieved the grace and renown of us all, and ye are reputed for the most valiant of all other.' 'Ah, sir,' said the knight, 'ye say as it pleaseth you: I would it were so: and if I have this day anything advanced myself to

serve you and to accomplish the vow that I made, it ought
not to be reputed to me any prowess.' 'Sir James,' said the
prince, 'I and all ours take you in this journey for the best
doer in arms, and to the intent to furnish you the better
to pursue the wars, I retain you for ever to be my knight
with five hundred marks of yearly revenues, the which I
shall assign you on mine heritage in England.' 'Sir,' said
the knight, 'God grant me to deserve the great goodness
that ye shew me': and so he took his leave of the prince,
for he was right feeble, and so his servants brought him to
his lodging. And as soon as he was gone, the earl of Warwick and the lord Cobham returned to the prince and presented to him the French king. The prince made lowly
reverence to the king and caused wine and spices to be
brought forth, and himself served the king in sign of great
love.

HOW THE ENGLISHMAN WON GREATLY AT THE
BATTLE OF POITIERS

THUS this battle was discomfited, as ye have heard, the
which was in the fields of Maupertuis a two leagues from
Poitiers the twenty-second day of September the year of
our Lord MCCCLVI. It begun in the morning[1] and ended at
noon, but as then all the Englishmen were not returned from
the chase; therefore the prince's banner stood on a bush to
draw all his men together, but it was well nigh night or all
came from the chase. And as it was reported, there was
slain all the flower of France, and there was taken with
the king and the lord Philip his son a seventeen earls, beside barons, knights and squires, and slain a five or six thousand of one and other. When every man was come from
the chase, they had twice as many prisoners as they were
in number in all. Then it was counselled among them because of the great charge and doubt to keep so many, that
they should put many of them to ransom incontinent in the
field, and so they did: and the prisoners found the Englishmen and Gascons right courteous; there were many that
day put to ransom and let go all only on their promise of

[1] 'Environ heure de prime.'

faith and truth to return again between that and Christmas
to Bordeaux with their ransoms. Then that night they
lay in the field beside whereas the battle had been: some
unarmed them, but not all, and unarmed all their prisoners, and every man made good cheer to his prisoner;
for that day whosoever took any prisoner, he was clear
his and might quit or ransom him at his pleasure. All
such as were there with the prince were all made rich
with honour and goods, as well by ransoming of prisoners
as by winning of gold, silver, plate, jewels, that was there
found: there was no man that did set anything by rich harness, whereof there was great plenty, for the Frenchmen
came thither richly beseen, weening to have had the journey
for them

HOW THE LORD JAMES AUDLEY GAVE TO HIS FOUR SQUIRES THE FIVE HUNDRED MARKS OF REVENUES THAT THE PRINCE HAD GIVEN HIM

WHEN sir James Audley was brought to his lodging, then
he sent for sir Peter Audley his brother and for the lord
Bartholomew of Burghersh, the lord Stephen of Cosington,
the lord of Willoughby and the lord Ralph Ferrers, all these
were of his lineage, and then he called before him his four
squires, that had served him that day well and truly. Then
he said to the said lords: 'Sirs, it hath pleased my lord the
prince to give me five hundred marks of revenues by year
in heritage, for the which gift I have done him but small
service with my body. Sirs, behold here these four squires,
who hath always served me truly and specially this day: that
honour that I have is by their valiantness. Wherefore I
will reward them: I give and resign into their hands the
gift that my lord the prince hath given me of five hundred
marks of yearly revenues, to them and to their heirs for
ever, in like manner as it was given me. I clearly disherit
me thereof and inherit them without any repeal[1] or condition.'
The lords and other that ere there, every man beheld other
and said among themselves: 'It cometh of a great nobleness

[1] 'Rappel,' *i. e.* power of recalling the gift. The word 'repeal' is a
correction of 'rebell.'

to give this gift.' They answered him with one voice: 'Sir, be it as God will; we shall bear witness in this behalf wheresoever we be come.' Then they departed from him, and some of them went to the prince, who the same night would make a supper to the French king and to the prisoners, for they had enough to do withal, of that the Frenchmen brought with them,[2] for the Englishmen wanted victual before, for some in three days had no bread before.

HOW THE PRINCE MADE A SUPPER TO THE FRENCH KING THE SAME DAY OF THE BATTLE

THE same day of the battle at night the prince made a supper in his lodging to the French king and to the most part of the great lords that were prisoners. The prince made the king and his son, the lord James of Bourbon, the lord John d'Artois, the earl of Tancarville, the earl of Estampes, the earl Dammartin, the earl of Joinville and the lord of Partenay to sit all at one board, and other lords, knights and squires at other tables; and always the prince served before the king as humbly as he could, and would not sit at the king's board for any desire that the king could make, but he said he was not sufficient to sit at the table with so great a prince as the king was. But then he said to the king: 'Sir, for God's sake make none evil nor heavy cheer, though God this day did not consent to follow your will; for, sir, surely the king my father shall bear you as much honour and amity as he may do, and shall accord with you so reasonably that ye shall ever be friends together after. And, sir, methinks ye ought to rejoice, though the journey be not as ye would have had it, for this day ye have won the high renown of prowess and have passed this day in valiantness all other of your party. Sir, I say not this to mock you, for all that be on our party, that saw every man's deeds, are plainly accorded by true sentence to give you the prize and chaplet.' Therewith the Frenchmen began to murmur and said among themselves how the prince had spoken nobly, and that by all estimation

[2] 'Who was to give the king of France a supper of his own provisions; for the French had brought great abundance with them, and provisions had failed among the English,' etc.

he should prove a noble man, if God send him life and to persevere in such good fortune.

HOW THE PRINCE RETURNED TO BORDEAUX
AFTER THE BATTLE OF POITIERS

WHEN supper was done, every man went to his lodging with their prisoners. The same night they put many to ransom and believed them on their faiths and troths, and ransomed them but easily, for they said they would set no knight's ransom so high, but that he might pay at his ease and maintain still his degree. The next day, when they had heard mass and taken some repast and that everything was trussed and ready, then they took their horses and rode towards Poitiers. The same night there was come to Poitiers the lord of Roye with a hundred spears: he was not at the battle, but he met the duke of Normandy near to Chauvigny, and the duke sent him to Poitiers to keep the town till they heard other tidings. When the lord of Roye knew that the Englishmen were so near coming to the city, he caused every man to be armed and every man to go to his defence to the walls, towers and gates; and the Englishmen passed by without any approaching, for they were so laded with gold, silver and prisoners, that in their returning they assaulted no fortress; they thought it a great deed if they might bring the French king, with their other prisoners and riches that they had won, in safeguard to Bordeaux. They rode but small journeys because of their prisoners and great carriages that they had: they rode in a day no more but four or five leagues and lodged ever betimes, and rode close together in good array saving the marshals' battles, who rode ever before with five hundred men of arms to open the passages as the prince should pass; but they found no encounters, for all the country was so frayed that every man drew to the fortresses.

As the prince rode, it was shewed him how the lord Audley had given to his four squires the gift of the five hundred marks that he had given unto him: then the prince sent for him and he was brought in his litter to the prince, who received him courteously and said: 'Sir James, we have knowledge that the revenues that we gave you, as soon as ye came to your lodging, you gave the same to four squires: we would know why ye did so, and whether the gift was agreeable to you or not.' 'Sir,' said the knight, 'it is of truth I have given it to them, and I shall shew you why I did so. These four squires that be here present have a long season served me well and truly in many great businesses and, sir, in this last battle they served me in such wise that an they had never done nothing else I was bound to reward them, and before the same day they had never nothing of me in reward. Sir, I am but a man alone; but by the aid and comfort of them I took on me to accomplish my vow long before made. I had been dead in the battle an they had not been: wherefore, sir, when I considered the love that they bare unto me, I had not been courteous if I would not a rewarded them. I thank God I have had and shall have enough as long as I live: I will never be abashed for lack of good. Sir, if I have done this without your pleasure, I require you to pardon me, for, sir, both I and my squires shall serve you as well as ever we did.' Then the prince said: 'Sir James, for anything that ye have done I cannot blame you, but can you good thank therefor; and for the valiantness of these squires, whom ye praise so much, I accord to them your gift, and I will render again to you six hundred marks in like manner as ye had the other.'

Thus the prince and his company did so much that they passed through Poitou and Saintonge without damage and came to Blaye, and there passed the river of Gironde and arrived in the good city of Bordeaux. It cannot be recorded the great feast and cheer that they of the city with the clergy made to the prince, and how honourably they were there received. The prince brought the French king into the abbey of Saint Andrew's, and there they lodged both, the king in one part and the prince in the other. The prince bought of the lords, knights and squires of Gascoyne the most part of the earls of the realm of France, such as were prisoners, and paid ready money for them. There was divers questions and challenges made between the knights and squires of Gascoyne for taking of the French king; howbeit Denis Morbeke by right of arms and by true

tokens that he shewed challenged him for his prisoner.
Another squire of Gascoyne called Bernard of Truttes said
how he had right to him: there was much ado and many
words before the prince and other lords that were there,
and because these two challenged each other to fight in that
quarrel, the prince caused the matter to rest till they came
in England and that no declaration should be made but
afore the king of England his father; but because the
French king himself aided to sustain the challenge of Denis
Morbeke, for he inclined more to him than to any other,
the prince therefore privily caused to be delivered to the
said sir Denis two thousand nobles to maintain withal his
estate.

Anon after the prince came to Bordeaux, the cardinal
of Perigord came thither, who was sent from the pope in
legation, as it was said. He was there more than fifteen
days or the prince would speak with him because of the
chatelain of Amposte and his men, who were against him
in the battle of Poitiers. The prince believed that the
cardinal sent them thither, but the cardinal did so much by
the means of the lord of Caumont, the lord of Montferrand and the captal of Buch, who were his cousins,
they shewed so good reasons to the prince, that he was
content to hear him speak. And when he was before the
prince, he excused himself so sagely that the prince and
his council held him excused, and so he fell again into the
prince's love and redeemed out his men by reasonable ransoms; and the chatelain was set to his ransom of ten thousand franks, the which he paid after. Then the cardinal
began to treat on the deliverance of the French king, but
I pass it briefly because nothing was done. Thus the prince,
the Gascons and Englishmen tarried still at Bordeaux till
it was Lent in great mirth and revel, and spent foolishly
the gold and silver that they had won. In England also
there was great joy when they heard tidings of the battle
of Poitiers, of the discomfiting of the Frenchmen and taking
of the king: great solemnities were made in all churches
and great fires and wakes throughout all England. The
knights and squires, such as were come home from that
journey, were much made of and praised more than other.

WAT TYLER'S REBELLION

HOW THE COMMONS OF ENGLAND REBELLED AGAINST THE NOBLEMEN

IN the mean season while this treaty was, there fell in England great mischief and rebellion of moving of the common people, by which deed England was at a point to have been lost without recovery. There was never realm nor country in so great adventure as it was in that time, and all because of the ease and riches that the common people were of, which moved them to this rebellion, as sometime they did in France, the which did much hurt, for by such incidents the realm of France hath been greatly grieved.

It was a marvellous thing and of poor foundation that this mischief began in England, and to give ensample to all manner of people I will speak thereof as it was done, as I was informed, and of the incidents thereof. There was an usage in England, and yet is in divers countries, that the noblemen hath great franchise over the commons and keepeth them in servage, that is to say, their tenants ought by custom to labour the lords' lands, to gather and bring home their corns, and some to thresh and to fan, and by servage to make their hay and to hew their wood and bring it home. All these things they ought to do by servage, and there be more of these people in England than in any other realm. Thus the noblemen and prelates are served by them, and especially in the county of Kent, Essex, Sussex and Bedford. These unhappy people of these said countries began to stir, because they said they were kept in great servage, and in the beginning of the world, they said, there were no bondmen, wherefore they maintained that none ought to be bond, without he did

treason to his lord, as Lucifer did to God; but they said
they could have no such battle,[1]   for they were neither
angels nor spirits, but men formed to the similitude of
their lords, saying why should they then be kept so under
like beasts; the which they said they would no longer
suffer, for they would be all one, and if they laboured or
did anything for their lords, they would have wages therefor
as well as other. And of this imagination was a foolish
priest in the country of Kent called John Ball, for the
which foolish words he had been three times in the bishop
of Canterbury's prison: for this priest used oftentimes on the
Sundays after mass, when the people were going out of
the minster, to go into the cloister and preach, and made
the people to assemble about him, and would say thus:
' Ah, ye good people, the matters goeth not well to pass in
England, nor shall not do till everything be common, and
that there be no villains nor gentlemen, but that we may
be all unied together, and that the lords be no greater
masters than we be. What have we deserved, or why
should we be kept thus in servage? We be all come from
one father and one mother, Adam and Eve: whereby can
they say or shew that they be greater lords than we be,
saving by that they cause us to win and labour for that
they dispend? They are clothed in velvet and camlet furred
with grise, and we be vestured with poor cloth: they have
their wines, spices and good bread, and we have the drawing out of the chaff[2] and drink water: they dwell in fair
houses, and we have the pain and travail, rain and wind in
the fields; and by that that cometh of our labours they keep
and maintain their estates: we be called their bondmen,
and without we do readily them service, we be beaten; and
we have no sovereign to whom we may complain, nor that
will hear us nor do us right. Let us go to the king, he is
young, and shew him what servage we be in, and shew him
how we will have it otherwise, or else we will provide us
of some remedy; and if we go together, all manner of
people that be now in any bondage will follow us to the

[1] The true text is, ' Mais ils n'avoient pas cette taille,' ' but they were not
of that nature.' The translator found the corruption ' bataille ' for ' taille.'
[2] Froissart says ' le seigle, le retrait et la paille,' ' the rye, the bran and the
straw.' The translator's French text had ' le seigle, le retraict de la paille.'

intent to be made free; and when the king seeth us, we shall have some remedy, either by fairness or otherwise.' Thus John Ball said on Sundays, when the people issued out of the churches in the villages; wherefore many of the mean people loved him, and such as intended to no goodness said how he said truth; and so they would murmur one with another in the fields and in the ways as they went together, affirming how John Ball said truth.

The archbishop of Canterbury, who was informed of the saying of this John Ball, caused him to be taken and put in prison a two or three months to chastise him: howbeit, it had been much better at the beginning that he had been condemned to perpetual prison or else to have died, rather than to have suffered him to have been again delivered out of prison; but the bishop had conscience to let him die. And when this John Ball was out of prison, he returned again to his error, as he did before.

Of his words and deeds there were much people in London informed, such as had great envy at them that were rich and such as were noble; and then they began to speak among them and said how the realm of England was right evil governed, and how that gold and silver was taken from them by them that were named noblemen: so thus these unhappy men of London began to rebel and assembled them together, and sent word to the foresaid countries that they should come to London and bring their people with them, promising them how they should find London open to receive them and the commons of the city to be of the same accord, saying how they would do so much to the king that there should not be one bondman in all England.

This promise moved so them of Kent, of Essex, of Sussex, of Bedford and of the countries about, that they rose and came towards London to the number of sixty thousand. And they had a captain called Water Tyler, and with him in company was Jack Straw and John Ball: these three were chief sovereign captains, but the head of all was Water Tyler, and he was indeed a tiler of houses, an ungracious patron. When these unhappy men began thus to stir, they of London, except such as were of their band, were greatly affrayed. Then the mayor of London and the rich men of

the city took counsel together, and when they saw the
people thus coming on every side, they caused the gates of
the city to be closed and would suffer no man to enter into
the city. But when they had well imagined, they advised
not so to do, for they thought they should thereby put their
suburbs in great peril to be brent; and so they opened again
the city, and there entered in at the gates in some place
a hundred, two hundred, by twenty and by thirty, and so
when they came to London, they entered and lodged: and
yet of truth the third part[3] of these people could not tell
what to ask or demand, but followed each other like beasts,
as the shepherds[4] did of old time, saying how they would
go conquer the Holy Land, and at last all came to nothing.
In like wise these villains and poor people came to London,
a hundred mile off, sixty mile, fifty mile, forty mile, and
twenty mile off, and from all countries about London, but
the most part came from the countries before named, and
as they came they demanded ever for the king. The gentlemen of the countries, knights and squires, began to doubt,
when they saw the people began to rebel; and though they
were in doubt, it was good reason; for a less occasion they
might have been affrayed. So the gentlemen drew together
as well as they might.

The same day that these unhappy people of Kent were
coming to London, there returned from Canterbury the king's
mother, princess of Wales, coming from her pilgrimage. She
was in great jeopardy to have been lost, for these people
came to her chare and dealt rudely with her, whereof the
good lady was in great doubt lest they would have done
some villany to her or to her damosels. Howbeit, God
kept her, and she came in one day from Canterbury to
London, for she never durst tarry by the way. The same
time king Richard her son was at the Tower of London:
there his mother found him, and with him there was the
earl of Salisbury, the archbishop of Canterbury, sir Robert
of Namur, the lord of Gommegnies and divers other, who
were in doubt of these people that thus gathered together,

---

[3] 'Bien les trois pars,' i. e. 'three-fourths.'
[4] 'Les pastoureaulx.' The reference no doubt is to the Pastoureaux of
1320, who were destroyed at Aigues-Mortes when attempting to obtain a
passage to the Holy Land.

and wist not what they demanded. This rebellion was well known in the king's court, or any of these people began to stir out of their houses; but the king nor his council did provide no remedy therefor, which was great marvel. And to the intent that all lords and good people and such as would nothing but good should take ensample to correct them that be evil and rebellious, I shall shew you plainly all the matter, as it was.

THE EVIL DEEDS THAT THESE COMMONS OF ENGLAND DID TO THE KING'S OFFICERS, AND HOW THEY SENT A KNIGHT TO SPEAK WITH THE KING

THE Monday before the feast of Corpus Christi the year of our Lord God a thousand three hundred and eighty-one these people issued out of their houses to come to London to speak with the king to be made free, for they would have had no bondman in England. And so first they came to Saint Thomas of Canterbury, and there John Ball had thought to have found the bishop of Canterbury, but he was at London with the king. When Wat Tyler and Jack Straw entered into Canterbury, all the common people made great feast, for all the town was of their assent; and there they took counsel to go to London to the king, and to send some of their company over the river of Thames into Essex, into Sussex and into the counties of Stafford and Bedford, to speak to the people that they should all come to the farther side of London and thereby to close London round about, so that the king should not stop their passages, and that they should all meet together on Corpus Christi day. They that were at Canterbury entered into Saint Thomas' church and did there much hurt, and robbed and brake up the bishop's chamber, and in robbing and bearing out their pillage they said: 'Ah, this chancellor of England hath had a good market to get together all this riches: he shall give us now account of the revenues of England and of the great profits that he hath gathered sith the king's coronation.' When they had this Monday thus broken the abbey of Saint Vincent, they departed in the morning and all the people of Canterbury with them, and so took the way to Rochester and sent their people to the villages about. And in their going they beat down and robbed houses of advocates and procurers of the king's court and of the archbishop, and had mercy of none. And when they were come to Rochester, they had there good cheer; for the people of that town tarried for them, for they were of the same sect, and then they went to the castle there and took the knight that had the rule thereof, he was called sir John Newton, and they said to him: 'Sir, it behoveth you to go with us and you shall be our sovereign captain and to do that we will have you.' The knight excused himself honestly and shewed them divers considerations and excuses, but all availed him nothing, for they said unto him: 'Sir John, if ye do not as we will have you, ye are but dead.' The knight, seeing these people in that fury and ready to slay him, he then doubted death and agreed to them, and so they took him with them against his inward will; and in like wise did they of other counties in England, as Essex, Sussex, Stafford, Bedford and Warwick, even to Lincoln; for they brought the knights and gentlemen into such obeisance, that they caused them to go with them, whether they would or not, as the lord Moylays, a great baron, sir Stephen of Hales and sir Thomas of Cosington and other.

Now behold the great fortune. If they might have come to their intents, they would have destroyed all the noblemen of England, and thereafter all other nations would have followed the same and have taken foot and ensample by them and by them of Gaunt and Flanders, who rebelled against their lord. The same year the Parisians rebelled in like wise and found out the mallets of iron, of whom there were more than twenty thousand, as ye shall hear after in this history; but first we will speak of them of England.

When these people thus lodged at Rochester departed, and passed the river and came to Brentford, alway keeping still their opinions, beating down before them and all about the places and houses of advocates and procurers, and striking off the heads of divers persons. And so long they went forward till they came within a four mile of London, and there lodged on a hill called Blackheath; and as they went, they said ever they were the king's men and the noble commons of England:[1] and when they of London knew that they were come so near to them, the mayor, as ye have heard before, closed the gates and kept straitly all the passages. This order caused the mayor, who was called Nicholas Walworth,[2] and divers other rich burgesses of the city, who were not of their sect; but there were in London of their unhappy opinions more than thirty thousand.

Then these people thus being lodged on Blackheath determined to send their knight to speak with the king and to shew him how all that they have done or will do is for him and his honour, and how the realm of England hath not been well governed a great space for the honour of the realm nor for the common profit by his uncles and by the clergy, and specially by the archbishop of Canterbury his chancellor; whereof they would have account. This knight durst do none otherwise, but so came by the river of Thames to the Tower. The king and they that were with him in the Tower, desiring to hear tidings, seeing this knight coming made him way, and was brought before the king into a chamber; and with the king was the princess his mother and his two brethren, the earl of Kent and the lord John Holland, the earl of Salisbury, the earl of Warwick, the earl of Oxford, the archbishop of Canterbury, the lord of Saint John's,[3] sir Robert of Namur, the lord of Vertaing, the lord of Gommegnies, sir Henry of Senzeille, the mayor of London and divers other notable burgesses. This knight sir John Newton, who was well known among them, for he was one of the king's officers, he kneeled down before the king and said: ' My right redoubted lord, let it not displease your grace the message that I must needs shew you, for, dear sir, it is by force and against my will.' ' Sir John,' said the king, ' say what ye will: I hold you excused.' ' Sir, the commons of this your realm hath sent me to you to desire you to come and speak with them on Blackheath; for they desire to have none but you: and, sir, ye need not to

---

[1] ' That they were for the king and the noble commons (or commonwealth) of England.'
[2] Froissart calls him John: his name was really William.
[3] That is, the grand prior of the Hospital.

have any doubt of your person, for they will do you no hurt; for they hold and will hold you for their king. But, sir, they say they will shew you divers things, the which shall be right necessary for you to take heed of, when they speak with you; of the which things, sir, I have no charge to shew you: but, sir, it may please you to give me an answer such as may appease them and that they may know for truth that I have spoken with you; for they have my children in hostage till I return again to them, and without I return again, they will slay my children incontinent.'

Then the king made him an answer and said: 'Sir, ye shall have an answer shortly.' Then the king took counsel what was best for him to do, and it was anon determined that the next morning the king should go down the river by water and without fail to speak with them. And when sir John Newton heard that answer, he desired nothing else and so took his leave of the king and of the lords and returned again into his vessel, and passed the Thames and went to Blackheath, where he had left more than threescore thousand men. And there he answered them that the next morning they should send some of their council to the Thames, and there the king would come and speak with them. This answer greatly pleased them, and so passed that night as well as they might, and the fourth part of them[*] fasted for lack of victual for they had none, wherewith they were sore displeased, which was good reason.

All this season the earl of Buckingham was in Wales, for there he had fair heritages by reason of his wife, who was daughter to the earl of Northumberland and Hereford; but the voice was all through London how he was among these people. And some said certainly how they had seen him there among them; and all was because there was one Thomas in their company, a man of the county of Cambridge, that was very like the earl. Also the lords that lay at Plymouth to go into Portugal were well informed of this rebellion and of the people that thus began to rise; wherefore they doubted lest their viage should have been broken, or else they feared lest the commons about Hampton, Winchester and Arundel would have come on them: wherefore

---

[*] 'Les quatre pars d'eux,' 'four-fifths of them.'

they weighed up their anchors and issued out of the haven with great pain, for the wind was sore against them, and so took the sea and there cast anchor abiding for the wind. And the duke of Lancaster, who was in the marches of Scotland between Moorlane and Roxburgh entreating with the Scots, where it was shewed him of the rebellion, whereof he was in doubt, for he knew well he was but little beloved with the commons of England; howbeit, for all those tidings, yet he did sagely demean himself as touching the treaty with the Scots. The earl Douglas, the earl of Moray, the earl of Sutherland and the earl Thomas Versy, and the Scots that were there for the treaty knew right well the rebellion in England, how the common people in every part began to rebel against the noblemen; wherefore the Scots thought that England was in great danger to be lost, and therefore in their treaties they were the more stiffer against the duke of Lancaster and his council.

Now let us speak of the commons of England and how they persevered.

HOW THE COMMONS OF ENGLAND ENTERED INTO LONDON, AND OF THE GREAT EVIL THAT THEY DID, AND OF THE DEATH OF THE BISHOP OF CANTERBURY AND DIVERS OTHER

In the morning on Corpus Christi day king Richard heard mass in the Tower of London, and all his lords, and then he took his barge with the earl of Salisbury, the earl of Warwick, the earl of Oxford and certain knights, and so rowed down along the Thames to Rotherhithe, whereas was descended down the hill a ten thousand men to see the king and to speak with him. And when they saw the king's barge coming, they began to shout, and made such a cry, as though all the devils of hell had been among them. And they had brought with them sir John Newton to the intent that, if the king had not come, they would have stricken him all to pieces, and so they had promised him. And when the king and his lords saw the demeanour of the people, the best assured of them were in dread; and so the king was counselled by his barons not to take any landing there, but so rowed up and down the river. And the king demanded of them what they would, and said how he was come thither to speak with them, and they said all with one voice: 'We would that ye should come aland, and then we shall shew you what we lack.' Then the earl of Salisbury answered for the king and said: 'Sirs, ye be not in such order nor array that the king ought to speak with you.' And so with those words no more said: and then the king was counselled to return again to the Tower of London, and so he did.

And when these people saw that, they were inflamed with ire and returned to the hill where the great band was, and there shewed them what answer they had and how the king was returned to the Tower of London. Then they cried all with one voice, 'Let us go to London,' and so they took their way thither; and in their going they beat down abbeys and houses of advocates and of men of the court, and so came into the suburbs of London, which were great and fair, and there beat down divers fair houses, and specially they brake up the king's prisons, as the Marshalsea and other, and delivered out all the prisoners that were within: and there they did much hurt, and at the bridge foot they threat them of London because the gates of the bridge were closed, saying how they would bren all the suburbs and so conquer London by force, and to slay and bren all the commons of the city. There were many within the city of their accord, and so they drew together and said: 'Why do we not let these good people enter into the city? they are your fellows, and that that they do is for us.' So therewith the gates were opened, and then these people entered into the city and went into houses and sat down to eat and drink. They desired nothing but it was incontinent brought to them, for every man was ready to make them good cheer and to give them meat and drink to appease them.

Then the captains, as John Ball, Jack Straw and Wat Tyler, went throughout London and a twenty thousand with them, and so came to the Savoy in the way to Westminster, which was a goodly house and it pertained to the duke of Lancaster. And when they entered, they slew the keepers thereof and robbed and pilled the house, and when they had so done, then they set fire on it and clean destroyed and brent it. And when they had done that outrage, they left not

therewith, but went straight to the fair hospital of the
Rhodes called Saint John's,[1] and there they brent house,
hospital, minster and all. Then they went from street to
street and slew all the Flemings that they could find in
church or in any other place, there was none respited from
death. And they brake up divers houses of the Lombards
and robbed them and took their goods at their pleasure, for
there was none that durst say them nay. And they slew
in the city a rich merchant called Richard Lyon, to whom
before that time Wat Tyler had done service in France;
and on a time this Richard Lyon had beaten him, while he
was his varlet, the which Wat Tyler then remembered and
so came to his house and strake off his head and caused it
to be borne on a spear-point before him all about the city.
Thus these ungracious people demeaned themselves like
people enraged and wood, and so that day they did much
sorrow in London.

And so against night they went to lodge at Saint Katherine's before the Tower of London, saying how they would
never depart thence till they had the king at their pleasure
and till he had accorded to them all [they would ask, and]
that they would ask accounts of the chancellor of England,
to know where all the good was become that he had levied
through the realm, and without he made a good account to
them thereof, it should not be for his profit. And so when
they had done all these evils to the strangers all the day,
at night they lodged before the Tower.

Ye may well know and believe that it was great pity for
the danger that the king and such as were with him were in.
For some time these unhappy people shouted and cried so
loud, as though all the devils of hell had been among them.
In this evening the king was counselled by his brethren and
lords and by sir Nicholas Walworth, mayor of London,
and divers other notable and rich burgesses, that in the
night time they should issue out of the Tower and enter into
the city, and so to slay all these unhappy people, while
they were at their rest and asleep; for it was thought that

[1] This is called afterwards 'l'Ospital de Saint Jehan du Temple,' and
therefore would probably be the Temple, to which the Hospitallers had suc-
ceeded. They had, however, another house at Clerkenwell, which also had
been once the property of the Templars.

many of them were drunken, whereby they should be slain like flies; also of twenty of them there was scant one in harness. And surely the good men of London might well have done this at their ease, for they had in their houses secretly their friends and servants ready in harness, and also sir Robert Knolles was in his lodging keeping his treasure with a sixscore ready at his commandment; in like wise was sir Perducas d'Albret, who was as then in London, insomuch that there might well [have] assembled together an eight thousand men ready in harness. Howbeit, there was nothing done, for the residue of the commons of the city were sore doubted, lest they should rise also, and the commons before were a threescore thousand or more. Then the earl of Salisbury and the wise men about the king said: 'Sir, if ye can appease them with fairness, it were best and most profitable, and to grant them everything that they desire, for if we should begin a thing the which we could not achieve, we should never recover it again, but we and our heirs ever to be disinherited.' So this counsel was taken and the mayor countermanded, and so commanded that he should not stir; and he did as he was commanded, as reason was. And in the city with the mayor there were twelve aldermen, whereof nine of them held with the king and the other three took part with these ungracious people, as it was after well known, the which they full dearly bought.

And on the Friday in the morning the people, being at Saint Katherine's near to the Tower, began to apparel themselves and to cry and shout, and said, without the king would come out and speak with them, they would assail the Tower and take it by force, and slay all them that were within. Then the king doubted these words and so was counselled that he should issue out to speak with them: and then the king sent to them that they should all draw to a fair plain place called Mile-end, whereas the people of the city did sport them in the summer season, and there the king to grant them that they desired; and there it was cried in the king's name, that whosoever would speak with the king let him go to the said place, and there he should not fail to find the king. Then the people began to depart, specially the commons of the villages, and went to the same place: but all went not thither, for they were not all of one condition; for there were some that desired nothing but riches and the utter destruction of the noblemen and to have London robbed and pilled; that was the principal matter of their beginning, the which they well shewed; for as soon as the Tower gate opened and that the king was issued out with his two brethren and the earl of Salisbury, the earl of Warwick, the earl of Oxford, sir Robert of Namur, the lord of Vertaing, the lord Gommegnies and divers other, then Wat Tyler, Jack Straw and John Ball and more than four hundred entered into the Tower and brake up chamber after chamber, and at last found the archbishop of Canterbury, called Simon, a valiant man and a wise, and chief chancellor of England, and a little before he had said mass before the king. These gluttons took him and strake off his head, and also they beheaded the lord of Saint John's and a friar minor, master in medicine, pertaining to the duke of Lancaster, they slew him in despite of his master, and a sergeant at arms called John Leg; and these four heads were set on four long spears and they made them to be borne before them through the streets of London and at last set them a-high on London bridge, as though they had been traitors to the king and to the realm. Also these gluttons entered into the princess' chamber and brake her bed, whereby she was so sore affrayed that she swooned; and there she was taken up and borne to the water side and put into a barge and covered, and so conveyed to a place called the Queen's Wardrobe;[2] and there she was all that day and night like a woman half dead, till she was comforted with the king her son, as ye shall hear after.

HOW THE NOBLES OF ENGLAND WERE IN GREAT PERIL TO HAVE BEEN DESTROYED, AND HOW THESE REBELS WERE PUNISHED AND SENT HOME TO THEIR OWN HOUSES

WHEN the king came to the said place of Mile-end without London, he put out of his company his two brethren, the earl

[2] The Queen's Wardrobe was in the 'Royal' (called by Froissart or his copyist 'la Réole'), a palace near Blackfriars.

of Kent and sir John Holland, and the lord of Gommegnies, for they durst not appear before the people: and when the king and his other lords were there, he found there a three-score thousand men of divers villages and of sundry countries in England; so the king entered in among them and said to them sweetly: 'Ah, ye good people, I am your king: what lack ye? what will ye say?' Then such as understood him said: 'We will that ye make us free for ever, ourselves, our heirs and our lands, and that we be called no more bond nor so reputed.' 'Sirs,' said the king, 'I am well agreed thereto. Withdraw you home into your own houses and into such villages as ye came from, and leave behind you of every village two or three, and I shall cause writings to be made and seal them with my seal, the which they shall have with them, containing everything that ye demand; and to the intent that ye shall be the better assured, I shall cause my banners to be delivered into every bailiwick, shire and countries.'

These words appeased well the common people, such as were simple and good plain men, that were come thither and wist not why. They said, 'It was well said, we desire no better.' Thus these people began to be appeased and began to withdraw them into the city of London. And the king also said a word, the which greatly contented them. He said: 'Sirs, among you good men of Kent ye shall have one of my banners with you, and ye of Essex another, and ye of Sussex, of Bedford, of Cambridge, of Yarmouth, of Stafford and of Lynn, each of you one; and also I pardon everything that ye have done hitherto, so that ye follow my banners and return home to your houses.' They all answered how they would so do: thus these people departed and went into London. Then the king ordained more than thirty clerks the same Friday, to write with all diligence letter patents and sealed with the king's seal, and delivered them to these people; and when they had received the writing, they departed and returned into their own countries: but the great venom remained still behind, for Wat Tyler, Jack Straw and John Ball said, for all that these people were thus appeased, yet they would not depart so, and they had of their accord more than thirty thousand. So they abode still and made no press to have the king's writing nor seal, for all their intents was to put the city to trouble in such wise as to slay all the rich and honest persons and to rob and pill their houses. They of London were in great fear of this, wherefore they kept their houses privily with their friends and such servants as they had, every man according to his puissance. And when these said people were this Friday thus somewhat appeased, and that they should depart as soon as they had their writings, every man home into his own country, then king Richard came into the Royal, where the queen his mother was, right sore affrayed: so he comforted her as well as he could and tarried there with her all that night.

Yet I shall shew you of an adventure that fell by these ungracious people before the city of Norwich, by a captain among them called Guilliam Lister of Stafford. The same day of Corpus Christi that these people entered into London and brent the duke of Lancaster's house, called the Savoy, and the hospital of Saint John's and brake up the king's prisons and did all this hurt, as ye have heard before, the same time there assembled together they of Stafford, of Lynn, of Cambridge, of Bedford and of Yarmouth; and as they were coming towards London, they had a captain among them called Lister. And as they came, they rested them before Norwich, and in their coming they caused every man to rise with them, so that they left no villains behind them. The cause why they rested before Norwich I shall shew you. There was a knight, captain of the town, called sir Robert Sale. He was no gentleman born, but he had the grace to be reputed sage and valiant in arms, and for his valiantness king Edward made him knight. He was of his body one of the biggest knights in all England. Lister and his company thought to have had this knight with them and to make him their chief captain, to the intent to be the more feared and beloved: so they sent to him that he should come and speak with them in the field, or else they would bren the town. The knight considered that it was better for him to go and speak with them rather than they should do that outrage to the town: then he mounted on his horse and issued out of the town all alone, and so came to speak with them. And when they saw him, they made him great cheer and honoured him much, desiring him to alight off his horse and to speak with them, and so he did: wherein he did great folly; for when he was alighted, they came round about him and began to speak fair to him and said: 'Sir Robert, ye are a knight and a man greatly beloved in this country and renowned a valiant man; and though ye be thus, yet we know you well, ye be no gentleman born, but son to a villain such as we be. Therefore come you with us and be our master, and we shall make you so great a lord, that one quarter of England shall be under your obeisance.' When the knight heard them speak thus, it was greatly contrarious to his mind, for he thought never to make any such bargain, and answered them with a felonous regard: 'Fly away, ye ungracious people, false and evil traitors that ye be: would you that I should forsake my natural lord for such a company of knaves as ye be, to my dishonour for ever? I had rather ye were all hanged, as ye shall be; for that shall be your end.' And with those words he had thought to have leapt again upon his horse, but he failed of the stirrup and the horse started away. Then they cried all at him and said: 'Slay him without mercy.' When he heard those words, he let his horse go and drew out a good sword and began to scrimmish with them, and made a great place about him, that it was pleasure to behold him. There was none that durst approach near him: there were some that approached near him, but at every stroke that he gave he cut off other leg, head or arm: there was none so hardy but that they feared him: he did there such deeds of arms that it was marvel to regard. But there were more than forty thousand of these unhappy people: they shot and cast at him, and he was unarmed: to say truth, if he had been of iron or steel, yet he must needs have been slain; but yet, or he died, he slew twelve out of hand, beside them that he hurt. Finally he was stricken to the earth, and they cut off his arms and legs and then strake his body all to pieces. This was the end of sir Robert Sale, which was great damage; for which deed afterward all the knights and squires of England were angry and sore displeased when they heard thereof.

Now let us return to the king. The Saturday the king departed from the Wardrobe in the Royal and went to Westminster and heard mass in the church there, and all his lords with him. And beside the church there was a little chapel with an image of our Lady, which did great miracles and in whom the kings of England had ever great trust and confidence. The king made his orisons before this image and did there his offering; and then he leapt on his horse, and all his lords, and so the king rode toward London; and when he had ridden a little way, on the left hand there was a way to pass without London.[1]

The same proper morning Wat Tyler, Jack Straw and John Ball had assembled their company to common together in a place called Smithfield, whereas every Friday there is a market of horses; and there were together all of affinity more than twenty thousand, and yet there were many still in the town, drinking and making merry in the taverns and paid nothing, for they were happy that made them best cheer. And these people in Smithfield had with them the king's banners, the which were delivered them the day before, and all these gluttons were in mind to overrun and to rob London the same day; for their captains said how they had done nothing as yet. 'These liberties that the king hath given us is to us but a small profit: therefore let us be all of one accord and let us overrun this rich and puissant city, or they of Essex, of Sussex, of Cambridge, of Bedford, of Arundel, of Warwick, of Reading, of Oxford, of Guildford, of Lynn, of Stafford, of Yarmouth, of Lincoln, of York and of Durham do come hither. For all these will come hither; Baker and Lister will bring them hither; and if we be first lords of London and have the possession of the riches that is therein, we shall not repent us; for if we leave it, they that come after will have it from us.'

To this counsel they all agreed; and therewith the king came the same way unware of them, for he had thought to have passed that way without London, and with him a forty horse. And when he came before the abbey of Saint Bartholomew and beheld all these people, then the king rested and said how he would go no farther till he knew

[1] Or rather, 'he found a place on the left hand to pass without London.'

what these people ailed, saying, if they were in any trouble, how he would rappease them again. The lords that were with him tarried also, as reason was when they saw the king tarry. And when Wat Tyler saw the king tarry, he said to his people: 'Sirs, yonder is the king: I will go and speak with him. Stir not from hence, without I make you a sign; and when I make you that sign, come on and slay all them except the king; but do the king no hurt, he is young, we shall do with him as we list and shall lead him with us all about England, and so shall we be lords of all the realm without doubt.' And there was a doublet-maker of London called John Tycle, and he had brought to these gluttons a sixty doublets, the which they ware: then he demanded of these captains who should pay him for his doublets; he demanded thirty mark. Wat Tyler answered him and said: 'Friend, appease yourself, thou shalt be well paid or this day be ended. Keep thee near me; I shall be thy creditor.' And therewith he spurred his horse and departed from his company and came to the king, so near him that his horse head touched the croup of the king's horse, and the first word that he said was this: 'Sir king, seest thou all yonder people?' 'Yea truly,' said the king, 'wherefore sayest thou?' 'Because,' said he, 'they be all at my commandment and have sworn to me faith and truth, to do all that I will have them.' 'In a good time,' said the king, 'I will well it be so.' Then Wat Tyler said, as he that nothing demanded but riot: 'What believest thou, king, that these people and as many more as be in London at my commandment, that they will depart from thee thus without having thy letters?' 'No,' said the king, 'ye shall have them: they be ordained for you and shall be delivered every one each after other. Wherefore, good fellows, withdraw fair and easily to your people and cause them to depart out of London; for it is our intent that each of you by villages and townships shall have letters patents, as I have promised you.'

With those words Wat Tyler cast his eyen on a squire that was there with the king bearing the king's sword, and Wat Tyler hated greatly the same squire, for the same squire had displeased him before for words between them. 'What,' said Tyler, 'art thou there? Give me thy dagger.' 'Nay,' said the squire, 'that will I not do: wherefore should I give it thee?' The king beheld the squire and said: 'Give it him; let him have it.' And so the squire took it him sore against his will. And when this Wat Tyler had it, he began to play therewith and turned it in his hand, and said again to the squire: 'Give me also that sword.' 'Nay,' said the squire, 'it is the king's sword: thou art not worthy to have it, for thou art but a knave; and if there were no more here but thou and I, thou durst not speak those words for as much gold in quantity as all yonder abbey.'[2] 'By my faith,' said Wat Tyler, 'I shall never eat meat till I have thy head': and with those words the mayor of London came to the king with a twelve horses well armed under their coats, and so he brake the press and saw and heard how Wat Tyler demeaned himself, and said to him: 'Ha, thou knave, how art thou so hardy in the king's presence to speak such words? It is too much for thee so to do.' Then the king began to chafe and said to the mayor: 'Set hands on him.' And while the king said so, Tyler said to the mayor: 'A God's name what have I said to displease thee?' 'Yes truly,' quoth the mayor, 'thou false stinking knave, shalt thou speak thus in the presence of the king my natural lord? I commit never to live, without thou shalt dearly abye it.'[3] And with those words the mayor drew out his sword and strake Tyler so great a stroke on the head, that he fell down at the feet of his horse, and as soon as he was fallen, they environed him all about, whereby he was not seen of his company. Then a squire of the king's alighted, called John Standish, and he drew out his sword and put it into Wat Tyler's belly, and so he died.

Then the ungracious people there assembled, perceiving their captain slain, began to murmur among themselves and said: 'Ah, our captain is slain, let us go and slay them all': and therewith they arranged themselves on the place in manner of battle, and their bows before them. Thus the king began a great outrage;[4] howbeit, all turned to the best:

[2] The full text has, 'for as much gold as that minster of Saint Paul is great.'
[3] 'Jamais je veux vivre, si tu ne le compares.'
[4] 'Outrage' here means 'act of boldness,' as elsewhere, e. g. 'si fist une grant apertise d'armes et un grant outrage.'

for as soon as Tyler was on the earth, the king departed
from all his company and all alone he rode to these people,
and said to his own men: 'Sirs, none of you follow me; let
me alone.' And so when he came before these ungracious
people, who put themselves in ordinance to revenge their
captain, then the king said to them: 'Sirs, what aileth you?
Ye shall have no captain but me: I am your king: be all in
rest and peace.' And so the most part of the people that
heard the king speak and saw him among them, were shame-
fast and began to wax peaceable and to depart; but some,
such as were malicious and evil, would not depart, but made
semblant as though they would do somewhat.

Then the king returned to his own company and demanded
of them what was best to be done. Then he was counselled
to draw into the field, for to fly away was no boot. Then
said the mayor: 'It is good that we do so, for I think surely
we shall have shortly some comfort of them of London and
of such good men as be of our part, who are purveyed and
have their friends and men ready armed in their houses.'
And in the mean time voice and bruit ran through London
how these unhappy people were likely to slay the king and
the mayor in Smithfield; through the which noise all manner
of good men of the king's party issued out of their houses
and lodgings well armed, and so came all to Smithfield
and to the field where the king was, and they were anon to
the number of seven or eight thousand men well armed.
And first thither came sir Robert Knolles and sir Perducas
d'Albret, well accompanied, and divers of the aldermen of
London, and with them a six hundred men in harness, and
a puissant man of the city, who was the king's draper,[5]
called Nicholas Bramber, and he brought with him a great
company; and ever as they came, they ranged them afoot
in order of battle: and on the other part these unhappy
people were ready ranged, making semblance to give battle,
and they had with them divers of the king's banners. There
the king made three knights, the one the mayor of London
sir Nicholas Walworth, sir John Standish and sir Nicholas
Bramber. Then the lords said among themselves: 'What

---

[5] 'Qui estoit des draps du roy.' He owned large estates in Essex and also
shops in London. He became one of the councillors of Richard II.

shall we do? We see here our enemies, who would gladly slay us, if they might have the better hand of us.' Sir Robert Knolles counselled to go and fight with them and slay them all; yet the king would not consent thereto, but said: 'Nay, I will not so: I will send to them commanding them to send me again my banners, and thereby we shall see what they will do. Howbeit, other by fairness or otherwise, I will have them.' 'That is well said, sir,' quoth the earl of Salisbury. Then these new knights were sent to them, and these knights made token to them not to shoot at them, and when they came so near them that their speech might be heard, they said: 'Sirs, the king commandeth you to send to him again his banners, and we think he will have mercy of you.' And incontinent they delivered again the banners and sent them to the king. Also they were commanded on pain of their heads, that all such as had letters of the king to bring them forth and to send them again to the king; and so many of them delivered their letters, but not all. Then the king made them to be all to-torn in their presence; and as soon as the king's banners were delivered again, these unhappy people kept none array, but the most part of them did cast down their bows, and so brake their array and returned into London. Sir Robert Knolles was sore displeased in that he might not go to slay them all: but the king would not consent thereto, but said he would be revenged of them well enough; and so he was after.

Thus these foolish people departed, some one way and some another; and the king and his lords and all his company right ordinately entered into London with great joy. And the first journey that the king made he went to the lady princess his mother, who was in a castle in the Royal called the Queen's Wardrobe, and there she had tarried two days and two nights right sore abashed, as she had good reason; and when she saw the king her son, she was greatly rejoiced and said: 'Ah, fair son, what pain and great sorrow that I have suffered for you this day!' Then the king answered and said: 'Certainly, madam, I know it well; but now rejoice yourself and thank God, for now it is time. I have this day recovered mine heritage and the realm of England, the which I had near lost.' Thus the king tarried that day with his mother, and every lord went peaceably to their own lodgings. Then there was a cry made in every street in the king's name, that all manner of men, not being of the city of London and have not dwelt there the space of one year, to depart; and if any such be found there the Sunday by the sun-rising, that they should be taken as traitors to the king and to lose their heads. This cry thus made, there was none that durst brake it, and so all manner of people departed and sparkled abroad every man to their own places. John Ball and Jack Straw were found in an old house hidden, thinking to have stolen away, but they could not, for they were accused by their own men. Of the taking of them the king and his lords were glad, and then strake off their heads and Wat Tyler's also, and they were set on London bridge, and the valiant men's heads taken down that they had set on the Thursday before. These tidings anon spread abroad, so that the people of the strange countries, which were coming towards London, returned back again to their own houses and durst come no farther.

THE BATTLE OF OTTERBURN

HOW THE EARL DOUGLAS WON THE PENNON OF SIR HENRY PERCY
AT THE BARRIERS BEFORE NEWCASTLE-UPON-TYNE, AND
HOW THE SCOTS BRENT THE CASTLE OF PONTLAND,
AND HOW SIR HENRY PERCY AND SIR RALPH
HIS BROTHER TOOK ADVICE TO FOLLOW
THE SCOTS TO CONQUER AGAIN THE
PENNON THAT WAS LOST AT
THE SCRIMMISH

WHEN the English lords saw that their squire returned not again at the time appointed, and could know nothing what the Scots did, nor what they were purposed to do, then they thought well that their squire was taken. The lords sent each to other, to be ready whensoever they should hear that the Scots were abroad: as for their messenger, they thought him but lost.

Now let us speak of the earl Douglas and other, for they had more to do than they that went by Carlisle. When the earls of Douglas, of Moray, of March, and Dunbar[1] departed from the great host, they took their way thinking to pass the water and to enter into the bishopric of Durham, and to ride to the town and then to return, brenning and exiling the country and so to come to Newcastle and to lodge there in the town in the despite of all the Englishmen. And as they determined, so they did assay to put it in use, for they rode a great pace under covert without doing of any pillage by the way or assaulting of any castle, tower or house, but so came into the lord Percy's land and passed the river of Tyne without any let a three leagues above Newcastle not far from Brancepeth, and at last entered into the bishopric of Durham, where they found a good country.

[1] George, earl of March and Dunbar: the text gives Mare, but there was at this time no earl of Mar.

Then they began to make war, to slay people and to bren villages and to do many sore displeasures.

As at that time the earl of Northumberland and the other lords and knights of that country knew nothing of their coming. When tidings came to Newcastle and to Durham that the Scots were abroad, and that they might well see by the fires and smoke abroad in the country, the earl sent to Newcastle his two sons and sent commandment to every man to draw to Newcastle, saying to his sons: 'Ye shall go to Newcastle and all the country shall assemble there, and I shall tarry at Alnwick, which is a passage that they must pass by. If we may enclose them, we shall speed well.' Sir Henry Percy and sir Ralph his brother obeyed their father's commandment and came thither with them of the country. The Scots rode burning and exiling the country, that the smoke thereof came to Newcastle. The Scots came to the gates of Durham and scrimmished there; but they tarried not long but returned, as they had ordained before to do, and that they found by the way took and destroyed it. Between Durham and Newcastle is but twelve leagues English and a good country: there was no town, without it were closed, but it was brent, and they repassed the river of Tyne where they had passed before, and then came before Newcastle and there rested. All the English knights and squires of the country of York and bishopric of Durham were assembled at Newcastle, and thither came the seneschal of York, sir Ralph Lumley, sir Matthew Redman, captain of Berwick, sir Robert Ogle, sir Thomas Grey, sir Thomas Holton, sir John Felton, sir John Lilleburn, sir Thomas Abingdon, the baron of Hilton, sir John Coppledike and divers other, so that the town was so full of people that they wist not where to lodge.

When these three Scottish earls who were chief captains had made their enterprise in the bishopric of Durham and had sore overrun the country, then they returned to Newcastle and there rested and tarried two days, and every day they scrimmished. The earl of Northumberland's two sons were two young lusty knights and were ever foremost at the barriers to scrimmish. There were many proper feats of arms done and achieved: there was fighting hand to hand:

among other there fought hand to hand the earl Douglas and sir Henry Percy, and by force of arms the earl Douglas won the pennon of sir Henry Percy's, wherewith he was sore displeased and so were all the Englishmen. And the earl Douglas said to sir Henry Percy: 'Sir, I shall bear this token of your prowess into Scotland and shall set it on high on my castle of Dalkeith, that it may be seen far off.' 'Sir,' quoth sir Henry, 'ye may be sure ye shall not pass the bounds of this country till ye be met withal in such wise that ye shall make none avaunt thereof.' 'Well, sir,' quoth the earl Douglas, 'come this night to my lodging and seek for your pennon: I shall set it before my lodging and see if ye will come to take it away.' So then it was late, and the Scots withdrew to their lodgings and refreshed them with such as they had. They had flesh enough: they made that night good watch, for they thought surely to be awaked for the words they had spoken, but they were not, for sir Henry Percy was counselled not so to do.

The next day the Scots dislodged and returned towards their own country, and so came to a castle and a town called Pontland, whereof sir Edmund of Alphel was lord, who was a right good knight. There the Scots rested, for they came thither betimes, and understood that the knight was in his castle. Then they ordained to assail the castle, and gave a great assault, so that by force of arms they won it and the knight within it. Then the town and castle was brent; and from thence the Scots went to the town and castle of Otterburn, an eight English mile from Newcastle[2] and there lodged. That day they made none assault, but the next morning they blew their horns and made ready to assail the castle, which was strong, for it stood in the marish. That day they assaulted till they were weary, and did nothing. Then they sowned the retreat and returned to their lodgings. Then the lords drew to council to determine what they

[2] Froissart says 'eight English leagues.' In the next chapter the distance becomes 'seven little leagues,' and later on, 'a six English miles,' where the original is 'lieues.' The actual distance is about thirty miles. The translator gives the form 'Combur' here, but 'Ottenburge' in the next chapter, as the name of the place. It is remarkable indeed how little trouble he seems to have taken generally to give English names correctly. In this chapter we have 'Nymyche' for 'Alnwick' and 'Pouclan' for 'Pontland,' forms rather less like the real names than those which he found in the French text, viz. Nynich and Ponclau.

should do. The most part were of the accord that the next day they should dislodge without giving of any assault and to draw fair and easily towards Carlisle. But the earl Douglas brake that counsel and said: 'In despite of sir Henry Percy, who said he would come and win again his pennon, let us not depart hence for two or three days. Let us assail this castle: it is pregnable: we shall have double honour. And then let us see if he will come and fetch his pennon: he shall be well defended.'[3] Every man accorded to his saying, what for their honour and for the love of him. Also they lodged there at their ease, for there was none that troubled them: they made many lodgings of boughs and great herbs and fortified their camp sagely with the marish that was thereby, and their carriages were set at the entry into the marishes and had all their beasts within the marish. Then they apparelled for to assault the next day: this was their intention.

Now let us speak of sir Henry Percy and of sir Ralph his brother and shew somewhat what they did. They were sore displeased that the earl Douglas had won the pennon of their arms: also it touched greatly their honours, if they did not as sir Henry Percy said he would; for he had said to the earl Douglas that he should not carry his pennon out of England, and also he had openly spoken it before all the knights and squires that were at Newcastle. The Englishmen there thought surely that the earl Douglas' band was but the Scots' vanguard and that their host was left behind. The knights of the country, such as were well expert in arms, spake against sir Henry Percy's opinion and said to him: 'Sir, there fortuneth in war oftentimes many losses. If the earl Douglas have won your pennon, he bought it dear, for he came to the gate to seek it and was well beaten:[4] another day ye shall win as much of him or more. Sir, we say this because we know well all the power of Scotland is abroad in the fields, and if we issue out and be not men enow to fight with them, and peradventure they have made this scrimmish with us to the intent to draw us out of the town, and the number that they be of, as it is said, above

[3] Froissart says, 'if he comes, it shall be defended.' The translator perhaps means 'he shall be prevented.'
[4] i. e. 'well fought with.'

forty thousand men, they may soon enclose us and do with us what they will. Yet it were better to lose a pennon than two or three hundred knights and squires and put all our country in adventure.' These words refrained sir Henry and his brother, for they would do nothing against counsel. Then tidings came to them by such as had seen the Scots and seen all their demeanour and what way they took and where they rested.

HOW SIR HENRY PERCY AND HIS BROTHER WITH A GOOD NUMBER
OF MEN OF ARMS AND ARCHERS WENT AFTER THE
SCOTS, TO WIN AGAIN HIS PENNON THAT
THE EARL DOUGLAS HAD WON BEFORE
NEWCASTLE-UPON-TYNE, AND HOW
THEY ASSAILED THE SCOTS BE-
FORE OTTERBURN IN THEIR
LODGINGS

IT was shewed to sir Henry Percy and to his brother and to the other knights and squires that were there, by such as had followed the Scots from Newcastle and had well advised their doing, who said to sir Henry and to sir Ralph: 'Sirs, we have followed the Scots privily and have discovered all the country. The Scots be at Pontland and have taken sir Edmund Alphel in his own castle, and from thence they be gone to Otterburn and there they lay this night. What they will do to-morrow we know not: they are ordained to abide there: and, sirs, surely their great host is not with them, for in all they pass not there a three thousand men.' When sir Henry heard that, he was joyful and said: 'Sirs, let us leap on our horses, for by the faith I owe to God and to my lord my father I will go seek for my pennon and dislodge them this same night.' Knights and squires that heard him agreed thereto and were joyous, and every man made him ready.

The same evening the bishop of Durham came thither with a good company, for he heard at Durham how the Scots were before Newcastle and how that the lord Percy's sons with other lords and knights should fight with the Scots: therefore the bishop of Durham to come to the rescue had assembled up all the country and so was coming to Newcastle. But sir Henry Percy would not abide his coming, for he had with him six hundred spears, knights and squires, and an eight thousand footmen. They thought that sufficient number to fight with the Scots, if they were not but three hundred spears and three thousand of other. Thus they departed from Newcastle after dinner and set forth in good order, and took the same way as the Scots had gone and rode to Otterburn, a seven little leagues from thence and fair way, but they could not ride fast because of their foot-men. And when the Scots had supped and some laid down to their rest, and were weary of travailing and assaulting of the castle all that day, and thought to rise early in the morning in cool of the day to give a new assault, therewith suddenly the Englishmen came on them and entered into the lodgings, weening it had been the masters' lodgings, and therein were but varlets and servants. Then the Englishmen cried, 'Percy, Percy!' and entered into the lodgings, and ye know well where such affray is noise is soon raised: and it fortuned well for the Scots, for when they saw the Englishmen came to wake them, then the lord sent a certain of their servants of foot-men to scrimmish with the Englishmen at the entry of the lodgings, and in the mean time they armed and apparelled them, every man under his banner and under his captain's pennon. The night was far on, but the moon shone so bright as an it had been in a manner day. It was in the month of August and the weather fair and temperate.

Thus the Scots were drawn together and without any noise departed from their lodgings and went about a little mountain, which was greatly for their advantage. For all the day before they had well advised the place and said among themselves: 'If the Englishmen come on us suddenly, then we will do thus and thus, for it is a jeopardous thing in the night if men of war enter into our lodgings. If they do, then we will draw to such a place, and thereby other we shall win or lose.' When the Englishmen entered into the field, at the first they soon overcame the varlets, and as they entered further in, always they found new men to busy them and to scrimmish with them. Then suddenly came the Scots

from about the mountain and set on the Englishmen or they
were ware, and cried their cries; whereof the Englishmen
were sore astonied. Then they cried 'Percy!' and the other
party cried 'Douglas!'

There began a cruel battle and at the first encounter many
were overthrown of both parties; and because the Englishmen were a great number and greatly desired to vanquish
their enemies, and rested at their pace[1] and greatly did put
aback the Scots, so that the Scots were near discomfited.
Then the earl James Douglas, who was young and strong and
of great desire to get praise and grace, and was willing to
deserve to have it, and cared for no pain nor travail, came
forth with his banner and cried, 'Douglas, Douglas!' and
sir Henry Percy and sir Ralph his brother, who had great
indignation against the earl Douglas because he had won
the pennon of their arms at the barriers before Newcastle,
came to that part and cried, 'Percy!' Their two banners
met and their men: there was a sore fight: the Englishmen
were so strong and fought so valiantly that they reculed
the Scots back. There were two valiant knights of Scots
under the banner of the earl Douglas, called sir Patrick of
Hepbourn and sir Patrick his son. They acquitted themselves that day valiantly: the earl's banner had been won,
an they had not been: they defended it so valiantly and in
the rescuing thereof did such feats of arms, that it was
greatly to their recommendation and to their heirs' for ever
after.

It was shewed me by such as had been at the same battle,
as well by knights and squires of England as of Scotland, at
the house of the earl of Foix,—for anon after this battle
was done I met at Orthez two squires of England called John
of Chateauneuf and John of Cantiron; also when I returned
to Avignon I found also there a knight and a squire of
Scotland; I knew them and they knew me by such tokens
as I shewed them of their country, for I, author of this book,
in my youth had ridden nigh over all the realm of Scotland,
and I was as then a fifteen days in the house of earl William
Douglas, father to the same earl James, of whom I spake
of now, in a castle of five leagues from Edinburgh in the

[1] In French, 'ilz se arresterent,' without 'and.'

country of Dalkeith;[2] the same time I saw there this earl
James, a fair young child, and a sister of his called the lady
Blanche,—and I was informed by both these parties[3] how
this battle was as sore a battle fought as lightly hath been
heard of before of such a number; and I believe it well, for
Englishmen on the one party and Scots on the other party
are good men of war, for when they meet there is a hard
fight without sparing, there is no ho between them as long
as spears, swords, axes or daggers will endure, but lay on
each upon other, and when they be well beaten[4] and that
the one party hath obtained the victory, they then glorify so
in their deeds of arms and are so joyful, that such as be
taken they shall be ransomed or they go out of the field, so
that shortly each of them is so content with other that at
their departing courteously they will say, 'God thank you';
but in fighting one with another there is no play nor sparing,
and this is true, and that shall well appear by this said
rencounter, for it was as valiantly foughten as could be devised, as ye shall hear.

HOW THE EARL JAMES DOUGLAS BY HIS VALIANTNESS EN-
COURAGED HIS MEN, WHO WERE RECULED AND IN A
MANNER DISCOMFITED, AND IN HIS SO DOING
HE WAS WOUNDED TO DEATH

KNIGHTS and squires were of good courage on both parties
to fight valiantly: cowards there had no place, but hardiness reigned with goodly feats of arms, for knights and
squires were so joined together at hand strokes, that archers
had no place of nother party. There the Scots shewed
great hardiness and fought merrily with great desire of
honour: the Englishmen were three to one: howbeit, I say
not but Englishmen did nobly acquit themselves, for ever
the Englishmen had rather been slain or taken in the place
than to fly. Thus, as I have said, the banners of Douglas
and Percy and their men were met each against other,

---

[2] 'Which is called in the country Dalkeith.' The French has 'que on
nomme au pays Dacquest,' of which the translator makes 'in the countrey
of Alquest.'
[3] 'By both sides,' *i. e.* Scotch and English.
[4] 'When they have well fought.'

envious who should win the honour of that journey. At the
beginning the Englishmen were so strong that they reculed
back their enemies: then the earl Douglas, who was of
great heart and high of enterprise, seeing his men recule
back, then to recover the place and to shew knightly valour
he took his axe in both his hands, and entered so into the
press that he made himself way in such wise, that none durst
approach near him, and he was so well armed that he
bare well off such strokes as he received.[1] Thus he went
ever forward like a hardy Hector, willing alone to conquer
the field and to discomfit his enemies: but at last he was encountered with three spears all at once, the one strake him on
the shoulder, the other on the breast and the stroke glinted
down to his belly, and the third strake him in the thigh, and
sore hurt with all three strokes, so that he was borne perforce to the earth and after that he could not be again
relieved. Some of his knights and squires followed him,
but not all, for it was night, and no light but by the shining
of the moon. The Englishmen knew well they had borne one
down to the earth, but they wist not who it was; for if
they had known that it had been the earl Douglas, they
had been thereof so joyful and so proud that the victory
had been theirs. Nor also the Scots knew not of that adventure till the end of the battle; for if they had known it,
they should have been so sore despaired and discouraged
that they would have fled away. Thus as the earl Douglas
was felled to the earth, he was stricken into the head with
an axe, and another stroke through the thigh: the Englishmen passed forth and took no heed of him: they thought none
otherwise but that they had slain a man of arms. On the
other part the earl George de la March and of Dunbar fought
right valiantly and gave the Englishmen much ado, and
cried, 'Follow Douglas,' and set on the sons of Percy: also
earl John of Moray with his banner and men fought valiantly and set fiercely on the Englishmen, and gave them so
much to do that they wist not to whom to attend.

[1] 'No man was so well armed that he did not fear the great strokes
which he gave.'

HOW IN THIS BATTLE SIR RALPH PERCY WAS SORE HURT AND
TAKEN PRISONER BY A SCOTTISH KNIGHT

OF all the battles and encounterings that I have made mention of herebefore in all this history, great or small, this battle that I treat of now was one of the sorest and best foughten without cowardice or faint hearts. For there was nother knight nor squire but that did his devoir and fought hand to hand: this battle was like the battle of Becherel,[1] the which was valiantly fought and endured. The earl of Northumberland's sons, sir Henry and sir Ralph Percy, who were chief sovereign captains, acquitted themselves nobly, and sir Ralph Percy entered in so far among his enemies that he was closed in and hurt, and so sore handled that his breath was so short, that he was taken prisoner by a knight of the earl of Moray's called sir John Maxwell. In the taking the Scottish knight demanded what he was, for it was in the night, so that he knew him not, and sir Ralph was so sore overcome and bled fast, that at last he said: 'I am Ralph Percy.' Then the Scot said: 'Sir Ralph, rescue or no rescue I take you for my prisoner: I am Maxwell.' 'Well,' quoth sir Ralph, 'I am content: but then take heed to me, for I am sore hurt, my hosen and my greaves are full of blood.' Then the knight saw by him the earl Moray and said: 'Sir, here I deliver to you sir Ralph Percy as prisoner; but, sir, let good heed be taken to him, for he is sore hurt.' The earl was joyful of these words and said: 'Maxwell, thou hast well won thy spurs.' Then he delivered sir Ralph Percy to certain of his men, and they stopped and wrapped his wounds: and still the battle endured, not knowing who had as then the better, for there were many taken and rescued again that came to no knowledge.

Now let us speak of the young James earl of Douglas, who did marvels in arms or he was beaten down. When he was overthrown, the press was great about him, so that he could not relieve, for with an axe he had his death's wound. His men followed him as near as they could, and there came to him sir James Lindsay his cousin and sir John and sir

---

[1] Or, according to another reading, 'Cocherel.'

Walter Sinclair and other knights and squires. And by him was a gentle knight of his, who followed him all the day, and a chaplain of his, not like a priest but like a valiant man of arms, for all that night he followed the earl with a good axe in his hands and still scrimmished about the earl there-as he lay, and reculed back some of the Englishmen with great strokes that he gave. Thus he was found fighting near to his master, whereby he had great praise, and thereby the same year he was made archdeacon of Aberdeen. This priest was called sir William of North Berwick: he was a tall man and a hardy and was sore hurt. When these knights came to the earl, they found him in an evil case and a knight of his lying by him called sir Robert Hart: he had a fifteen wounds in one place and other. Then sir John Sinclair demanded of the earl how he did. 'Right evil, cousin,' quoth the earl, 'but thanked be God there hath been but a few of mine ancestors that hath died in their beds: but, cousin, I require you think to revenge me, for I reckon myself but dead, for my heart fainteth oftentimes. My cousin Walter and you, I pray you raise up again my banner which lieth on the ground, and my squire Davie Collemine slain: but, sirs, shew nother to friend nor foe in what case ye see me in; for if mine enemies knew it, they would rejoice, and our friends discomforted.' The two brethren of Sinclair and sir James Lindsay did as the earl had desired them and raised up again his banner and cried 'Douglas!' Such as were behind and heard that cry drew together and set on their enemies valiantly and reculed back the Englishmen and many overthrown, and so drave the Englishmen back beyond the place whereas the earl lay, who was by that time dead, and so came to the earl's banner, the which sir John Sinclair held in his hands, and many good knights and squires of Scotland about him, and still company drew to the cry of 'Douglas.' Thither came the earl Moray with his banner well accompanied, and also the earl de la March and of Dunbar, and when they saw the Englishmen recule and their company assembled together, they renewed again the battle and gave many hard and sad strokes.

HOW THE SCOTS WON THE BATTLE AGAINST THE ENGLISHMEN
BESIDE OTTERBURN, AND THERE WAS TAKEN PRISONERS SIR
HENRY AND SIR RALPH PERCY, AND HOW AN ENGLISH
SQUIRE WOULD NOT YIELD HIM, NO MORE WOULD
A SCOTTISH SQUIRE, AND SO DIED BOTH ; AND
HOW THE BISHOP OF DURHAM AND HIS
COMPANY WERE DISCOMFITED
AMONG THEMSELVES

To say truth, the Englishmen were sorer travailed than the
Scots, for they came the same day from Newcastle-upon-
Tyne, a six English miles, and went a great pace to the
intent to find the Scots, which they did; so that by their
fast going they were near out of breath, and the Scots were
fresh and well rested, which greatly availed them when
time was of their business; for in the last scrimmish they
reculed back the Englishmen in such wise, that after that
they could no more assemble together, for the Scots passed
through their battles.   And it fortuned that sir Henry
Percy and the lord of Montgomery, a valiant knight of Scotland, fought together hand to hand right valiantly without
letting of any other, for every man had enough to do.   So
long they two fought that per force of arms sir Henry
Percy was taken prisoner by the said lord of Montgomery.

The knights and squires of Scotland, as sir Marc Adre-
man,[1] sir Thomas Erskine, sir William, sir James and sir
Alexander Lindsay, the lord of Fenton, sir John of Saint-
Moreaulx,[2] sir Patrick of Dunbar, sir John and sir Walter
Sinclair, sir John Maxwell, sir Guy Stuart, sir John Hali-
burton, sir Alexander Ramsay, Robert Collemine[3] and his
two sons John and Robert; who were there made knights,
and a hundred knights and squires that I cannot name, all
these right valiantly did acquit themselves.   And on the
English party, before that the lord Percy was taken and
after, there fought valiantly sir Ralph Lumley, sir Matthew
Redman, sir Thomas Ogle, sir Thomas Gray, sir Thomas
Helton, sir Thomas Abingdon, sir John Lilleburn, sir
William Walsingham, the baron of Helton, sir John of

[1] Perhaps ' Malcolm Drummond.'
[2] The true reading seems to be ' Sandilands.'   [3] Perhaps ' Coningham.'

Colpedich,[4] the seneschal of York and divers other foot-men. Whereto should I write long process? This was a sore battle and well foughten; and as fortune is always changeable, though the Englishmen were more in number than the Scots and were right valiant men of war and well expert, and that at the first front they reculed back the Scots, yet finally the Scots obtained the place and victory, and all the foresaid Englishmen taken, and a hundred more, saving sir Matthew Redman, captain of Berwick, who when he knew no remedy nor recoverance, and saw his company fly from the Scots and yielded them on every side, then he took his horse and departed to save himself.

The same season about the end of this discomfiture there was an English squire called Thomas Waltham, a goodly and a valiant man, and that was well seen, for of all that night he would nother fly nor yet yield him. It was said he had made a vow at a feast in England, that the first time that ever he saw Englishmen and Scots in battle, he would so do his devoir to his power, in such wise that either he would be reputed for the best doer on both sides or else to die in the pain. He was called a valiant and a hardy man and did so much by his prowess, that under the banner of the earl of Moray he did such valiantness in arms, that the Scots had marvel thereof, and so was slain in fighting: the Scots would gladly have taken him alive, but he would never yield, he hoped ever to have been rescued. And with him there was a Scottish squire slain, cousin to the king of Scots, called Simon Glendowyn; his death was greatly complained of the Scots.

This battle was fierce and cruel till it came to the end of the discomfiture; but when the Scots saw the Englishmen recule and yield themselves, then the Scots were courteous and set them to their ransom, and every man said to his prisoner: 'Sirs, go and unarm you and take your ease; I am your master:' and so made their prisoners as good cheer as though they had been brethren, without doing to them any damage. The chase endured a five English miles, and if the Scots had been men enow, there had none scaped, but other they had been taken or slain. And if Archambault

[4] Either 'Copeland' or 'Copeldike.'

Douglas and the earl of Fife, the earl Sutherland and other
of the great company who were gone towards Carlisle had
been there, by all likelihood they had taken the bishop of
Durham and the town of Newcastle-upon-Tyne. I shall
shew you how. The same evening that the Percies departed
from Newcastle, as ye have heard before, the bishop of
Durham with the rearband came to Newcastle and supped:
and as he sat at the table, he had imagination in himself how
he did not acquit himself well to see the Englishmen in the
field and he to be within the town. Incontinent he caused
the table to be taken away and commanded to saddle his
horses and to sown the trumpets, and called up men in
the town to arm themselves and to mount on their horses,
and foot-men to order themselves to depart. And thus every
man departed out of the town to the number of seven thousand, two thousand on horseback and five thousand afoot;
they took their way toward Otterburn, whereas the battle had
been. And by that time they had gone two mile[1] from
Newcastle tidings came to them how their men were fighting with the Scots. Therewith the bishop rested there, and
incontinent came more flying fast, that they were out of
breath. Then they were demanded how the matter went.
They answered and said: 'Right evil; we be all discomfited:
here cometh the Scots chasing of us.' These tidings troubled
the Englishmen, and began to doubt. And again the third
time men came flying as fast as they might. When the men
of the bishopric of Durham heard of these evil tidings, they
were abashed in such wise that they brake their array, so
that the bishop could not hold together the number of five
hundred. It was thought that if the Scots had followed
them in any number, seeing that it was night, that in the
entering into the town, and the Englishmen so abashed, the
town had been won.

The bishop of Durham, being in the field, had good will
to have succoured the Englishmen and recomforted his men
as much as he could; but he saw his own men fly as well
as other. Then he demanded counsel of sir William Lucy
and of sir Thomas Clifford and of other knights, what was
best to do. These knights for their honour would give him

[1] The word 'lieue' is translated 'mile' throughout.

no counsel; for they thought to return again and do nothing should sown greatly to their blame, and to go forth might be to their great damage; and so stood still and would give none answer, and the longer they stood, the fewer they were, for some still stale away. Then the bishop said: 'Sirs, all things considered, it is none honour to put all in peril, nor to make of one evil damage twain. We hear how our company be discomfited, and we cannot remedy it: for to go to recover them, we know not with whom nor with what number we shall meet. Let us return fair and easily for this night to Newcastle, and to-morrow let us draw together and go look on our enemies.' Every man answered: 'As God will, so be it.' Therewith they returned to Newcastle. Thus a man may consider the great default that is in men that be abashed and discomfited: for if they had kept them together and have turned again such as fled, they had discomfited the Scots. This was the opinion of divers; and because they did not thus, the Scots had the victory.

HOW SIR MATTHEW REDMEN DEPARTED FROM THE BATTLE
TO SAVE HIMSELF; AND HOW SIR JAMES LINDSAY WAS
TAKEN PRISONER BY THE BISHOP OF DURHAM; AND
HOW AFTER THE BATTLE SCURRERS WERE SENT
FORTH TO DISCOVER THE COUNTRY

I SHALL shew you of sir Matthew Redman, who was on horseback to save himself, for he alone could not remedy the matter. At his departing sir James Lindsay was near to him and saw how sir Matthew departed, and this sir James, to win honour, followed in chase sir Matthew Redman, and came so near him that he might have striken him with his spear, if he had list. Then he said: 'Ah, sir knight, turn; it is a shame thus to fly: I am James of Lindsay: if ye will not turn, I shall strike you on the back with my spear.' Sir Matthew spake no word, but strake his horse with the spurs sorer than he did before. In this manner he chased him more than three miles, and at last sir Matthew Redman's horse foundered and fell under him. Then he stept forth on the earth and drew out his sword, and took courage to defend himself; and the Scot thought to have stricken him on the breast, but sir Matthew Redman swerved from the stroke, and the spear-point entered into the earth. Then sir Matthew strake asunder the spear with his sword; and when sir James Lindsay saw how he had lost his spear, he cast away the truncheon and lighted afoot, and took a little battle-axe that he carried at his back and handled it with his one hand quickly and deliverly, in the which feat Scots be well expert, and then he set at sir Matthew and he defended himself properly. Thus they tourneyed together, one with an axe and the other with a sword, a long season, and no man to let them. Finally sir James Lindsay gave the knight such strokes and held him so short, that he was put out of breath in such wise that he yielded himself, and said: 'Sir James Lindsay, I yield me to you.' 'Well,' quoth he, 'and I receive you, rescue or no rescue.' 'I am content,' quoth Redman, 'so ye deal with me like a good companion.' 'I shall not fail that,' quoth Lindsay, and so put up his sword. 'Well, sir,' quoth Redman, 'what will you now that I shall do? I am your prisoner, ye have conquered me. I would gladly go again to Newcastle, and within fifteen days I shall come to you into Scotland, whereas ye shall assign me.' 'I am content,' quoth Lindsay: 'ye shall promise by your faith to present yourself within this three weeks at Edinboro, and wheresoever ye go, to repute yourself my prisoner.' All this sir Matthew sware and promised to fulfil. Then each of them took their horses and took leave each of other. Sir James returned, and his intent was to go to his own company the same way that he came, and sir Matthew Redman to Newcastle.

Sir James Lindsay could not keep the right way as he came: it was dark and a mist, and he had not ridden half a mile, but he met face to face with the bishop of Durham and more than five hundred Englishmen with him. He might well escaped if he had would, but he supposed it had been his own company, that had pursued the Englishmen. When he was among them, one demanded of him what he was. 'I am,' quoth he, 'sir James Lindsay.' The bishop heard those words and stept to him and said: 'Lindsay, ye are taken: yield ye to me.' 'Who be you?' quoth Lindsay. 'I am,' quoth he, 'the bishop of Durham.' 'And from whence come you, sir?' quoth Lindsay. 'I come from the battle,' quoth the bishop, 'but I struck never a stroke there: I go back to Newcastle for this night, and ye shall go with me.' 'I may not choose,' quoth Lindsay, 'sith ye will have it so. I have taken and I am taken; such is the adventures of arms.' 'Whom have ye taken?' quoth the bishop. 'Sir,' quoth he, 'I took in the chase sir Matthew Redman.' 'And where is he?' quoth the bishop. 'By my faith, sir, he is returned to Newcastle: he desired me to trust him on his faith for three weeks, and so have I done.' 'Well,' quoth the bishop, 'let us go to Newcastle, and there ye shall speak with him.' Thus they rode to Newcastle together, and sir James Lindsay was prisoner to the bishop of Durham.

Under the banner of the earl de la March and of Dunbar was taken a squire of Gascoyne, called John of Chateauneuf, and under the banner of the earl of Moray was taken his companion John de Cantiron. Thus the field was clean avoided, or the day appeared. The Scots drew together and took guides and sent out scurrers to see if any men were in the way from Newcastle, to the intent that they would not be troubled in their lodgings; wherein they did wisely, for when the bishop of Durham was come again to Newcastle and in his lodging, he was sore pensive and wist not what to say nor do; for he heard say how his cousins the Percies were slain or taken, and all the knights that were with them. Then he sent for all the knights and squires that were in the town; and when they were come, he demanded of them if they should leave the matter in that case, and said: 'Sirs, we shall bear great blame if we thus return without looking on our enemies.' Then they concluded by the sun-rising every man to be armed, and on horseback and afoot to depart out of the town and to go to Otterburn to fight with the Scots. This was warned through the town by a trumpet, and every man armed them and assembled before the bridge, and by the sun-rising they departed by the gate towards Berwick and took the way towards Otterburn to the number of ten thousand, what afoot and a-horseback. They were not gone past two mile from Newcastle, when the Scots were signified that the bishop of Durham was coming to themward to fight: this they knew by their spies, such as they had set in the fields.

After that sir Matthew Redman was returned to Newcastle and had shewed to divers how he had been taken prisoner by sir James Lindsay, then it was shewed him how the bishop of Durham had taken the said sir James Lindsay and how that he was there in the town as his prisoner. As soon as the bishop was departed, sir Matthew Redman went to the bishop's lodging to see his master, and there he found him in a study, lying in a window,[1] and said: 'What, sir James Lindsay, what make you here?' Then sir James came forth of the study to him and gave him good morrow, and said: 'By my faith, sir Matthew, fortune hath brought me hither; for as soon as I was departed from you, I met by chance the bishop of Durham, to whom I am prisoner, as ye be to me. I believe ye shall not need to come to Edinboro to me to make your finance: I think rather we shall make an exchange one for another, if the bishop be so content.' 'Well, sir,' quoth Redman, 'we shall accord right well together, ye shall dine this day with me: the bishop and our men be gone forth to fight with your men, I cannot tell what shall fall, we shall know at their return.' 'I am content to dine with you,' quoth Lindsay. Thus these two knights dined together in Newcastle.

When the knights of Scotland were informed how the bishop of Durham came on them with ten thousand men, they drew to council to see what was best for them to do, other to depart or else to abide the adventure. All things considered, they concluded to abide, for they said they could not be in a better nor a stronger place than they were in already: they had many prisoners and they could not carry them away, if they should have departed; and also they had many of their men hurt and also some of their prisoners, whom they thought they would not leave behind them. Thus they drew together and ordered so their field, that there was no entry but one way, and they set all their prisoners together and made them to promise how that, rescue or no

[1] Or rather, 'very pensive leaning against a window,' and afterwards the expression 'came forth of the study to him' should be 'broke off his thought and came towards him.'

rescue, they should be their prisoners. After that they made all their minstrels to blow up all at once and made the greatest revel of the world. Lightly it is the usage of Scots, that when they be thus assembled together in arms, the footmen beareth about their necks horns in manner like hunters, some great, some small, and of all sorts, so that when they blow all at once, they make such a noise, that it may be heard nigh four miles off: thus they do to abash their enemies and to rejoice themselves. When the bishop of Durham with his banner and ten thousand men with him were approached within a league, then the Scots blew their horns in such wise, that it seemed that all the devils in hell had been among them, so that such as heard them and knew not of their usage were sore abashed. This blowing and noise endured a long space and then ceased: and by that time the Englishmen were within less than a mile. Then the Scots began to blow again and made a great noise, and as long endured as it did before. Then the bishop approached with his battle well ranged in good order and came within the sight of the Scots, as within two bow-shot or less: then the Scots blew again their horns a long space. The bishop stood still to see what the Scots would do and aviewed them well and saw how they were in a strong ground greatly to their advantage. Then the bishop took counsel what was best for him to do; but all things well advised, they were not in purpose to enter in among the Scots to assail them, but returned without doing of anything, for they saw well they might rather lose than win.

When the Scots saw the Englishmen recule and that they should have no battle, they went to their lodgings and made merry, and then ordained to depart from thence. And because that sir Ralph Percy was sore hurt, he desired of his master that he might return to Newcastle or into some place, whereas it pleased him, unto such time as he were whole of his hurts, promising, as soon as he were able to ride, to return into Scotland, other to Edinboro or into any other place appointed. The earl of March, under whom he was taken, agreed thereto and delivered him a horse litter and sent him away; and by like covenant divers other knights and squires were suffered to return and took term other to return or else to pay their finance, such as they were appointed unto. It was shewed me by the information of the Scots, such as had been at this said battle that was between Newcastle and Otterburn in the year of our Lord God a thousand three hundred fourscore and eight, the nineteenth day of August, how that there were taken prisoners of the English party a thousand and forty men, one and other, and slain in the field and in the chase eighteen hundred and forty, and sore hurt more than a thousand: and of the Scots there were a hundred slain, and taken in the chase more than two hundred; for as the Englishmen fled, when they saw any advantage they returned again and fought: by that means the Scots were taken and none otherwise. Every man may well consider that it was a well fought field, when there were so many slain and taken on both parties.

HOW THE SCOTS DEPARTED AND CARRIED WITH THEM THE EARL DOUGLAS DEAD, AND BURIED HIM IN THE ABBEY OF MELROSE; AND HOW SIR ARCHAMBAULT DOUGLAS AND HIS COMPANY DEPARTED FROM BEFORE CARLISLE AND RETURNED INTO SCOTLAND

AFTER this battle thus finished, every man returned,[1] and the earl Douglas' dead body chested and laid in a chare, and with him sir Robert Hart and Simon Glendowyn, then they prepared to depart: so they departed and led with them sir Henry Percy and more than forty knights of England, and took the way to the abbey of Melrose. At their departing they set fire in their lodgings, and rode all the day, and yet lay that night in the English ground: none denied them. The next day they dislodged early in the morning and so came that day to Melrose. It is an abbey of black monks on the border between both realms. There they rested and buried the earl James Douglas. The second day after his obsequy was done reverently, and on his body laid a tomb of stone and his banner hanging over him. Whether there were as then any more earls of Douglas, to whom the land returned, or not, I cannot tell;

[1] That is, 'After the battle was over and every man had returned,' but it should be, 'After all this was done and everything was gathered together.'

for I, sir John Froissart, author of this book, was in Scotland in the earl's castle of Dalkeith, living earl William, at which time he had two children, a son and a daughter; but after there were many of the Douglases, for I have seen a five brethren, all squires, bearing the name of Douglas, in the king of Scotland's house, David; they were sons to a knight in Scotland called sir James Douglas, and they bare in their arms gold, three oreilles gules, but as for the heritage, I know not who had it: as for sir Archambault Douglas, of whom I have spoken before in this history in divers places, who was a valiant knight, and greatly redoubted of the Englishmen, he was but a bastard.

When these Scots had been at Melrose abbey and done there all that they came thither for, then they departed each from other and went into their own countries, and such as had prisoners, some led them away with them and some were ransomed and suffered to return. Thus the Englishmen found the Scots right courteous and gentle in their deliverance and ransom, so that they were well content. This was shewed me in the country of Bearn in the earl of Foix's house by a knight named John of Chateauneuf, who was taken prisoner at the same journey under the banner of the earl of March and Dunbar: and he greatly praised the said earl, for he suffered him to pass in manner as he desired himself.

Thus these men of war of Scotland departed, and ransomed their prisoners as soon as they might right courteously, and so returned little and little into their own countries. And it was shewed me and I believe it well, that the Scots had by reason of that journey two hundred thousand franks for ransoming of prisoners: for sith the battle that was before Stirling in Scotland, whereas sir Robert of Bruce, sir William Douglas, sir Robert Versy, sir Simon Fraser and other Scots chased the Englishmen three days, they never had journey so profitable nor so honourable for them, as this was. When tidings came to the other company of the Scots that were beside Carlisle, how their company had distressed the Englishmen beside Otterburn, they were greatly rejoiced, and displeased in their minds that they had not been there. Then they determined to dislodge and to draw into their own countries, seeing their other company were withdrawn. Thus they dislodged and entered into Scotland.

Now let us leave to speak of the Scots and of the Englishmen for this time, and let us return to the young Charles of France, who with a great people went into Almaine, to bring the duke of Gueldres to reason.

When the French king and all his army were past the river of Meuse at the bridge of Morsay, they took the way of Ardennes and of Luxembourg, and always the pioneers were before, beating woods and bushes and making the ways plain. The duke of Juliers and his country greatly doubted the coming of the French king, for they knew well they should have the first assault and bear the first burden: and the land of Juliers is a plain country; in one day the men of war should do much damage there, and destroy and waste all, except the castles and good towns. Thus the French king entered into the country of Luxembourg and came to an abbey, whereas Wenceslas sometime duke of Brabant was buried. There the king tarried two days: then he departed and took the way through Bastogne, and lodged within a league whereas the duchess of Brabant lay. She sent word of her being there to the duke of Burgoyne, and he brought her into the field to speak with the king, who received her right honourably, and there communed together. Then the duchess returned to Bastogne, and thither she was conveyed with sir John of Vienne and sir Guy of Tremouïlle; and the next day the king went forward, approaching to the land of his enemies, and came to the entering into Almaine, on the frontiers of the duchy of Juliers. But or he came so far forward, Arnold bishop of Liege had been with the king and had greatly entreated for the duke of Juliers, that the king should not be miscontent with him, though he were father to the duke of Gueldres; for he excused him of the defiance that his son had made, affirming how it was not by his knowledge nor consent, wherefore, he said, it were pity that the father should bear the default of the son. This excuse was not sufficient to the king nor to his uncles: for the intent of the king and his council was, without the duke of

Juliers would come and make other manner of excuse, and to yield himself to the king's pleasure, his country should be the first that should bear the burden. Then the bishop of Liege and the lords of Hesbaing and the councils of the good towns offered to the king and his council wholly the bishopric of Liege for his army to pass and repass paying for their expenses, and to rest and refresh them there as long as it pleased them. The king thanked them, and so did his uncles, and would not refuse their offer, for he knew not what need he should have after.

THE HOLY GRAIL FROM THE
BOOK OF KING ARTHUR

BY
SIR THOMAS MALORY

INTRODUCTORY NOTE

THE *earliest extant form of the story of the Holy Grail is the French metrical romance of "Perceval" or "Le Conte du Graal" of Chrétien de Troies, written about 1175. Chrétien died leaving the poem unfinished, and it was continued by three other authors till it reached the vast size of 63,000 lines. The religious signification of the Grail is supposed to have been attached to it early in the thirteenth century by Robert de Boron, and, perhaps a little later, in the French prose "Quest of the Holy Grail," Galahad takes the place of Perceval as the hero of the story. The later history of the various versions of the legend is highly intricate, and in many points uncertain. It was from a form of it embodied in the French prose "Lancelot" that Sir Thomas Malory drew the chapters of his "Morte d'Arthur" which are here reprinted, and which, more than the earlier versions, are the source from which the legend has passed into modern English poetry.*

Until a few years ago Malory himself was little more than a name, our information about him being limited to the statement in Caxton's edition of the "Morte d'Arthur" that he was the author. It now appears probable, however, that Sir Thomas Malory was an English knight born about 1400, of an old Warwickshire family. He served in the French wars under Richard Beauchamp, Earl of Warwick, "whom all Europe recognized as embodying the knightly ideal of the age," and may well have owed his enthusiasm for chivalry to his association with this distinguished nobleman. He died in 1471.

Malory's book is a compilation from French and English sources. These are chosen without much discrimination, and put together without great skill in arrangement. But the author's wholehearted enthusiasm for chivalrous ideals and the noble simplicity and fine rhythm of his prose have combined to give his work a unique place in English literature. In it the age of chivalry is summed up and closed. It is not without reason that the date of its publication by Caxton, 1485, should be conventionally accepted as the end of the Middle Ages in England. Romance had passed under the printing press, and a new age had begun.

THE HOLY GRAIL

BEING BOOKS XIII, XIV, XV, XVI and XVII OF THE BOOK OF KING ARTHUR AND OF HIS NOBLE KNIGHTS OF THE ROUND TABLE

THE THIRTEENTH BOOK.

CHAPTER I

HOW AT THE VIGIL OF THE FEAST OF PENTECOST ENTERED INTO THE HALL BEFORE KING ARTHUR A DAMOSEL, AND DESIRED SIR LAUNCELOT FOR TO COME AND DUB A KNIGHT, AND HOW HE WENT WITH HER

AT the vigil of Pentecost, when all the fellowship of the Round Table were come unto Camelot and there heard their service, and the tables were set ready to the meat, right so entered into the hall a full fair gentlewoman on horseback, that had ridden full fast, for her horse was all besweated. Then she there alit, and came before the king and saluted him; and he said: Damosel, God thee bless.

109

Sir, said she, for God's sake say me where Sir Launcelot is. Yonder ye may see him, said the king. Then she went unto Launcelot and said: Sir Launcelot, I salute you on King Pelles' behalf, and I require you come on with me hereby into a forest. Then Sir Launcelot asked her with whom she dwelled. I dwell, said she, with King Pelles. What will ye with me? said Launcelot. Ye shall know, said she, when ye come thither. Well, said he, I will gladly go with you. So Sir Launcelot bad his squire saddle his horse and bring his arms; and in all haste he did his commandment. Then came the queen unto Launcelot, and said: Will ye leave us at this high feast? Madam, said the gentlewoman, wit ye well he shall be with you tomorn by dinner time. If I wist, said the queen, that he should not be with us here tomorn he should not go with you by my good will. Right so departed Sir Launcelot with the gentlewoman, and rode until that he came into a forest and into a great valley, where they saw an abbey of nuns; and there was a squire ready and opened the gates, and so they entered and descended off their horses; and there came a fair fellowship about Sir Launcelot, and welcomed him, and were passing glad of his coming. And then they led him unto the Abbess's chamber and unarmed him; and right so he was ware upon a bed lying two of his cousins, Sir Bors and Sir Lionel, and then he waked them; and when they saw him they made great joy. Sir, said Sir Bors unto Sir Launcelot, what adventure hath brought you hither, for we weened tomorn to have found you at Camelot? As God me help, said Sir Launcelot, a gentlewoman brought me hither, but I know not the cause. In the meanwhile that they thus stood talking together, therein came twelve nuns that brought with them Galahad, the which was passing fair and well made, that unnethe in the world men might not find his match: and all those ladies wept. Sir, said they all, we bring you here this child the which we have nourished, and we pray you to make him a knight, for of a more worthier man's hand may he not receive the order of knighthood. Sir Launcelot beheld the young squire and saw him seemly and demure as a dove, with all manner of good features, that he weened of his age never to have seen so fair a man of form. Then said Sir

Launcelot: Cometh this desire of himself? He and all they
said yea. Then shall he, said Sir Launcelot, receive the high
order of knighthood as tomorn at the reverence of the high
feast. That night Sir Launcelot had passing good cheer;
and on the morn at the hour of prime, at Galahad's desire,
he made him knight and said: God make him a good man,
for of beauty faileth you not as any that liveth.

CHAPTER II

HOW THE LETTERS WERE FOUND WRITTEN IN THE SIEGE
PERILOUS, AND OF THE MARVELLOUS ADVENTURE
OF THE SWORD IN A STONE

Now fair sir, said Sir Launcelot, will ye come with me
unto the court of King Arthur? Nay, said he, I will not go
with you as at this time. Then he departed from them and
took his two cousins with him, and so they came unto Camelot by the hour of underne on Whitsunday. By that time the
king and the queen were gone to the minster to hear their
service. Then the king and the queen were passing glad of
Sir Bors and Sir Lionel, and so was all the fellowship. So
when the king and all the knights were come from service,
the barons espied in the sieges of the Round Table all about,
written with golden letters: Here ought to sit he, and he
ought to sit here. And thus they went so long till that they
came to the Siege Perilous, where they found letters newly
written of gold which said: Four hundred winters and four
and fifty accomplished after the passion of our Lord Jesu
Christ ought this siege to be fulfilled. Then all they said:
This is a marvellous thing and an adventurous. In the name
of God, said Sir Launcelot; and then accounted the term of
the writing from the birth of our Lord unto that day. It
seemeth me, said Sir Launcelot, this siege ought to be fulfilled this same day, for this is the feast of Pentecost after
the four hundred and four and fifty year; and if it would
please all parties, I would none of these letters were seen this
day, till he be come that ought to achieve this adventure.
Then made they to ordain a cloth of silk, for to cover these

letters in the Siege Perilous. Then the king bad haste unto dinner. Sir, said Sir Kay the Steward, if ye go now to your meat ye shall break your old custom of your court, for ye have not used on this day to sit at your meat or that ye have seen some adventure. Ye say sooth, said the king, but I had so great joy of Sir Launcelot and of his cousins, which be come to the court whole and sound, so that I bethought me not of mine old custom. So, as they stood speaking, in came a squire and said unto the king: Sir, I bring unto you marvellous tidings. What be they? said the king. Sir, there is here beneath at the river a great stone which I saw fleet above the water, and therein I saw sticking a sword. The king said: I will see that marvel. So all the knights went with him, and when they came to the river they found there a stone fleeting, as it were of red marble, and therein stuck a fair rich sword, and in the pommel thereof were precious stones wrought with subtil letters of gold. Then the barons read the letters which said in this wise: Never shall man take me hence, but only he by whose side I ought to hang, and he shall be the best knight of the world. When the king had seen the letters, he said unto Sir Launcelot: Fair sir, this sword ought to be yours, for I am sure ye be the best knight of the world. Then Sir Launcelot answered full soberly: Certes, sir, it is not my sword; also, Sir, wit ye well I have no hardiness to set my hand to it, for it longed not to hang by my side. Also, who that assayeth to take the sword and faileth of it, he shall receive a wound by that sword that he shall not be whole long after. And I will that ye wit that this same day shall the adventures of the Sangreal, that is called the Holy Vessel, begin.

CHAPTER III

HOW SIR GAWAINE ESSAYED TO DRAW OUT THE SWORD, AND HOW AN OLD MAN BROUGHT IN GALAHAD

Now, fair nephew, said the king unto Sir Gawaine, essay ye, for my love. Sir, he said, save your good grace I shall not do that. Sir, said the king, essay to take the sword and at my commandment. Sir, said Gawaine, your commandment I will obey. And therewith he took up the sword by the handles, but he might not stir it. I thank you, said the king to Sir Gawaine. My lord Sir Gawaine, said Sir Launcelot, now wit ye well this sword shall touch you so sore that ye shall will ye had never set your hand thereto for the best castle of this realm. Sir, he said, I might not withsay mine uncle's will and commandment. But when the king heard this he repented it much, and said unto Sir Percivale that he should essay, for his love. And he said: Gladly, for to bear Sir Gawaine fellowship. And therewith he set his hand on the sword and drew it strongly, but he might not move it. Then were there more that durst be so hardy, to set their hands thereto. Now may ye go to your dinner, said Sir Kay unto the King, for a marvellous adventure have ye seen. So the king and all went unto the court, and every knight knew his own place, and set him therein, and young men that were knights served them. So when they were served, and all sieges fulfilled save only the Siege Perilous, anon there befell a marvellous adventure, that all the doors and windows of the palace shut by themself. Not for then the hall was not greatly darked; and therewith they abashed both one and other. Then King Arthur spake first and said: By God, fair fellows and lords, we have seen this day marvels, but or night I suppose we shall see greater marvels. In the meanwhile came in a good old man, and an ancient, clothed all in white, and there was no knight knew from whence he came. And with him he brought a young knight, both on foot, in red arms, without sword or shield, save a scabbard hanging by his side. And these words he said: Peace be with you, fair lords. Then the old man said unto Arthur: Sir, I bring here a young knight, the which is of king's lineage, and of the kindred of Joseph of Aramathie, whereby the marvels of this court, and of strange realms, shall be fully accomplished.

CHAPTER IV

HOW THE OLD MAN BROUGHT GALAHAD TO THE SIEGE PERILOUS AND SET HIM THEREIN, AND HOW ALL THE KNIGHTS MARVELLED

THE king was right glad of his words, and said unto the good man: Sir, ye be right welcome, and the young knight with you. Then the old man made the young man to unarm him, and he was in a coat of red sendel, and bare a mantle upon his shoulder that was furred with ermine, and put that upon him. And the old knight said unto the young knight: Sir, follow me. And anon he led him unto the Siege Perilous, where beside sat Sir Launcelot; and the good man lift up the cloth, and found there letters that said thus: This is the siege of Galahad, the haut prince. Sir, said the old knight, wit ye well that place is yours. And then he set him down surely in that siege. And then he said to the old man: Sir, ye may now go your way, for well have ye done that ye were commanded to do; and recommend me unto my grandsire, King Pelles, and unto my lord Petchere, and say them on my behalf, I shall come and see them as soon as ever I may. So the good man departed; and there met him twenty noble squires, and so took their horses and went their way. Then all the knights of the Table Round marvelled greatly of Sir Galahad, that he durst sit there in that Siege Perilous, and was so tender of age; and wist not from whence he came but all only by God; and said: This is he by whom the Sangreal shall be achieved, for there sat never none but he, but he were mischieved. Then Sir Launcelot beheld his son and had great joy of him. Then Bors told his fellows: Upon pain of my life this young knight shall come unto great worship. This noise was great in all the court, so that it came to the queen. Then she had marvel what knight it might be that durst adventure him to sit in the Siege Perilous. Many said unto the queen he resembled much unto Sir Launcelot. I may well suppose, said the queen, that Sir Launcelot begat him on King Pelles' daughter, by the which he was made to lie by, by enchantment, and his name is Galahad. I would fain see him, said the queen, for he must needs be a noble man, for so is his father that him begat, I report me unto all the Table Round. So when the meat was done that the king and all were risen, the king yede unto the Siege Perilous and lift up the cloth, and found there the name of Galahad; and then he shewed it unto Sir Gawaine, and said: Fair nephew, now have we among us Sir Galahad, the good knight that shall worship us all; and upon pain of my life he shall achieve the Sangreal, right as Sir Launcelot had done us to understand. Then came King Arthur unto Galahad and said: Sir, ye be welcome, for ye shall move many good knights to the quest of the Sangreal, and ye shall achieve that never knights might bring to an end. Then the king took him by the hand, and went down from the palace to shew Galahad the adventures of the stone.

CHAPTER V

HOW KING ARTHUR SHEWED THE STONE HOVING ON THE WATER TO GALAHAD, AND HOW HE DREW OUT THE SWORD

THE queen heard thereof, and came after with many ladies, and shewed them the stone where it hoved on the water. Sir, said the king unto Sir Galahad, here is a great marvel as ever I saw, and right good knights have essayed and failed. Sir, said Galahad, that is no marvel, for this adventure is not theirs but mine; and for the surety of this sword I brought none with me, for here by my side hangeth the scabbard. And anon he laid his hand on the sword, and lightly drew it out of the stone, and put it in the sheath, and said unto the king: Now it goeth better than it did aforehand. Sir, said the king, a shield God shall send you. Now have I that sword that sometime was the good knight's, Balin le Savage, and he was a passing good man of his hands; and with this sword he slew his brother Balan, and that was great pity, for he was a good knight, and either slew other through a dolorous stroke that Balin gave unto my grandfather King Pelles, the which is not yet whole, nor not

shall be till I heal him. Therewith the king and all espied
where came riding down the river a lady on a white palfrey
toward them. Then she saluted the king and the queen,
and asked if that Sir Launcelot was there. And then he
answered himself: I am here, fair lady. Then she said all
with weeping: How your great doing is changed sith this
day in the morn. Damosel, why say you so? said Launcelot. I say you sooth, said the damosel, for ye were this day
the best knight of the world, but who should say so now, he
should be a liar, for there is now one better than ye, and
well it is proved by the adventures of the sword whereto ye
durst not set to your hand; and that is the change and
leaving of your name. Wherefore I make unto you a
remembrance, that ye shall not ween from henceforth that
ye be the best knight of the world. As touching unto that,
said Launcelot, I know well I was never the best. Yes,
said the damosel, that were ye, and are yet, of any sinful
man of the world. And, Sir king, Nacien, the hermit,
sendeth thee word, that thee shall befall the greatest worship
that ever befell king in Britain; and I say you wherefore,
for this day the Sangreal appeared in thy house and fed thee
and all thy fellowship of the Round Table. So she departed
and went that same way that she came.

CHAPTER VI

HOW KING ARTHUR HAD ALL THE KNIGHTS TOGETHER
FOR TO JOUST IN THE MEADOW BESIDE
CAMELOT OR THEY DEPARTED

Now, said the king, I am sure at this quest of the Sangreal
shall all ye of the Table Round depart, and never shall I see
you again whole together; therefore I will see you all whole
together in the meadow of Camelot to joust and to tourney,
that after your death men may speak of it that such good
knights were wholly together such a day. As unto that
counsel and at the king's request they accorded all, and took
on their harness that longed unto jousting. But all this
moving of the king was for this intent, for to see Galahad

proved; for the king deemed he should not lightly come again unto the court after his departing. So were they assembled in the meadow both more and less. Then Sir Galahad, by the prayer of the king and the queen, did upon him a noble jesseraunce, and also he did on his helm, but shield would he take none for no prayer of the king. And then Sir Gawaine and other knights prayed him to take a spear. Right so he did; and the queen was in a tower with all her ladies, for to behold that tournament. Then Sir Galahad dressed him in middes of the meadow, and began to break spears marvellously, that all men had wonder of him; for he there surmounted all other knights, for within a while he had defouled many good knights of the Table Round save twain, that was Sir Launcelot and Sir Percivale.

CHAPTER VII

HOW THE QUEEN DESIRED TO SEE GALAHAD; AND HOW
AFTER, ALL THE KNIGHTS WERE REPLENISHED
WITH THE HOLY SANGREAL, AND HOW THEY
AVOWED THE ENQUEST OF THE SAME

THEN the king, at the queen's request, made him to alight and to unlace his helm, that the queen might see him in the visage. When she beheld him she said: Soothly I dare well say that Sir Launcelot begat him, for never two men resembled more in likeness, therefore it is no marvel though he be of great prowess. So a lady that stood by the queen said: Madam, for God's sake ought he of right to be so good a knight? Yea, forsooth, said the queen, for he is of all parties come of the best knights of the world and of the highest lineage; for Sir Launcelot is come but of the eighth degree from our Lord Jesu Christ, and Sir Galahad is of the ninth degree from our Lord Jesu Christ, therefore I dare say they be the greatest gentlemen of the world. And then the king and all estates went home unto Camelot, and so went to evensong to the great minster, and so after upon that to supper, and every knight sat in his own place as they were toforehand. Then anon they heard cracking and crying of thunder, that them thought the place should all to drive. In the midst of this blast entered a sunbeam more clearer by seven times than ever they saw day, and all they were alighted of the grace of the Holy Ghost. Then began every knight to behold other, and either saw other, by their seeming, fairer than ever they saw afore. Not for then there was no knight might speak one word a great while, and so they looked every man on other as they had been dumb. Then there entered into the hall the Holy Greal covered with white samite, but there was none might see it, nor who bare it. And there was all the hall fulfilled with good odours, and every knight had such meats and drinks as he best loved in this world. And when the Holy Greal had been borne through the hall, then the Holy Vessel departed suddenly, that they wist not where it became: then had they all breath to speak. And then the king yielded thank- ings to God, of His good grace that he had sent them Certes, said the king, we ought to thank our Lord Jesu greatly for that he hath shewed us this day, at the reverence of this high feast of Pentecost. Now, said Sir Gawaine, we have been served this day of what meats and drinks we thought on; but one thing beguiled us, we might not see the holy Grail, it was so preciously covered. Wherefore I will make here avow, that tomorn, without longer abiding, I shall labour in the quest of the Sangreal, that I shall hold me out a twelvemonth and a day, or more if need be, and never shall I return again unto the court till I have seen it more openly than it hath been seen here; and if I may not speed I shall return again as he that may not be against the will of our Lord Jesu Christ. When they of the Table Round heard Sir Gawaine say so, they arose up the most part and made such avows as Sir Gawaine had made. Anon as King Arthur heard this he was greatly displeased, for he wist well they might not again say their avows. Alas, said King Arthur unto Sir Gawaine, ye have nigh slain me with the avow and promise that ye have made; for through you ye have bereft me the fairest fellowship and the truest of knighthood that ever were seen together in any realm of the world; for when they depart from hence I am sure they all shall never meet more in this world, for they shall die many in the quest. And so it forthinketh me a little, for I have loved them as well as my life, wherefore it shall grieve me right sore, the departition of this fellowship: for I have had an old custom to have them in my fellowship.

CHAPTER VIII

HOW GREAT SORROW WAS MADE OF THE KING AND THE QUEEN AND LADIES FOR THE DEPARTING OF THE KNIGHTS, AND HOW THEY DEPARTED

AND therewith the tears filled in his eyes. And then he said: Gawaine, Gawaine, ye have set me in great sorrow, for I have great doubt that my true fellowship shall never meet here more again. Ah, said Sir Launcelot, comfort yourself; for it shall be unto us a great honour and much more than if we died in any other places, for of death we be siccar. Ah, Launcelot, said the king, the great love that I have had unto you all the days of my life maketh me to say such doleful words; for never Christian king had never so many worthy men at his table as I have had this day at the Round Table, and that is my great sorrow. When the queen, ladies, and gentlewomen, wist these tidings, they had such sorrow and heaviness that there might no tongue tell it, for those knights had held them in honour and charity. But among all other Queen Guenever made great sorrow. I marvel, said she, my lord would suffer them to depart from him. Thus was all the court troubled for the love of the departition of those knights. And many of those ladies that loved knights would have gone with their lovers; and so had they done, had not an old knight come among them in religious clothing; and then he spake all on high and said: Fair lords, which have sworn in the quest of the Sangreal, thus sendeth you Nacien, the hermit, word, that none in this quest lead lady nor gentlewoman with him, for it is not to do in so high a service as they labour in; for I warn you plain, he that is not clean of his sins he shall not see the mysteries of our Lord Jesu Christ. And for this cause they left these ladies and gentlewomen. After this the queen came unto Galahad and asked him of whence he was, and of what country. He told her of whence he was. And son unto Launcelot, she said he was. As to that, he said neither yea or nay. So God me help, said the queen, of your father ye need not to shame you, for he is the goodliest knight, and of the best men of the world come, and of the strain of all parties, of kings. Wherefore ye ought of right to be, of your deeds, a passing good man; and certainly, she said, ye resemble him much. Then Sir Galahad was a little ashamed and said: Madam, sith ye know in certain, wherefore do ye ask it me? for he that is my father shall be known openly and all betimes. And then they went to rest them. And in the honour of the highness of Galahad he was led into King Arthur's chamber, and there rested in his own bed. And as soon as it was day the king arose, for he had no rest of all that night for sorrow. Then he went unto Gawaine and to Sir Launcelot that were arisen for to hear mass. And then the king again said: Ah Gawaine, Gawaine, ye have betrayed me; for never shall my court be amended by you, but ye will never be sorry for me as I am for you. And therewith the tears began to run down by his visage. And therewith the king said: Ah, knight Sir Launcelot, I require thee thou counsel me, for I would that this quest were undone an it might be. Sir, said Sir Launcelot, ye saw yesterday so many worthy knights that then were sworn that they may not leave it in no manner of wise. That wot I well, said the king, but it shall so heavy me at their departing that I wot well there shall no manner of joy remedy me. And then the king and the queen went unto the minister. So anon Launcelot and Gawaine commanded their men to bring their arms. And when they all were armed save their shields and their helms, then they came to their fellowship, which were all ready in the same wise, for to go to the minster to hear their service. Then after the service was done the king would wit how many had undertaken the quest of the Holy Grail; and to account them he prayed them all. Then found they by tale an hundred and fifty, and all were knights of the Round Table. And then they put on their helms and departed, and recommended them all wholly unto the queen: and there was weeping and great sorrow. Then the queen departed into her chamber so that no man should apperceive her great sorrows. When Sir Launcelot missed the queen he went into her chamber, and when she saw him she cried aloud: O Sir Launcelot, ye have betrayed me and put me to death, for to leave thus my lord. Ah, madam, said Sir Launcelot, I pray you be not displeased, for I shall come as soon as I may with my worship. Alas, said she, that ever I saw you; but he that suffered death upon the cross for all mankind be to you good conduct and safety, and all the whole fellowship. Right so departed Sir Launcelot, and found his fellowship that abode his coming. And so they mounted upon their horses and rode through the streets of Camelot; and there was weeping of the rich and poor, and the king turned away and might not speak for weeping. So within a while they came to a city, and a castle that hight Vagon. There they entered into the castle, and the lord of that castle was an old man that hight Vagon, and he was a good man of his living, and set open the gates, and made them all the good cheer that he might. And so on the morrow they were all accorded that they should depart every each from other; and then they departed on the morrow with weeping and mourning cheer, and every knight took the way that him best liked.

CHAPTER IX

HOW GALAHAD GAT HIM A SHIELD, AND HOW THEY SPED THAT PRESUMED TO TAKE DOWN THE SAID SHIELD

Now rideth Sir Galahad yet without shield, and so he rode four days without any adventure. And at the fourth day after evensong he came to a White Abbey, and there he was received with great reverence, and led to a chamber, and there he was unarmed; and then was he ware of two knights of the Round Table, one was King Bagdemagus, and that other was Sir Uwaine. And when they saw him they went unto him and made of him great solace, and so they went to supper. Sirs, said Sir Galahad, what adventure brought you hither? Sir, said they, it is told us that within this place is a shield that no man may bear about his neck but if that he be mischieved or dead within three days, or else maimed for ever. Ah sir, said King Bagdemagus, I shall it bear to-morrow for to essay this strange adventure. In the name of God, said Sir Galahad. Sir, said Bagdemagus, an I may not achieve the adventure of this shield ye shall take it upon you, for I am sure ye shall not fail. Sir, said Galahad, I agree right well thereto, for I have no shield. So on the morn they arose and heard mass. Then King Bagdemagus asked where the adventurous shield was. Anon a monk led him behind an altar where the shield hung as white as any snow, but in the middes was a red cross. Sir, said the monk, this shield ought not to be hanged about no knight's neck but he be the worthiest knight of the world, and therefore I counsel you knights to be well advised. Well, said King Bagdemagus, I wot well that I am not the best knight of the world, but yet shall I essay to bear it. And so he bare it out of the monastery; and then he said unto Sir Galahad: If it will please you I pray you abide here still, till ye know how I shall speed. I shall abide you here, said Galahad. Then King Bagdemagus took with him a squire, the which should bring tidings unto Sir Galahad how he sped. Then when they had ridden a two mile and came in a fair valley afore an hermitage, then they saw a goodly knight come from that part in white armour, horse and all; and he came as fast as his horse might run, with his spear in the rest, and King Bagdemagus dressed his spear against him and brake it upon the white knight. But the other struck him so hard that he brake the mails, and thrust him through the right shoulder, for the shield covered him not as at that time; and so he bare him from his horse. And therewith he alighted and took the white shield from him, saying: Knight, thou hast done thyself great folly, for this shield ought not to be borne but by him that shall have no peer that liveth. And then he came to King Bagdemagus' squire and said: Bear this shield unto the good knight Sir Galahad, that thou left in the abbey, and greet him well from me. Sir, said the squire, what is your name? Take thou no heed of my name, said the knight, for it is not for thee to know nor for none earthly man. Now, fair sir, said the squire, at the reverence of Jesu Christ, tell me for what cause this shield may not be borne but if the bearer thereof be mischieved. Now sith thou hast conjured me so, said the knight, this shield behoveth unto no man but unto Galahad. And the squire went unto Bagdemagus and asked whether he were sore wounded or not. Yea, forsooth, said he, I shall escape hard from the death. Then he fetched his horse, and brought him with great pain unto an abbey. Then was he taken down softly and unarmed, and laid in a bed, and there was looked to his wounds. And as the book telleth, he lay there long, and escaped hard with the life.

CHAPTER X

HOW GALAHAD DEPARTED WITH THE SHIELD, AND HOW KING EVELAKE HAD RECEIVED THE SHIELD OF JOSEPH OF ARAMATHIE

SIR GALAHAD, said the squire, that knight that wounded Bagdemagus sendeth you greeting, and bad that ye should bear this shield, wherethrough great adventures should befall. Now blessed be God and fortune, said Galahad. And then he asked his arms, and mounted upon his horse, and hung the white shield about his neck, and commended them unto God. And Sir Uwaine said he would bear him fellowship if it pleased him. Sir, said Galahad, that may ye not, for I must go alone, save this squire shall bear me fellowship: and so departed Uwaine. Then within a while came Galahad there as the white knight abode him by the hermitage, and every each saluted other courteously. Sir, said Galahad, by this shield be many marvels fallen? Sir, said the knight, it befell after the passion of our Lord Jesu Christ thirty-two year, that Joseph of Aramathie, the gentle knight, the which took down our Lord off the holy Cross, at that time he departed from Jerusalem with a great party of his kindred with him. And so he laboured till that they came to a city that hight Sarras. And at that same hour that

Joseph came to Sarras there was a king that hight Evelake, that had great war against the Saracens, and in especial against one Saracen, the which was King Evelake's cousin, a rich king and a mighty, which marched nigh this land, and his name was called Tolleme la Feintes. So on a day these two met to do battle. Then Joseph, the son of Joseph of Aramathie, went to King Evelake and told him he should be discomfit and slain, but if he left his belief of the old law and believed upon the new law. And then there he shewed him the right belief of the Holy Trinity, to the which he agreed unto with all his heart; and there this shield was made for King Evelake, in the name of Him that died upon the Cross. And then through his good belief he had the better of King Tolleme. For when Evelake was in the battle there was a cloth set afore the shield, and when he was in the greatest peril he let put away the cloth, and then his enemies saw a figure of a man on the Cross, where-through they all were discomfit. And so it befell that a man of King Evelake's was smitten his hand off, and bare that hand in his other hand; and Joseph called that man unto him and bade him go with good devotion touch the Cross. And as soon as that man had touched the Cross with his hand it was as whole as ever it was tofore. Then soon after there fell a great marvel, that the cross of the shield at one time vanished away that no man wist where it became. And then King Evelake was baptised, and for the most part all the people of that city. So, soon after Joseph would depart, and King Evelake would go with him whether he would or nold. And so by fortune they came into this land, that at that time was called Great Britain; and there they found a great felon paynim, that put Joseph into prison. And so by fortune tidings came unto a worthy man that hight Mondrames, and he assembled all his people for the great renown he had heard of Joseph; and so he came into the land of Great Britain and disinherited this felon paynim and consumed him; and therewith delivered Joseph out of prison. And after that all the people were turned to the Christian faith.

CHAPTER XI

HOW JOSEPH MADE A CROSS ON THE WHITE SHIELD WITH HIS BLOOD, AND HOW GALAHAD WAS BY A MONK BROUGHT TO A TOMB

Not long after that Joseph was laid in his deadly bed. And when King Evelake saw that he made much sorrow, and said: For thy love I have left my country, and sith ye shall depart out of this world, leave me some token of yours that I may think on you. Joseph said: That will I do full gladly; now bring me your shield that I took you when ye went into battle against King Tolleme. Then Joseph bled sore at the nose, so that he might not by no mean be staunched. And there upon that shield he made a cross of his own blood. Now may ye see a remembrance that I love you, for ye shall never see this shield but ye shall think on me, and it shall be always as fresh as it is now. And never shall man bear this shield about his neck but he shall repent it, unto the time that Galahad, the good knight, bare it; and the last of my lineage shall have it about his neck, that shall do many marvellous deeds. Now, said King Evelake, where shall I put this shield, that this worthy knight may have it? Ye shall leave it there as Nacien, the hermit, shall be put after his death; for thither shall that good knight come the fifteenth day after that he shall receive the order of knighthood: and so that day that they set is this time that he have his shield, and in the same abbey lieth Nacien, the hermit. And then the white knight vanished away. Anon as the squire had heard these words, he alit off his hackney and kneeled down at Galahad's feet, and prayed him that he might go with him till he had made him knight. If I would not refuse you? Then will ye make me a knight? said the squire, and that order, by the grace of God, shall be well set in me. So Sir Galahad granted him, and turned again unto the abbey where they came from; and there men made great joy of Sir Galahad. And anon as he was alit there was a monk brought him unto a tomb in a churchyard, where there was such a noise that who that heard it should

verily nigh be mad or lose his strength: and Sir, they said,
we deem it is a fiend.

CHAPTER XII

OF THE MARVEL THAT SIR GALAHAD SAW AND HEARD
IN THE TOMB, AND HOW HE MADE
MELIAS KNIGHT

Now lead me thither, said Galahad. And so they did,
all armed save his helm. Now, said the good man, go to
the tomb and lift it up. So he did, and heard a great noise;
and piteously it said, that all men might hear it: Sir Galahad,
the servant of Jesu Christ, come thou not nigh me, for thou
shalt make me go again there where I have been so long.
But Galahad was nothing afraid, but lifted up the stone;
and there came out so foul a smoke, and after he saw the
foulest figure leap thereout that ever he saw in the likeness
of a man; and then he blessed him and wist well it was a
fiend. Then heard he a voice say: Galahad, I see there
environ about thee so many angels that my power may not
dare thee. Right so Sir Galahad saw a body all armed lie
in that tomb, and beside him a sword. Now, fair brother,
said Galahad, let us remove this body, for it is not worthy
to lie in this churchyard, for he was a false Christian man.
And therewith they all departed and went to the abbey.
And anon as he was unarmed a good man came and set
him down by him and said: Sir, I shall tell you what
betokeneth all that ye saw in the tomb; for that covered
body betokeneth the duresse of the world, and the great sin
that our Lord found in the world. For there was such
wretchedness that the father loved not the son, nor the son
loved not the father; and that was one of the causes that
our Lord took flesh and blood of a clene maiden, for our sins
were so great at that time that wellnigh all was wickedness.
Truly, said Galahad, I believe you right well. So Sir
Galahad rested him there that night; and upon the morn
he made the squire knight, and asked him his name, and of
what kindred he was come. Sir, said he, men calleth me
Melias de Lile, and I am the son of the king of Denmark.

Now, fair sir, said Galahad, sith that ye be come of kings and queens, now look that knighthood be well set in you, for ye ought to be a mirror unto all chivalry. Sir, said Sir Melias, ye say sooth. But, sir, sithen ye have made me a knight ye must of right grant me my first desire that is reasonable. Ye say sooth, said Galahad. Melias said: Then that ye will suffer me to ride with you in this quest of the Sangreal, till that some adventure depart us. I grant you, sir. Then men brought Sir Melias his armour and his spear and his horse, and so Sir Galahad and he rode forth all that week or they found any adventure. And then upon a Monday in the morning, as they were departed from an abbey, they came to a cross which departed two ways, and in that cross were letters written that said thus: Now, ye knights errant, the which goeth to seek knights adventurous, see here two ways; that one way defendeth thee that thou ne go that way, for he shall not go out of the way again but if he be a good man and a worthy knight; and if thou go on the left hand, thou shalt not lightly there win prowess, for thou shalt in this way be soon essayed. Sir, said Melias to Galahad, if it like you to suffer me to take the way on the left hand, tell me, for there I shall well prove my strength. It were better, said Galahad, ye rode not that way, for I deem I should better escape in that way than ye. Nay, my lord, I pray you let me have that adventure. Take it in God's name, said Galahad.

CHAPTER XIII

OF THE ADVENTURE THAT MELIAS HAD, AND HOW GALAHAD REVENGED HIM, AND HOW MELIAS WAS CARRIED INTO AN ABBEY

AND then rode Melias into an old forest, and therein he rode two days and more. And then he came into a fair meadow, and there was a fair lodge of boughs. And then he espied in that lodge a chair, wherein was a crown of gold, subtily wrought. Also there were cloths covered upon the earth, and many delicious meats set thereon. Sir Melias beheld this adventure, and thought it marvellous, but he had no hunger, but of the crown of gold he took much keep;

and therewith he stooped down and took it up, and rode his
way with it. And anon he saw a knight came riding after
him that said: Knight, set down that crown which is not
yours, and therefore defend you. Then Sir Melias blessed
him and said: Fair lord of heaven, help and save thy new-
made knight. And then they let their horses run as fast as
they might, so that the other knight smote Sir Melias
through hauberk and through the left side, that he fell to
the earth nigh dead. And then he took the crown and went
his way; and Sir Melias lay still and had no power to stir.
In the meanwhile by fortune there came Sir Galahad and
found him there in peril of death. And then he said: Ah,
Melias, who hath wounded you? therefore it had been better
to have ridden the other way. And when Sir Melias heard
him speak: Sir, he said, for God's love let me not die in
this forest, but bear me unto the abbey here beside, that I
may be confessed and have my rights. It shall be done,
said Galahad, but where is he that hath wounded you?
With that Sir Galahad heard in the leaves cry on high:
Knight, keep thee from me. Ah sir, said Melias, beware,
for that is he that hath slain me. Sir Galahad answered:
Sir knight, come on your peril. Then either dressed to
other, and came together as fast as their horses might run,
and Galahad smote him so that his spear went through his
shoulder, and smote him down off his horse, and in the
falling Galahad's spear brake. With that came out another
knight out of the leaves, and brake a spear upon Galahad
or ever he might turn him. Then Galahad drew out his
sword and smote off the left arm of him, so that it fell to
the earth. And then he fled, and Sir Galahad pursued fast
after him. And then he turned again unto Sir Melias,
and there he alit and dressed him softly on his horse tofore
him, for the truncheon of his spear was in his body; and
Sir Galahad start up behind him, and held him in his arms,
and so brought him to the abbey, and there unarmed him
and brought him to his chamber. And then he asked his
Saviour. And when he had received Him he said unto Sir
Galahad: Sir, let death come when it pleaseth him. And
therewith he drew out the truncheon of the spear out of his
body: and then he swooned. Then came there an old monk

which sometime had been a knight, and beheld Sir Melias. And anon he ransacked him; and then he said unto Sir Galahad: I shall heal him of his wound, by the grace of God, within the term of seven weeks. Then was Sir Galahad glad, and unarmed him, and said he would abide there three days. And then he asked Sir Melias how it stood with him. Then he said he was turned unto helping, God be thanked.

CHAPTER XIV

HOW SIR GALAHAD DEPARTED, AND HOW HE WAS COMMANDED TO GO TO THE CASTLE OF MAIDENS TO DESTROY THE WICKED CUSTOM

Now will I depart, said Galahad, for I have much on hand, for many good knights be full busy about it, and this knight and I were in the same quest of the Sangreal. Sir, said the good man, for his sin he was thus wounded; and I marvel, said the good man, how ye durst take upon you so rich a thing as the high order of knighthood without clene confession, and that was the cause ye were bitterly wounded. For the way on the right hand betokeneth the highway of our Lord Jesu Christ, and the way of a good true good liver. And the other way betokeneth the way of sinners and of misbelievers. And when the devil saw your pride and presumption, for to take you in the quest of the Sangreal, that made you to be overthrown, for it may not be achieved but by virtuous living. Also, the writing on the cross was a signification of heavenly deeds, and of knightly deeds in God's works, and no knightly deeds in worldly works. And pride is head of all deadly sins, that caused this knight to depart from Galahad. And where thou tookest the crown of gold thou sinnest in covetise and in theft: all this were no knightly deeds. And this Galahad, the holy knight, the which fought with the two knights, the two knights signify the two deadly sins which were wholly in this knight Melias; and they might not withstand you, for ye are without deadly sin. Now departed Galahad from thence, and betaught

(E)   HC—Vol. 35

them all unto God. Sir Melias said: My lord Galahad, as
soon as I may ride I shall seek you. God send you health,
said Galahad, and so took his horse and departed, and rode
many journeys forward and backward, as adventure would
lead him. And at the last it happened him to depart from
a place or a castle the which was named Abblasoure; and
he had heard no mass, the which he was wont ever to hear
or ever he departed out of any castle or place, and kept
that for a custom. Then Sir Galahad came unto a mountain
where he found an old chapel, and found there nobody, for
all, all was desolate; and there he kneeled tofore the altar,
and besought God of wholesome counsel. So as he prayed
he heard a voice that said: Go thou now, thou adventurous
knight, to the Castle of Maidens, and there do thou away the
wicked customs.

CHAPTER XV

HOW SIR GALAHAD FOUGHT WITH THE KNIGHTS OF
THE CASTLE, AND DESTROYED THE
WICKED CUSTOM

WHEN Sir Galahad heard this he thanked God, and took
his horse; and he had not ridden but half a mile, he saw in
a valley afore him a strong castle with deep ditches, and
there ran beside it a fair river that hight Severn; and there
he met with a man of great age, and either saluted other,
and Galahad asked him the castle's name. Fair sir, said he,
it is the Castle of Maidens. That is a cursed castle, said
Galahad, and all they that be conversant therein, for all
pity is out thereof, and all hardiness and mischief is therein.
Therefore, I counsel you, sir knight, to turn again. Sir, said
Galahad, wit you well I shall not turn again. Then looked
Sir Galahad on his arms that nothing failed him, and then
he put his shield afore him; and anon there met him seven
fair maidens, the which said unto him: Sir knight, ye ride
here in a great folly, for ye have the water to pass over.
Why should I not pass the water? said Galahad. So rode
he away from them and met with a squire that said: Knight,
those knights in the castle defy you, and defenden you ye go

no further till that they wit what ye would. Fair sir, said Galahad, I come for to destroy the wicked custom of this castle. Sir, an ye will abide by that ye shall have enough to do. Go you now, said Galahad, and haste my needs. Then the squire entered into the castle. And anon after there came out of the castle seven knights, and all were brethren. And when they saw Galahad they cried: Knight, keep thee, for we assure thee nothing but death. Why, said Galahad, will ye all have ado with me at once? Yea, said they, thereto mayest thou trust. Then Galahad put forth his spear and smote the foremost to the earth, that near he brake his neck. And therewithal the other smote him on his shield great strokes, so that their spears brake. Then Sir Galahad drew out his sword, and set upon them so hard that it was marvel to see it, and so through great force he made them to forsake the field; and Galahad chased them till they entered into the castle, and so passed through the castle at another gate. And there met Sir Galahad an old man clothed in religious clothing, and said: Sir, have here the keys of this castle. Then Sir Galahad opened the gates, and saw so much people in the streets that he might not number them, and all said: Sir, ye be welcome, for long have we abiden here our deliverance. Then came to him a gentlewoman and said: These knights be fled, but they will come again this night, and here to begin again their evil custom. What will ye that I shall do? said Galahad. Sir, said the gentlewoman, that ye send after all the knights hither that hold their lands of this castle, and make them to swear for to use the customs that were used heretofore of old time. I will well, said Galahad. And there she brought him an horn of ivory, bounden with gold richly, and said: Sir, blow this horn which will be heard two mile about this castle. When Sir Galahad had blown the horn he set him down upon a bed. Then came a priest to Galahad, and said: Sir, it is past a seven year agone that these seven brethren came into this castle, and harboured with the lord of this castle, that hight the Duke Lianour, and he was lord of all this country. And when they espied the duke's daughter, that was a full fair woman, then by their false covin they made debate betwixt themself, and the duke of his goodness would have departed them, and there they slew him and his eldest son. And then they took the maiden and the treasure of the castle. And then by great force they held all the knights of this castle against their will under their obeisance, and in great service and truage, robbing and pillaging the poor common people of all that they had. So it happened on a day the duke's daughter said: Ye have done unto me great wrong to slay mine own father, and my brother, and thus to hold our lands: not for then, she said, ye shall not hold this castle for many years, for by one knight ye shall be overcome. Thus she prophesied seven years agone. Well, said the seven knights, sithen ye say so, there shall never lady nor knight pass this castle but they shall abide maugre their heads, or die therefor, till that knight be come by whom we shall lose this castle. And therefore is it called the Maidens' Castle, for they have devoured many maidens. Now, said Galahad, is she here for whom this castle was lost? Nay sir, said the priest, she was dead within these three nights after that she was thus enforced; and sithen have they kept her younger sister, which endureth great pains with more other ladies. By this were the knights of the country come, and then he made them do homage and fealty to the king's daughter, and set them in great ease of heart. And in the morn there came one to Galahad and told him how that Gawaine, Gareth, and Uwaine, had slain the seven brethren. I suppose well, said Sir Galahad, and took his armour and his horse, and commended them unto God.

CHAPTER XVI

HOW SIR GAWAINE CAME TO THE ABBEY FOR TO FOLLOW GALAHAD, AND HOW HE WAS SHRIVEN TO A HERMIT

Now, saith the tale, after Sir Gawaine departed, he rode many journeys, both toward and froward. And at the last he came to the abbey where Sir Galahad had the white shield, and there Sir Gawaine learned the way to sewe after Sir Galahad; and so he rode to the abbey where Melias lay

sick, and there Sir Melias told Sir Gawaine of the marvellous
adventures that Sir Galahad did. Certes, said Sir Gawaine,
I am not happy that I took not the way that he went, for
an I may meet with him I will not depart from him lightly,
for all marvellous adventures that Sir Galahad achieveth.
Sir, said one of the monks, he will not of your fellowship.
Why? said Sir Gawaine. Sir, said he, for ye be wicked
and sinful, and he is full blessed. Right as they thus stood
talking there came in riding Sir Gareth. And then they
made joy either of other. And on the morn they heard
mass, and so departed. And by the way they met with Sir
Uwaine les Avoutres, and there Sir Uwaine told Sir Gawaine
how he had met with none adventure sith he departed from
the court. Nor we, said Sir Gawaine. And either promised
other of the three knights not to depart while they were in
that quest, but if fortune caused it. So they departed and
rode by fortune till that they came by the Castle of Maidens;
and there the seven brethren espied the three knights, and
said: Sithen, we be flemyd by one knight from this castle,
we shall destroy all the knights of King Arthur's that we
may overcome, for the love of Sir Galahad. And therewith
the seven knights set upon the three knights, and by fortune
Sir Gawaine slew one of the brethren, and each one of his
fellows slew another, and so slew the remnant. And then
they took the way under the castle, and there they lost the
way that Sir Galahad rode, and there every each of them
departed from other; and Sir Gawaine rode till he came
to an hermitage, and there he found the good man saying
his evensong of Our Lady; and there Sir Gawaine asked
harbour for charity, and the good man granted it him gladly.
Then the good man asked him what he was. Sir, he said,
I am a knight of King Arthur's that am in the quest of the
Sangreal, and my name is Sir Gawaine. Sir, said the good
man, I would wit how it standeth betwixt God and you.
Sir, said Sir Gawaine, I will with a good will shew you my
life if it please you; and there he told the hermit How a
monk of an abbey called me wicked knight. He might well
say it, said the hermit, for when ye were first made knight
you should have taken you to knightly deeds and virtuous
living, and ye have done the contrary, for ye have lived

mischievously many winters; and Sir Galahad is a maid
and sinner never, and that is the cause he shall achieve
where he goeth that ye nor none such shall not attain, nor
none in your fellowship, for ye have used the most untruest
life that ever I heard knight live. For certes had ye not
been so wicked as ye are, never had the seven brethren been
slain by you and your two fellows. For Sir Galahad himself
alone beat them all seven the day tofore, but his living
is such he shall slay no man lightly. Also I may say you
the Castle of Maidens betokeneth the good souls that were
in prison afore the Incarnation of Jesu Christ. And the
seven knights betoken the seven deadly sins that reigned that
time in the world; and I may liken the good Galahad unto
the son of the High Father, that light within a maid, and
bought all the souls out of thrall: so did Sir Galahad deliver
all the maidens out of the woful castle. Now, Sir Gawaine,
said the good man, thou must do penance for thy sin. Sir,
what penance shall I do? Such as I will give, said the good
man. Nay, said Sir Gawaine, I may do no penance; for
we knights adventurous oft suffer great woe and pain. Well,
said the good man, and then he held his peace. And on the
morn Sir Gawaine departed from the hermit, and betaught
him unto God. And by adventure he met with Sir Aglovale
and Sir Griflet, two knights of the Table Round. And they
two rode four days without finding of any adventure, and at
the fifth day they departed. And every each held as befel
them by adventure. Here leaveth the tale of Sir Gawaine
and his fellows, and speak we of Sir Galahad.

CHAPTER XVII

HOW SIR GALAHAD MET WITH SIR LAUNCELOT AND
SIR PERCIVALE, AND SMOTE THEM DOWN,
AND DEPARTED FROM THEM

So when Sir Galahad was departed from the Castle of
Maidens he rode till he came to a waste forest, and there
he met with Sir Launcelot and Sir Percivale, but they knew
him not, for he was new disguised. Right so Sir Launcelot,

his father, dressed his spear and brake it upon Sir Galahad, and Galahad smote him so again that he smote down horse and man. And then he drew his sword, and dressed him unto Sir Percivale, and smote him so on the helm, that it rove to the coif of steel; and had not the sword swerved Sir Percivale had been slain, and with the stroke he fell out of his saddle. This jousts was done tofore the hermitage where a recluse dwelled. And when she saw Sir Galahad ride, she said: God be with thee, best knight of the world. Ah certes, said she, all aloud that Launcelot and Percivale might hear it: An yonder two knights had known thee as well as I do they would not have encountered with thee. When Sir Galahad heard her say so he was adread to be known: therewith he smote his horse with his spurs and rode a great pace froward them. Then perceived they both that he was Galahad; and up they gat on their horses, and rode fast after him, but in a while he was out of their sight. And then they turned again with heavy cheer. Let us spere some tidings, said Percivale, at yonder recluse. Do as ye list, said Sir Launcelot. When Sir Percivale came to the recluse she knew him well enough, and Sir Launcelot both. But Sir Launcelot rode overthwart and endlong in a wild forest, and held no path but as wild adventure led him. And at the last he came to a stony cross which departed two ways in waste land; and by the cross was a stone that was of marble, but it was so dark that Sir Launcelot might not wit what it was. Then Sir Launcelot looked by him, and saw an old chapel, and there he weened to have found people; and Sir Launcelot tied his horse till a tree, and there he did off his shield and hung it upon a tree. And then he went to the chapel door, and found it waste and broken. And within he found a fair altar, full richly arrayed with cloth of clene silk, and there stood a fair clean candlestick, which bare six great candles, and the candlestick was of silver. And when Sir Launcelot saw this light he had great will for to enter into the chapel, but he could find no place where he might enter; then was he passing heavy and dismayed. Then he returned and came to his horse and did off his saddle and bridle, and let him pasture, and unlaced his helm, and ungirt his sword, and laid him down to sleep upon his shield tofore the cross.

CHAPTER XVIII

AND so he fell on sleep; and half waking and sleeping
he saw come by him two palfreys all fair and white, the
which bare a litter, therein lying a sick knight. And when
he was nigh the cross he there abode still. All this Sir
Launcelot saw and beheld, for he slept not verily; and he
heard him say: O sweet Lord, when shall this sorrow leave
me? and when shall the holy vessel come by me, where-
through I shall be blessed? For I have endured thus long,
for little trespass. A full great while complained the knight
thus, and always Sir Launcelot heard it. With that Sir
Launcelot saw the candlestick with the six tapers come
before the cross, and he saw nobody that brought it. Also
there came a table of silver, and the holy vessel of the
Sangreal, which Launcelot had seen aforetime in King
Pescheour's house. And therewith the sick knight set him
up, and held up both his hands, and said: Fair sweet Lord,
which is here within this holy vessel; take heed unto me
that I may be whole of this malady. And therewith on his
hands and on his knees he went so nigh that he touched
the holy vessel and kissed it, and anon he was whole; and
then he said: Lord God, I thank thee, for I am healed of
this sickness. So when the holy vessel had been there a
great while it went unto the chapel with the chandelier
and the light, so that Launcelot wist not where it was
become; for he was overtaken with sin that he had no power
to rise ageyne the holy vessel; wherefore after that many
men said of him shame, but he took repentance after that.
Then the sick knight dressed him up and kissed the cross;
anon his squire brought him his arms, and asked his lord
how he did. Certes, said he, I thank God right well, through
the holy vessel I am healed. But I have marvel of this
sleeping knight that had no power to awake when this holy

vessel was brought hither. I dare right well say, said the squire, that he dwelleth in some deadly sin whereof he was never confessed. By my faith, said the knight, whatsomever he be he is unhappy, for as I deem he is of the fellowship of the Round Table, the which is entered into the quest of the Sangreal. Sir, said the squire, here I have brought you all your arms save your helm and your sword, and therefore by mine assent now may ye take this knight's helm and his sword: and so he did. And when he was clene armed he took Sir Launcelot's horse, for he was better than his; and so departed they from the Cross.

CHAPTER XIX

HOW A VOICE SPAKE TO SIR LAUNCELOT, AND HOW HE FOUND HIS HORSE AND HIS HELM BORNE AWAY, AND AFTER WENT AFOOT

THEN anon Sir Launcelot waked, and set him up, and bethought him what he had seen there, and whether it were dreams or not. Right so heard he a voice that said: Sir Launcelot, more harder than is the stone, and more bitter than is the wood, and more naked and barer than is the leaf of the fig tree; therefore go thou from hence, and withdraw thee from this holy place. And when Sir Launcelot heard this he was passing heavy and wist not what to do, and so departed sore weeping, and cursed the time that he was born. For then he deemed never to have had worship more. For those words went to his heart, till that he knew wherefore he was called so. Then Sir Launcelot went to the cross and found his helm, his sword, and his horse taken away. And then he called himself a very wretch, and most unhappy of all knights; and there he said: My sin and my wickedness have brought me unto great dishonour. For when I sought worldly adventures for worldly desires, I ever achieved them and had the better in every place, and never was I discomfit in no quarrel, were it right or wrong. And now I take upon me the adventures of holy things, and now I see and understand that mine old sin hindereth me and shameth me, so that I had no power to stir nor speak when the holy blood appeared afore me. So thus he sorrowed till it was day, and heard the fowls sing: then somewhat he was comforted. But when Sir Launcelot missed his horse and his harness then he wist well God was displeased with him. Then he departed from the cross on foot into a forest; and so by prime he came to an high hill, and found an hermitage and a hermit therein which was going unto mass. And then Launcelot kneeled down and cried on Our Lord mercy for his wicked works. So when mass was done Launcelot called him, and prayed him for charity for to hear his life. With a good will, said the good man. Sir, said he, be ye of King Arthur's court and of the fellowship of the Round Table? Yea forsooth, and my name is Sir Launcelot du Lake that hath been right well said of, and now my good fortune is changed, for I am the most wretch of the world. The hermit beheld him and had marvel how he was so abashed. Sir, said the hermit, ye ought to thank God more than any knight living, for He hath caused you to have more worldly worship than any knight that now liveth. And for your presumption to take upon you in deadly sin for to be in His presence, where His flesh and His blood was, that caused you ye might not see it with worldly eyes; for He will not appear where such sinners be, but if it be unto their great hurt and unto their great shame; and there is no knight living now that ought to give God so great thank as ye, for He hath given you beauty, seemliness, and great strength above all other knights; and therefore ye are the more beholding unto God than any other man, to love Him and dread Him, for your strength and manhood will little avail you an God be against you.

CHAPTER XX

HOW SIR LAUNCELOT WAS SHRIVEN, AND WHAT SORROW
HE MADE, AND OF THE GOOD ENSAMPLES
WHICH WERE SHEWED HIM

THEN Sir Launcelot wept with heavy cheer, and said: Now I know well ye say me sooth. Sir, said the good man, hide none old sin from me. Truly, said Sir Launcelot, that were me full loth to discover. For this fourteen year I never discovered one thing that I have used, and that may I now wyte my shame and my misadventure. And then he told there that good man all his life. And how he had loved a queen unmeasurably and out of measure long. And all my great deeds of arms that I have done, I did for the most part for the queen's sake, and for her sake would I do battle were it right or wrong; and never did I battle all only for God's sake, but for to win worship and to cause me to be the better beloved, and little or nought I thanked God of it. Then Sir Launcelot said: I pray you counsel me. I will counsel you, said the hermit, if ye will ensure me that ye will never come in that queen's fellowship as much as ye may forbear. And then Sir Launcelot promised him he nold, by the faith of his body. Look that your heart and your mouth accord, said the good man, and I shall ensure you ye shall have more worship than ever ye had. Holy father, said Sir Launcelot, I marvel of the voice that said to me marvellous words, as ye have heard toforehand. Have ye no marvel, said the good man, thereof, for it seemeth well God loveth you; for men may understand a stone is hard of kind, and namely one more than another; and that is to understand by thee, Sir Launcelot, for thou wilt not leave thy sin for no goodness that God hath sent thee; therefore thou art more than any stone, and never wouldst thou be made neysshe nor by water nor by fire, and that is the hete of the Holy Ghost may not enter in thee. Now take heed, in all the world men shall not find one knight to whom Our Lord hath given so much of grace as He hath given you, for He hath given you fairness with seemliness, He hath given thee wit, discretion to know good from evil. He hath given thee prowess and hardiness, and given thee to work so largely that thou hast had at all days the better wheresomever thou came; and now Our Lord will suffer thee no longer, but that thou shalt know Him whether thou wilt or nylt. And why the voice called thee bitterer than wood, for where overmuch sin dwelleth, there may be but little sweetness, wherefore thou art likened to an old rotten tree. Now have I shewed thee why thou art harder than the stone and bitterer than the tree. Now shall I shew thee why thou art more naked and barer than the fig tree. It befel that Our Lord on Palm Sunday preached in Jerusalem, and there He found in the people that all hardness was harboured in them, and there He found in all the town not one that would harbour him. And then He went without the town, and found in the middes of the way a fig tree, the which was right fair and well garnished of leaves, but fruit had it none. Then Our Lord cursed the tree that bare no fruit; that betokeneth the fig tree unto Jerusalem, that had leaves and no fruit. So thou, Sir Launcelot, when the Holy Grail was brought afore thee, He found in thee no fruit, nor good thought nor good will, and defouled with lechery. Certes, said Sir Launcelot, all that you have said is true, and from henceforward I cast me, by the grace of God, never to be so wicked as I have been, but as to follow knighthood and to do feats of arms. Then the good man enjoined Sir Launcelot such penance as he might do and to pursue knighthood, and so assoiled him, and prayed Sir Launcelot to abide with him all that day. I will well, said Sir Launcelot, for I have neither helm, nor horse, nor sword. As for that, said the good man, I shall help you or tomorn at even of an horse, and all that longed unto you. And then Sir Launcelot repented him greatly.

Here leaveth of the history of syr launcelot.
And here foloweth of sir Percyvale
de galys which is the xiiii
book.

THE FOURTEENTH BOOK

CHAPTER I

HOW SIR PERCIVALE CAME TO A RECLUSE AND ASKED COUN-
SEL, AND HOW SHE TOLD HIM THAT SHE
WAS HIS AUNT

NOW saith the tale, that when Sir Launcelot was
ridden after Sir Galahad, the which had all these
adventures above said, Sir Percivale turned again
unto the recluse, where he deemed to have tidings of that
knight that Launcelot followed. And so he kneeled at her
window, and the recluse opened it and asked Sir Percivale
what he would. Madam, he said, I am a knight of King
Arthur's court, and my name is Sir Percivale de Galis.
When the recluse heard his name she had great joy of him,
for mickle she had loved him tofore any other knight, for she
ought to do so, for she was his aunt. And then she commanded the gates to be opened, and there he had all the cheer
that she might make him, and all that was in her power was
at his commandment. So on the morn Sir Percivale went to
the recluse and asked her if she knew that knight with the
white shield. Sir, said she, why would ye wit? Truly,
madam, said Sir Percivale, I shall never be well at ease till
that I know of that knight's fellowship, and that I may fight
with him, for I may not leave him so lightly, for I have the
shame yet. Ah, Percivale, said she, would ye fight with
him? I see well ye have great will to be slain as your
father was through outrageousness. Madam, said Sir Percivale, it seemeth by your words that ye know me. Yea, said
she, I well ought to know you, for I am your aunt, although
I be in a priory place. For some called me sometime the
queen of the Waste Lands, and I was called the queen
of most riches in the world; and it pleased me never my
riches so much as doth my poverty. Then Sir Percivale
wept for very pity when that he knew it was his aunt.
Ah, fair nephew, said she, when heard ye tidings of your

mother? Truly, said he, I heard none of her, but I dream of her much in my sleep; and therefore I wot not whether she be dead or on live. Certes, fair nephew, said she, your mother is dead, for after your departing from her she took such a sorrow that anon, after she was confessed, she died. Now, God have mercy on her soul, said Sir Percivale, it sore forthinketh me; but all we must change the life. Now, fair aunt, tell me what is the knight? I deem it be he that bare the red arms on Whitsunday. Wit you well, said she, that this is he, for otherwise ought he not to do, but to go in red arms; and that same knight hath no peer, for he worketh all by miracle, and he shall never be overcome of none earthly man's hand.

CHAPTER II

HOW MERLIN LIKENED THE ROUND TABLE TO THE WORLD, AND HOW THE KNIGHTS THAT SHOULD ACHIEVE THE SANGREAL SHOULD BE KNOWN

ALSO Merlin made the Round Table in tokening of roundness of the world, for by the Round Table is the world signified by right, for all the world, Christian and heathen, repair unto the Round Table; and when they are chosen to be of the fellowship of the Round Table they think them more blessed and more in worship than if they had gotten half the world; and ye have seen that they have lost their fathers and their mothers, and all their kin, and their wives and their children, for to be of your fellowship. It is well seen by you; for since ye have departed from your mother ye would never see her, ye found such fellowship at the Round Table. When Merlin had ordained the Round Table he said, by them which should be fellows of the Round Table the truth of the Sangreal should be well known. And men asked him how men might know them that should best do and to achieve the Sangreal? Then he said there should be three white bulls that should achieve it, and the two should be maidens, and the third should be chaste. And that one of the three should pass his father as much as the lion passeth the leopard, both of strength and hardiness. They that heard Merlin say so said thus unto Merlin: Sithen there shall be such a knight, thou shouldest ordain by thy crafts a siege, that no man should sit in it but he all only that shall pass all other knights. Then Merlin answered that he would do so. And then he made the Siege Perilous, in the which Galahad sat in at his meat on Whitsunday last past. Now, madam, said Sir Percivale, so much have I heard of you that by my good will I will never have ado with Sir Galahad but by way of kindness; and for God's love, fair aunt, can ye teach me some way where I may find him? for much would I love the fellowship of him. Fair nephew, said she, ye must ride unto a castle the which is called Goothe, where he hath a cousin-germain, and there may ye be lodged this night. And as he teacheth you, pursue after as fast as ye can; and if he can tell you no tidings of him, ride straight unto the Castle of Carbonek, where the maimed king is there lying, for there shall ye hear true tidings of him.

CHAPTER III

HOW SIR PERCIVALE CAME INTO A MONASTERY, WHERE HE FOUND KING EVELAKE, WHICH WAS AN OLD MAN

THEN departed Sir Percivale from his aunt, either making great sorrow. And so he rode till evensong time. And then he heard a clock smite; and then he was ware of an house closed well with walls and deep ditches, and there he knocked at the gate and was let in, and he alit and was led unto a chamber, and soon he was unarmed. And there he had right good cheer all that night; and on the morn he heard his mass, and in the monastery he found a priest ready at the altar. And on the right side he saw a pew closed with iron, and behind the altar he saw a rich bed and a fair, as of cloth of silk and gold. Then Sir Percivale espied that therein was a man or a woman, for the visage was covered; then he left off his looking and heard his

service. And when it came to the sacring, he that lay
within that percloos dressed him up, and uncovered his
head; and then him beseemed a passing old man, and he
had a crown of gold upon his head, and his shoulders were
naked and unhilled unto his navel. And then Sir Percivale
espied his body was full of great wounds, both on the
shoulders, arms, and visage. And ever he held up his
hands against our Lord's body, and cried: Fair, sweet
Father, Jesu Christ, forget not me. And so he lay down,
but always he was in his prayers and orisons; and him
seemed to be of the age of three hundred winter. And
when the mass was done the priest took Our Lord's body
and bare it to the sick king. And when he had used it he
did off his crown, and commanded the crown to be set on
the altar. Then Sir Percivale asked one of the brethren
what he was. Sir, said the good man, ye have heard much
of Joseph of Aramathie, how he was sent by Jesu Christ
into this land for to teach and preach the holy Christian
faith; and therefore he suffered many persecutions the
which the enemies of Christ did unto him, and in the city
of Sarras he converted a king whose name was Evelake.
And so this king came with Joseph into this land, and ever
he was busy to be thereas the Sangreal was; and on a time
be nighed it so nigh that Our Lord was displeased with
him, but ever he followed it more and more, till God struck
him almost blind. Then this king cried mercy, and said:
Fair Lord, let me never die till the good knight of my
blood of the ninth degree be come, that I may see him
openly that he shall achieve the Sangreal, that I may kiss
him.

CHAPTER IV

HOW SIR PERCIVALE SAW MANY MEN OF ARMS BEARING A DEAD KNIGHT, AND HOW HE FOUGHT AGAINST THEM

WHEN the king thus had made his prayers he heard a
voice that said: Heard be thy prayers, for thou shalt not
die till he have kissed thee. And when that knight shall
come the clearness of your eyes shall come again, and thou

shalt see openly, and thy wounds shall be healed, and erst shall they never close. And this befel of King Evelake, and this same king hath lived this three hundred winters this holy life, and men say the knight is in the court that shall heal him. Sir, said the good man, I pray you tell me what knight that ye be, and if ye be of King Arthur's court and of the Table Round. Yea, forsooth, said he, and my name is Sir Percivale de Galis. And when the good man understood his name he made great joy of him. And then Sir Percivale departed and rode till the hour of noon. And he met in a valley about a twenty men of arms, which bare in a bier a knight deadly slain. And when they saw Sir Percivale they asked him of whence he was. And he answered: Of the court of King Arthur. Then they cried all at once: Slay him. Then Sir Percivale smote the first to the earth and his horse upon him. And then seven of the knights smote upon his shield all at once, and the remnant slew his horse so that he fell to the earth. So had they slain him or taken him had not the good knight, Sir Galahad, with the red arms come there by adventure into those parts. And when he saw all those knights upon one knight he cried: Save me that knight's life. And then he dressed him toward the twenty men of arms as fast as his horse might drive, with his spear in the rest, and smote the foremost horse and man to the earth. And when his spear was broken he set his hand to his sword, and smote on the right hand and on the left hand that it was marvel to see, and at every stroke he smote one down or put him to a rebuke, so that they would fight no more but fled to a thick forest, and Sir Galahad followed them. And when Sir Percivale saw him chase them so, he made great sorrow that his horse was away. And then he wist well it was Sir Galahad. And then he cried aloud: Ah, fair knight, abide and suffer me to do thankings unto thee, for much have ye done for me. But ever Sir Galahad rode so fast that at the last he passed out of his sight. And as fast as Sir Percivale might he went after him on foot, crying. And then he met with a yeoman riding upon an hackney, the which led in his hand a great steed blacker than any bear. Ah, fair friend, said Sir Percivale, as ever I may do for you, and to be your true knight in the first place ye will require me, that ye will lend me that black steed, that I might overtake a knight the which rideth afore me. Sir knight, said the yeoman, I pray you hold me excused of that, for that I may not do. For wit ye well, the horse is such a man's horse, that an I lent it you or any man, that he would slay me. Alas, said Sir Percivale, I had never so great sorrow as I have had for losing of yonder knight. Sir, said the yeoman, I am right heavy for you, for a good horse would beseem you well; but I dare not deliver you this horse but if ye would take him from me. That will I not do, said Sir Percivale. And so they departed; and Sir Percivale set him down under a tree, and made sorrow out of measure. And as he was there, there came a knight riding on the horse that the yeoman led, and he was clene armed.

CHAPTER V

HOW A YEOMAN DESIRED HIM TO GET AGAIN AN HORSE AND HOW SIR PERCIVALE'S HACKNEY WAS SLAIN, AND HOW HE GAT AN HORSE

AND anon the yeoman came pricking after as fast as ever he might, and asked Sir Percivale if he saw any knight riding on his black steed. Yea, sir forsooth, said he; why, sir, ask ye me that? Ah, sir, that steed he hath benome me with strength; wherefor my lord will slay me in what place he findeth me. Well, said Sir Percivale, what wouldst thou that I did? Thou seest well that I am on foot, but an I had a good horse I should bring him soon again. Sir, said the yeoman, take mine hackney and do the best ye can, and I shall serve you on foot to wit how that ye shall speed. Then Sir Percivale alit upon that hackney, and rode as fast as he might, and at the last he saw that knight. And then he cried: Knight, turn again; and he turned and set his spear again Sir Percivale, and he smote the hackney in the middes of the breast that he fell down dead to the earth, and there he had a great fall, and the other rode his way. And then Sir Percivale was wood worth, and cried: Abide, wicked knight; coward and false-hearted knight, turn again and fight with me on foot. But he answered not, but passed on his way. When Sir Percivale saw he would not turn he cast away his helm and sword, and said: Now am I a very wretch, cursed and most unhappy above all other knights. So in this sorrow he abode all that day till it was night; and then he was faint, and laid him down and slept till it was midnight; and then he awakened and saw afore him a woman which said unto him right fiercely: Sir Percivale, what dost thou here? He answered, I do neither good nor great ill. If thou wilt ensure me, said she, that thou wilt fulfil my will when I summon thee, I shall lend thee mine own horse which shall bear thee whither thou wilt. Sir Percivale was glad of her proffer, and ensured her to fulfil all her desire. Then abide me here, and I shall go and fetch you an horse. And so she came soon again and brought an horse with her that was inly black. When Percivale beheld that horse he marvelled that it was so great and so well apparelled; and not for then he was so hardy, and he leapt upon him, and took none heed of himself. And so anon as he was upon him he thrust to him with his spurs, and so he rode by a forest, and the moon shone clear. And within an hour and less he bare him four days' journey thence, until he came to a rough water the which roared, and his horse would have borne him into it.

CHAPTER VI

OF THE GREAT DANGER THAT SIR PERCIVALE WAS IN BY HIS HORSE, AND HOW HE SAW A SERPENT AND A LION FIGHT

AND when Sir Percivale came nigh the brim, and saw the water so boistous, he doubted to overpass it. And then he made a sign of the cross on his forehead. When the fiend felt him so charged he shook off Sir Percivale, and he went into the water crying and roaring, making great sorrow, and it seemed unto him that the water brent. Then Sir Percivale perceived it was a fiend, the which would have brought him unto his perdition. Then he commended himself unto God, and prayed Our Lord to keep him from all such temptations; and so he prayed all that night till on the morn that it was day; then he saw that he was in a wild mountain the which was closed with the sea nigh all about, that he might see no land about him which might relieve him, but wild beasts. And then he went into a valley, and there he saw a young serpent bring a young lion by the neck, and so he came by Sir Percivale. With that came a great lion crying and roaring after the serpent. And as fast as Sir Percivale saw this he marvelled, and hied him thither, but anon the lion had overtaken the serpent and began battle with him. And then Sir Percivale thought to help the lion for he was the more natural beast of the two; and therewith he drew his sword, and set his shield afore him, and there he gave the serpent such a buffet that he had a deadly wound. When the lion saw that, he made no resemblant to fight with him, but made him all the cheer that a beast might make a man. Then Percivale perceived that, and cast down his shield which was broken; and then he did off his helm for to gather wind, for he was greatly enchafed with the serpent: and the lion went alway about him fawning as a spaniel. And then he stroked him on the neck and on the shoulders. And then he thanked God of the fellowship of that beast. And about noon the lion took his little whelp and trussed him and bare him there he came from. Then was Sir Percivale alone. And as the tale telleth, he was one of the men of the world at that time which most believed in our Lord Jesu Christ, for in those days there were but few folks that believed in God perfectly. For in those days the son spared not the father no more than a stranger. And so Sir Percivale comforted himself in our Lord Jesu, and besought God no temptation should bring him out of God's service, but to endure as his true champion. Thus when Sir Percivale had prayed he saw the lion come toward him, and then he couched down at his feet. And so all that night the lion and he slept together; and when Sir Percivale slept he dreamed a marvellous dream, that there two ladies met with him, and that one sat upon a lion, and that other sat upon a serpent, and that one of them was young, and the other was old; and the youngest him thought said: Sir

Percivale, my lord saluteth thee, and sendeth thee word that thou array thee and make thee ready, for tomorn thou must fight with the strongest champion of the world. And if thou be overcome thou shalt not be quit for losing of any of thy members, but thou shalt be shamed for ever to the world's end. And then he asked her what was her lord. And she said the greatest lord of all the world: and so she departed suddenly that he wist not where.

CHAPTER VII

OF THE VISION THAT SIR PERCIVALE SAW, AND HOW HIS VISION WAS EXPOUNDED, AND OF HIS LION

THEN came forth the other lady that rode upon the serpent, and she said: Sir Percivale, I complain me of you that ye have done unto me, and have not offended unto you. Certes, madam, he said, unto you nor no lady I never offended. Yes, said she, I shall tell you why. I have nourished in this place a great while a serpent, which served me a great while, and yesterday ye slew him as he gat his prey. Say me for what cause ye slew him, for the lion was not yours. Madam, said Sir Percivale, I know well the lion was not mine, but I did it for the lion is of more gentler nature than the serpent, and therefore I slew him; meseemeth I did not amiss against you. Madam, said he, what would ye that I did? I would, said she, for the amends of my beast that ye become my man. And then he answered: That will I not grant you. No, said she, truly ye were never but my servant syn ye received the homage of Our Lord Jesu Christ. Therefore, I ensure you in what place I may find you without keeping I shall take you as he that sometime was my man. And so she departed from Sir Percivale and left him sleeping, the which was sore travailed of his advision. And on the morn he arose and blessed him, and he was passing feeble. Then was Sir Percivale ware in the sea, and saw a ship come sailing toward him; and Sir Percivale went unto the ship and found it covered within and without with white samite.

And at the board stood an old man clothed in a surplice, in likeness of a priest. Sir, said Sir Percivale, ye be welcome. God keep you, said the good man. Sir, said the old man, of whence be ye? Sir, said Sir Percivale, I am of King Arthur's court. and a knight of the Table Round, the which am in the quest of the Sangreal; and here am I in great duresse, and never like to escape out of this wilderness. Doubt not, said the good man, an ye be so true a knight as the order of chivalry requireth, and of heart as ye ought to be, ye should not doubt that none enemy should slay you. What are ye? said Sir Percivale. Sir, said the old man, I am of a strange country, and hither I come to comfort you. Sir, said Sir Percivale, what signifieth my dream that I dreamed this night? And there he told him altogether: She which rode upon the lion betokeneth the new law of holy church, that is to understand, faith, good hope, belief, and baptism. For she seemed younger than the other it is great reason, for she was born in the resurrection and the passion of our Lord Jesu Christ. And for great love she came to thee to warn thee of thy great battle that shall befall thee. With whom, said Sir Percivale, shall I fight? With the most champion of the world, said the old man; for as the lady said, but if thou quit thee well thou shalt not be quit by losing of one member, but thou shalt be shamed to the world's end. And she that rode on the serpent signifieth the old law, and that serpent betokeneth a fiend. And why she blamed thee that thou slewest her servant, it betokeneth nothing; the serpent that thou slewest betokeneth the devil that thou rodest upon to the rock. And when thou madest a sign of the cross, there thou slewest him, and put away his power. And when she asked thee amends and to become her man, and thou saidst thou wouldst not, that was to make thee to believe on her and leave thy baptism. So he commanded Sir Percivale to depart, and so he leapt over the board and the ship, and all went away he wist not whither. Then he went up unto the rock and found the lion which always kept him fellowship, and he stroked him upon the back and had great joy of him.

CHAPTER VIII

HOW SIR PERCIVALE SAW A SHIP COMING TO HIM-WARD,
AND HOW THE LADY OF THE SHIP TOLD HIM
OF HER DISHERITANCE

By that Sir Percivale had abiden there till mid-day he saw a ship came rowing in the sea as all the wind of the world had driven it. And so it drove under that rock. And when Sir Percivale saw this he hied him thither, and found the ship covered with silk more blacker than any bear, and therein was a gentlewoman of great beauty, and she was clothed richly that none might be better. And when she saw Sir Percivale she said: Who brought you in this wilderness where ye be never like to pass hence, for ye shall die here for hunger and mischief? Damosel, said Sir Percivale, I serve the best man of the world, and in his service he will not suffer me to die, for who that knocketh shall enter, and who that asketh shall have, and who that seeketh him he hideth him not. But then she said: Sir Percivale, wot ye what I am? Yea, said he. Now who taught you my name? said she. Now, said Sir Percivale, I know you better than ye ween. And I came out of the waste forest where I found the red knight with the white shield, said the damosel. Ah, damosel, said he, with that knight would I meet passing fain. Sir knight, said she, an ye will ensure me by the faith that ye owe unto knighthood that ye shall do my will what time I summon you, and I shall bring you unto that knight. Yea, said he, I shall promise you to fulfil your desire. Well, said she, now shall I tell you. I saw him in the forest chasing two knights unto a water, the which is called Mortaise; and they drove him into that water for dread of death, and the two knights passed over, and the red knight passed after, and there his horse was drenched, and he, through great strength, escaped unto the land: thus she told him, and Sir Percivale was passing glad thereof. Then she asked him if he had ate any meat late. Nay, madam, truly I ate no meat nigh this three days, but late here I spake with a good man that fed

me with his good words and holy, and refreshed me greatly.
Ah, sir knight, said she, that same man is an enchanter and
a multiplier of words. For an ye believe him ye shall plainly
be shamed, and die in this rock for pure hunger, and be
eaten with wild beasts; and ye be a young man and a goodly
knight, and I shall help you an ye will. What are ye,
said Sir Percivale, that proffered me thus great kindness?
I am, said she, a gentlewoman that am disherited, which
was sometime the richest woman of the world. Damosel,
said Sir Percivale, who hath disherited you? for I have great
pity of you. Sir, said she, I dwelled with the greatest man
of the world, and he made me so fair and clear that there
was none like me; and of that great beauty I had a little
pride more than I ought to have had. Also I said a word
that pleased him not. And then he would not suffer me to
be any longer in his company, and so drove me from mine
heritage, and so disherited me, and he had never pity of me
nor of none of my council, nor of my court. And sithen, sir
knight, it hath befallen me so, and through me and mine I
have benome him many of his men, and made them to
become my men. For they ask never nothing of me but I
give it them, that and much more. Thus I and all my servants were against him night and day. Therefore I know
now no good knight, nor no good man, but I get them on
my side an I may. And for that I know that thou art a
good knight, I beseech you to help me; and for ye be a
fellow of the Round Table, wherefore ye ought not to fail
no gentlewoman which is disherited, an she besought you
of help.

CHAPTER IX

HOW SIR PERCIVALE PROMISED HER HELP, AND HOW
HE REQUIRED HER OF LOVE, AND HOW HE
WAS SAVED FROM THE FIEND

THEN Sir Percivale promised her all the help that he
might; and then she thanked him. And at that time the
weather was hot. Then she called unto her a gentlewoman
and bad her bring forth a pavilion; and so she did, and

pyght it upon the gravel. Sir, said she, now may ye rest you in this heat of the day. Then he thanked her, and she put off his helm and his shield, and there he slept a great while. And then he awoke and asked her if she had any meat, and she said: Yea, also ye shall have enough. And so there was set enough upon the table, and thereon so much that he had marvel, for there was all manner of meats that he could think on. Also he drank there the strongest wine that ever he drank, him thought, and therewith he was a little chafed more than he ought to be; with that he beheld the gentlewoman, and him thought she was the fairest creature that ever he saw. And then Sir Percivale proffered her love, and prayed her that she would be his. Then she refused him, in a manner, when he required her, for the cause he should be the more ardent on her, and ever he ceased not to pray her of love. And when she saw him well enchafed, then she said: Sir Percivale, wit you well I shall not fulfil your will but if ye swear from henceforth ye shall be my true servant, and to do nothing but that I shall command you. Will ye ensure me this as ye be a true knight? Yea, said he, fair lady, by the faith of my body. Well, said she, now shall ye do with me what so it please you; and now wit ye well ye are the knight in the world that I have most desire for. And then two squires were commanded to make a bed in middes of the pavilion. And anon she was unclothed and laid therein. And then Sir Percivale laid him down by her naked; and by adventure and grace he saw his sword lie on the ground naked, in whose pommel was a red cross and the sign of the crucifix therein, and bethought him on his knighthood and his promise made toforehand unto the good man; then he made a sign of the cross in his forehead, and therewith the pavilion turned up so down, and then it changed unto a smoke, and a black cloud, and then he was adread and cried aloud:

CHAPTER X

FAIR sweet father, Jesu Christ, ne let me not be shamed, the which was nigh lost had not thy good grace been. And then he looked into a ship, and saw her enter therein, which said: Sir Percivale, ye have betrayed me. And so she went with the wind roaring and yelling, that it seemed all the water brent after her. Then Sir Percivale made great sorrow, and drew his sword unto him, saying: Sithen my flesh will be my master I shall punish it; and therewith he rove himself through the thigh that the blood start about him, and said: O good Lord, take this in recompensation of that I have done against thee, my Lord. So then he clothed him and armed him, and called himself a wretch, saying: How nigh was I lost, and to have lost that I should never have gotten again, that was my virginity, for that may never be recovered after it is once lost. And then he stopped his bleeding wound with a piece of his shirt. Thus as he made his moan he saw the same ship come from Orient that the good man was in the day afore, and the noble knight was ashamed with himself, and therewith he fell in a swoon. And when he awoke he went unto him weakly, and there he saluted this good man. And then he asked Sir Percivale: How hast thou done sith I departed? Sir, said he, here was a gentlewoman and led me into deadly sin. And there he told him altogether. Knew ye not the maid? said the good man. Sir, said he, nay, but well I wot the fiend sent her hither to shame me. O good knight, said he, thou art a fool, for that gentlewoman was the master fiend of hell, the which hath power above all devils, and that was the old lady that thou sawest in thine advision riding on the serpent. Then he told Sir Percivale how our Lord Jesu Christ beat him out of heaven for his sin, the which was the most brightest angel of heaven, and therefore he lost his heritage: And that was the champion that thou foughtest withal, the which had overcome thee had not the grace of God been. Now beware Sir Percivale, and taken this for an ensample. And then the good man vanished away. Then Sir Percivale took his arms, and entered into the ship, and so departed from thence.

Here endeth the fourtenthe booke, whiche is of syr percyval. And here foloweth of syre launce- lot, whiche is the fyftenth book.

THE FIFTEENTH BOOK

CHAPTER I

HOW SIR LAUNCELOT CAME TO A CHAPEL, WHERE HE
FOUND DEAD, IN A WHITE SHIRT, A MAN OF
RELIGION, OF AN HUNDRED WINTER OLD

WHEN the hermit had kept Sir Launcelot three days, the hermit gat him a horse, an helm, and a sword. And then he departed about the hour of noon. And then he saw a little house. And when he came near he saw a chapel, and there beside he saw an old man that was clothed all in white full richly; and then Sir Launcelot said: God save you. God keep you, said the good man, and make you a good knight. Then Sir Launcelot alit and entered into the chapel and there he saw an old man dead, in a white shirt of passing fine cloth. Sir, said the good man, this man that is dead ought not to be in such clothing as ye see him in, for in that he brake the oath of his order, for he hath been more than an hundred winter a man of a religion. And then the good man and Sir Launcelot went into the chapel; and the good man took a stole about his neck, and a book, and then he conjured on that book; and with that they saw in an hideous figure and horrible, that there was no man so hard-hearted nor so hard but he should have been afeard. Then said the fiend: Thou hast travailed me greatly; now tell me what thou wilt with me. I will, said the good man, that thou tell me how my fellow became dead, and whether he be saved or damned. Then he said with an horrible voice: He is not lost but saved. How may that be? said the good man; it seemed to me that he lived not well, for he brake his order for to wear a shirt where he ought to wear none, and who that trespasseth against our order doth not well. Not so, said the fiend, this man that lieth here dead was come of a great lineage. And there was a lord that hight the Earl de Vale, that held great war against this man's nephew, the which hight Aguarus. And so this Aguarus saw the earl was bigger than he. Then he went for to take counsel of his uncle, the which lieth here dead as ye may see. And then he asked leave, and went out of his hermitage for to maintain his nephew against the mighty earl; and so it happed that this man that lieth here dead did so much by his wisdom and hardiness that the earl was taken, and three of his lords, by force of this dead man.

CHAPTER II

OF A DEAD MAN, HOW MEN WOULD HAVE HEWN HIM, AND IT WOULD NOT BE, AND HOW SIR LAUNCELOT TOOK THE HAIR OF THE DEAD MAN

THEN was there peace betwixt the earl and this Aguarus, and great surety that the earl should never war against him. Then this dead man that here lieth came to this hermitage again; and then the earl made two of his nephews for to be avenged upon this man. So they came on a day, and found this dead man at the sacring of his mass, and they abode him till he had said mass. And then they set upon him and drew out swords to have slain him; but there would no sword bite on him more than upon a gad of steel, for the high Lord which he served he him preserved. Then made they a great fire, and did off all his clothes, and the hair off his back. And then this dead man hermit said unto them: Ween you to burn me? It shall not lie in your power nor to perish me as much as a thread an there were any on my body. No, said one of them, it shall be essayed. And then they despoiled him, and put upon him this shirt, and cast him in a fire, and there he lay all that night till it was day in that fire, and was not dead, and so in the morn I came and found him dead; but I found neither thread nor skin tamyd, and so took him out of the fire with great fear, and led him here as ye may see. And now may ye suffer me to go my way, for I have said you the sooth. And then he departed with a great tempest. Then was the good man and Sir Launcelot more gladder than they were tofore. And then Sir Launcelot dwelled with that good man that night. Sir, said the good man, be ye not Sir Launcelot du Lake? Yea, sir, said he. What seek ye in this country? Sir, said Sir Launcelot, I go to seek the adventures of the Sangreal. Well, said he, seek it ye may well, but though it were here ye shall have no power to see it no more than a blind man should see a bright sword, and that is long on your sin, and else ye were more abler than any man living. And then Sir Launcelot began to weep. Then said the good man: Were ye confessed sith ye entered into the quest of the Sangreal? Yea, sir, said Sir Launcelot. Then upon the morn when the good man had sung his mass, then they buried the dead man. Then Sir Launcelot said: Father, what shall I do? Now, said the good man, I require you take this hair that was this holy man's and put it next thy skin, and it shall prevail thee greatly. Sir, and I will do it, said Sir Launcelot. Also I charge you that ye eat no flesh as long as ye be in the quest of the Sangreal, nor ye shall drink no wine, and that ye hear mass daily an ye may do it. So he took the hair and put it upon him, and so departed at evensong-time. And so rode he into a forest, and there he met with a gentlewoman riding upon a white palfrey, and then she asked him: Sir knight, whither ride ye? Certes, damosel, said Launcelot, I wot not whither I ride but as fortune leadeth me. Ah, Sir Launcelot, said she, I wot what adventure ye seek, for ye were afore time nearer than ye be now, and yet shall ye see it more openly than ever ye did, and that shall ye understand in short time. Then Sir Launcelot asked her where he might be harboured that night. Ye shall not find this day nor night, but tomorn ye shall find harbour good, and ease of that ye be in doubt of. And then he commended her unto God. Then he rode till that he came to a Cross, and took that for his host as for that night.

CHAPTER III

OF A VISION THAT SIR LAUNCELOT HAD, AND HOW HE TOLD IT TO AN HERMIT, AND DESIRED COUNSEL OF HIM

AND so he put his horse to pasture, and did off his helm and his shield, and made his prayers unto the Cross that he never fall in deadly sin again. And so he laid him down to sleep. And anon as he was on sleep it befell him there an advision, that there came a man afore him all by compass of stars, and that man had a crown of gold on his head, and that man led in his fellowship seven kings and two knights. And all these worshipped the Cross, kneeling upon their knees, holding up their hands toward the heaven. And all they said: Fair sweet Father of heaven, come and visit us, and yield unto us every each as we have deserved. Then looked Launcelot up to the heaven, and him seemed the clouds did open, and an old man came down, with a company of angels, and alit among them, and gave unto every each his blessing, and called them his servants, and good and true knights. And when this old man had said thus he came to one of those knights, and said: I have lost all that I have set in thee, for thou hast ruled thee against me as a warrior, and used wrong wars with vain glory, more for the pleasure of the world than to please me, therefore thou shalt be confounded without thou yield me my treasure. All this advision saw Sir Launcelot at the Cross. And on the morn he took his horse and rode till midday; and there by adventure he met with the same knight that took his horse, helm, and his sword, when he slept when the Sangreal appeared afore the Cross. When Sir Launcelot saw him he saluted him not fair, but cried on high: Knight, keep thee, for thou hast done to me great unkindness. And then they put afore them their spears, and Sir Launcelot came so

fiercely upon him that he smote him and his horse down to
the earth, that he had nigh broken his neck. Then Sir
Launcelot took the knight's horse that was his own aforehand, and descended from the horse he sat upon, and
mounted upon his own horse, and tied the knight's own
horse to a tree that he might find that horse when that he
was arisen. Then Sir Launcelot rode till night and by
adventure he met an hermit, and each of them saluted
other; and there he rested with that good man all night,
and gave his horse such as he might get. Then said the
good man unto Launcelot: Of whence be ye? Sir, said
he, I am of Arthur's court, and my name is Sir Launcelot
du Lake that am in the quest of the Sangreal, and therefore
I pray you to counsel me of a vision the which I had at the
Cross. And so he told him all.

CHAPTER IV

HOW THE HERMIT EXPOUNDED TO SIR LAUNCE-
LOT HIS VISION, AND TOLD HIM THAT SIR
GALAHAD WAS HIS SON

Lo, Sir Launcelot, said the good man, there thou mightest
understand the high lineage that thou art come of, and
thine advision betokeneth. After the passion of Jesu Christ
forty year, Joseph of Aramathie preached the victory of
King Evelake, that he had in the battles the better of his
enemies. And of the seven kings and the two knights:
the first of them is called Nappus, an holy man; and the
second hight Nacien, in remembrance of his grandsire, and
in him dwelled our lord Jesu Christ; and the third was
called Helias le Grose; and the fourth hight Lisais; and
the fifth hight Jonas, he departed out of his country and
went into Wales, and took there the daughter of Manuel,
whereby he had the land of Gaul, and he came to dwell
in this country. And of him came King Launcelot thy
grandsire, the which there wedded the king's daughter of
Ireland, and he was as worthy a man as thou art, and of
him came King Ban, thy father, the which was the last

of the seven kings. And by thee, Sir Launcelot, it signifieth that the angels said thou were none of the seven fellowships. And the last was the ninth knight, he was signified to a lion, for he should pass all manner of earthly knights that is Sir Galahad, the which thou gat on King Pelles' daughter; and thou ought to thank God more than any other man living, for of a sinner earthly thou hast no peer as in knighthood, nor never shall be. But little thank hast thou given to God for all the great virtues that God hath lent thee. Sir, said Launcelot, ye say that that good knight is my son. That oughtest thou to know and no man better, said the good man, for thou knewest the daughter of King Pelles fleshly, and on her thou begattest Galahad, and that was he that at the feast of Pentecost sat in the Siege Perilous; and therefore make thou it known openly that he is one of thy begetting on King Pelles' daughter, for that will be your worship and honour, and to all thy kindred. And I counsel you in no place press not upon him to have ado with him. Well, said Launcelot, meseemeth that good knight should pray for me unto the High Father, that I fall not to sin again. Trust thou well, said the good man, thou farest mickle the better for his prayer; but the son shall not bear the wickedness of the father, nor the father shall not bear the wickedness of the son, but every each shall bear his own burden. And therefore beseek thou only God, and he will help thee in all thy needs. And then Sir Launcelot and he went to supper, and so laid him to rest, and the hair pricked so Sir Launcelot's skin which grieved him full sore, but he took it meekly, and suffered the pain. And so on the morn he heard his mass and took his arms, and so took his leave.

CHAPTER V

HOW SIR LAUNCELOT JOUSTED WITH MANY KNIGHTS, AND HOW HE WAS TAKEN

AND then mounted upon his horse, and rode into a forest, and held no highway. And as he looked afore

him he saw a fair plain, and beside that a fair castle, and
afore the castle were many pavilions of silk and of diverse
hue. And him seemed that he saw there five hundred
knights riding on horseback; and there were two parties:
they that were of the castle were all on black horses and
their trappours black, and they that were without were all
on white horses and trappours, and every each hurtled to
other that it marvelled Sir Launcelot. And at the last him
thought they of the castle were put to the worse. Then
thought Sir Launcelot for to help there the weaker party
in increasing of his chivalry. And so Sir Launcelot thrust
in among the party of the castle, and smote down a knight,
horse and man, to the earth. And then he rushed here
and there, and did marvellous deeds of arms. And then
he drew out his sword, and struck many knights to the
earth, so that all those that saw him marvelled that ever
one knight might do so great deeds of arms. But always
the white knights held them nigh about Sir Launcelot, for
to tire him and wind him. But at the last, as a man may
not ever endure, Sir Launcelot waxed so faint of fighting
and travailing, and was so weary of his great deeds, but
he might not lift up his arms for to give one stroke, so
that he weened never to have borne arms; and then they
all took and led him away into a forest, and there made
him to alight and to rest him. And then all the fellowship
of the castle were overcome for the default of him. Then
they said all unto Sir Launcelot: Blessed be God that ye
be now of our fellowship, for we shall hold you in our
prison; and so they left him with few words. And then
Sir Launcelot made great sorrow, For never or now was
I never at tournament nor jousts but I had the best, and
now I am shamed; and then he said: Now I am sure
that I am more sinfuller than ever I was. Thus he rode
sorrowing, and half a day he was out of despair, till that
he came into a deep valley. And when Sir Launcelot
saw he might not ride up into the mountain, he there alit
under an apple tree, and there he left his helm and his
shield, and put his horse unto pasture. And then he laid
him down to sleep. And then him thought there came
an old man afore him, the which said: Ah, Launcelot of

evil faith and poor belief, wherefore is thy will turned so lightly toward thy deadly sin? And when he had said thus he vanished away, and Launcelot wist not where he was become. Then he took his horse, and armed him; and as he rode by the way he saw a chapel where was a recluse, which had a window that she might see up to the altar. And all aloud she called Launcelot, for that he seemed a knight errant. And then he came, and she asked him what he was, and of what place, and where about he went to seek.

CHAPTER VI

HOW SIR LAUNCELOT TOLD HIS VISION UNTO A WOMAN, AND HOW SHE EXPOUNDED IT UNTO HIM

AND then he told her all together word by word, and the truth how it befell him at the tournament. And after told her his advision that he had had that night in his sleep, and prayed her to tell him what it might mean, for he was not well content with it. Ah, Launcelot, said she, as long as ye were knight of earthly knighthood ye were the most marvellous man of the world, and most adventurous. Now, said the lady, sithen ye be set among the knights of heavenly adventures, if adventure fell thee contrary at that tournament have thou no marvel, for that tournament yesterday was but a tokening of Our Lord. And not for then there was none enchantment, for they at the tournament were earthly knights. The tournament was a token to see who should have most knights, either Eliazar, the son of King Pelles, or Argustus, the son of King Harlon. But Eliazar was all clothed in white, and Argustus was covered in black, the which were come. All what this betokeneth I shall tell you. The day of Pentecost, when King Arthur held his court, it befell that earthly kings and knights took a tournament together, that is to say the quest of the Sangreal. The earthly knights were they the which were clothed all in black, and the covering betokeneth the sins whereof they be not confessed. And they with the covering of white betokeneth virginity, and they that chose chastity. And thus was the quest begun in them. Then thou beheld the sinners and the good men, and when thou sawest the sinners overcome, thou inclinest to that party for bobaunce and pride of the world, and all that must be left in that quest, for in this quest thou shalt have many fellows and thy betters. For thou art so feeble of evil trust and good belief, this made it when thou were there where they took thee and led thee into the forest. And anon there appeared the Sangreal unto the white knights, but thou was so feeble of good belief and faith that thou mightest not abide it for all the teaching of the good man, but anon thou turnest to the sinners, and that caused thy misadventure that thou should'st know good from evil and vain glory of the world, the which is not worth a pear. And for great pride thou madest great sorrow that thou haddest not overcome all the white knights with the covering of white by whom was betokened virginity and chastity; and therefore God was wroth with you, for God loveth no such deeds in this quest. And this advision signifieth that thou were of evil faith and of poor belief, the which will make thee to fall into the deep pit of hell if thou keep thee not. Now have I warned thee of thy vain glory and of thy pride, that thou hast many times erred against thy Maker. Beware of everlasting pain, for of all earthly knights I have most pity of thee, for I know well thou hast not thy peer of any earthly sinful man. And so she commended Sir Launcelot to dinner. And after dinner he took his horse and commended her to God, and so rode into a deep valley, and there he saw a river and an high mountain. And through the water he must needs pass, the which was hideous; and then in the name of God he took it with good heart. And when he came over he saw an armed knight, horse and man black as any bear; without any word he smote Sir Launcelot's horse to the earth; and so he passed on, he wist not where he was become. And then he took his helm and his shield, and thanked God of his adventure.

Here leveth of the story of syr launcelot.
And speke we of sir gawayne, the
whiche is the xvi. book

THE SIXTEENTH BOOK

CHAPTER I

HOW SIR GAWAINE WAS NIGH WEARY OF THE QUEST OF THE SANGREAL, AND OF HIS MARVELLOUS DREAM

WHEN Sir Gawaine was departed from his fellowship he rode long without any adventure. For he found not the tenth part of adventure as he was wont to do. For Sir Gawaine rode from Whitsuntide until Michaelmas and found none adventure that pleased him. So on a day it befell Gawaine met with Sir Ector de Maris, and either made great joy of other that it were marvel to tell. And so they told every each other, and complained them greatly that they could find none adventure. Truly, said Sir Gawaine unto Sir Ector, I am nigh weary of this quest, and loth I am to follow further in strange countries. One thing marvelled me, said Sir Ector, I have met with twenty knights, fellows of mine, and all they complain as I do. I have marvel, said Sir Gawaine, where that Sir Launcelot, your brother, is. Truly, said Sir Ector, I cannot hear of him, nor of Sir Galahad, Percivale, nor Sir Bors. Let them be, said Sir Gawaine, for they four have no peers. And if one thing were not in Sir Launcelot he had no fellow of none earthly man; but he is as we be, but if he took more pain upon him. But an these four be met together they will be loth that any man meet with them; for an they fail of the Sangreal it is in waste of all the remnant to recover it. Thus as Ector and Gawaine rode more than eight days. And on a Saturday they found an old chapel, the which was wasted that there seemed no man thither repaired; and there they alit, and set their spears at the door, and in they entered into the chapel, and there made their orisons a great while, and set them down in the sieges of the chapel. And as they spake of one thing and other, for heaviness they fell on sleep, and there befel them both marvellous adventures. Sir Gawaine him seemed he came into a meadow full of herbs and flowers, and there he saw a rack of bulls, an hundred and fifty, that were proud and black, save three of them were all white, and one had a black spot, and the other two were so fair and so white that they might be no whiter. And these three bulls which were so fair were tied with two strong cords. And the remnant of the bulls said among them: Go we hence to seek better pasture. And so some went, and some came again, but they were so lean that they might not stand upright; and of the bulls that were so white, that one came again and no more. But when this white bull was come again among these other there rose up a great cry for lack of wind that failed them; and so they departed one here and another there: this advision befell Gawaine that night.

CHAPTER II

OF THE VISION OF SIR ECTOR, AND HOW HE JOUSTED WITH SIR UWAINE LES AVOUTRES, HIS SWORN BROTHER

But to Ector de Maris befell another vision the contrary. For it seemed him that his brother, Sir Launcelot, and he alit out of a chair and leapt upon two horses, and the one said to the other: Go we seek that we shall not find. And him thought that a man beat Sir Launcelot, and despoiled him, and clothed him in another array, the which was all full of knots, and set him upon an ass, and so he rode till he came to the fairest well that ever he saw; and Sir Launcelot alit and would have drunk of that well. And when he stooped to drink of the water the water sank from him. And when Sir Launcelot saw that, he turned and went thither as the head came from. And in the meanwhile he trowed that himself and Sir Ector rode till they came to a rich man's house where there was a wedding. And there he saw a king the which said: Sir knight, here is no place for you. And then he turned again unto the chair that he came from. Thus within a while both Gawaine and Ector awaked, and either told other of their advision, the which marvelled them greatly. Truly, said Ector, I shall never be merry till I hear tidings of my brother Launcelot. Now as they sat thus talking they saw an hand showing unto the elbow, and was covered with red samite, and upon that hung a bridle not right rich, and held within the fist a great candle which burned right clear, and so passed afore them, and entered into the chapel, and then vanished away and they wist not where. And anon came down a voice which said: Knights of full evil faith and of poor belief, these two things have failed you, and therefore ye may not come to the adventures of the Sangreal. Then first spake Gawaine and said: Ector, have ye heard these words? Yea truly, said Sir Ector, I heard all. Now go we, said Sir Ector, unto some hermit that will tell us of our advision, for it seemeth me we labour all in vain. And so they departed and rode into a valley, and there met with a squire which rode on an hackney, and they saluted him fair. Sir, said Gawaine, can thou teach us to any hermit? Here is one in a little mountain, but it is so rough there may no horse go thither, and therefore ye must go upon foot; there shall ye find a poor house, and there is Nacien the hermit, which is the holiest man in this country. And so they departed either from other. And then in a valley they met with a knight all armed, which proffered them to joust as far as he saw them. In the name of God, said Sir Gawaine, sith I departed from Camelot there was none proffered me to joust but once. And now, sir, said Ector, let me joust with him. Nay, said Gawaine, ye shall not but if I be beat; it shall not forethink me then if ye go after me. And then either embraced other to joust and came together as fast as their horses might run, and brast their shields and the mails, and the one more than the other; and Gawaine was wounded in the left side, but the other knight was smitten through the breast, and the spear came out on the other side, and so they fell both out of their saddles, and in the falling they brake both their spears. Anon Gawaine arose and set his hand to his sword, and cast his shield afore him. But all for naught was it, for the knight had no power to rise against him. Then said Gawaine: Ye must yield you as an overcome man, or else I may slay you. Ah, sir knight, said he, I am but dead, for God's sake and of your gentleness lead me here unto an abbey that I may receive my Creator. Sir, said Gawaine, I know no house of religion hereby. Sir, said the knight, set me on an horse tofore you, and I shall teach you. Gawaine set him up in the saddle, and he leapt up behind him for to sustain him, and so came to an abbey where they were well received; and anon he was unarmed, and received his Creator. Then he prayed Gawaine to draw out the truncheon of the spear out of his body. Then Gawaine asked him what he was that knew him not. I am, said he, of King Arthur's court, and was a fellow of the Round Table, and we were brethren sworn together; and now Sir Gawaine, thou hast slain me, and my name is Uwaine les Avoutres, that sometime was son unto King Uriens, and was in the quest of the Sangreal; and now forgive it thee God, for it shall ever be said that the one sworn brother hath slain the other.

CHAPTER III

HOW SIR GAWAINE AND SIR ECTOR CAME TO AN HERMITAGE TO BE CONFESSED, AND HOW THEY TOLD TO THE HERMIT THEIR VISIONS

ALAS, said Gawaine, that ever this misadventure is befallen me. No force, said Uwaine, sith I shall die this death, of a much more worshipfuller man's hand might I not die; but when ye come to the court recommend me unto my lord, King Arthur, and all those that be left on live, and for old brotherhood think on me. Then began Gawaine to weep, and Ector also. And then Uwaine himself and Sir Gawaine drew out the truncheon of the spear, and anon departed the soul from the body. Then Sir Gawaine and Sir Ector buried him as men ought to bury a king's son, and made write upon his name, and by whom he was slain. Then departed Gawaine and Ector as heavy as they might for their misadventure, and so rode till that they came to the rough mountain, and there they tied their horses and went on foot to the hermitage. And when they were come up they saw a poor house, and beside the chapel a little courtelage, where Nacien the hermit gathered worts, as he which had tasted none other meat of a great while. And when he saw the errant knights he came toward them and saluted them, and they him again. Fair lords, said he, what adventure brought you hither? Sir, said Gawaine, to speak with you for to be confessed. Sir, said the hermit, I am ready. Then they told him so much that he wist well what they were. And then he thought to counsel them if he might. Then began Gawaine first and told him of his advision that he had had in the chapel, and Ector told him all as it is afore rehearsed. Sir, said the hermit unto Sir Gawaine, the fair meadow and the rack therein ought to be understood the Round Table, and by the meadow ought to be understood humility and patience, those be the things which be always green and quick; for men may no time overcome humility and patience, therefore was the Round Table founded; and the chivalry hath been at all times so by the fraternity which was there that she might not be overcome; for men said she was founded in patience and in humility. At the rack ate an hundred and fifty bulls; but they ate not in the meadow, for their hearts should be set in humility and patience, and the bulls were proud and black save only three. By the bulls is to understand the fellowship of the Round Table, which for their sin and their wickedness be black. Blackness is to say without good or virtuous works. And the three bulls which were white save only one that was spotted: the two white betoken Sir Galahad and Sir Percivale, for they be maidens clene and without spot; and the third that had a spot signifieth Sir Bors de Ganis, which trespassed but once in his virginity, but sithen he kept himself so well in chastity that all is forgiven him and his misdeeds. And why those three were tied by the necks, they be three knights in virginity and chastity, and there is no pride smitten in them. And the black bulls which said: Go we hence, they were those which at Pentecost at the high feast took upon them to go in the quest of the Sangreal without confession: they might not enter in the meadow of humility and patience. And therefore they returned into waste countries, that signifieth death, for there shall die many of them: every each of them shall slay other for sin, and they that shall escape shall be so lean that it shall be marvel to see them. And of the three bulls without spot, the one shall come again, and the other two never.

CHAPTER IV

HOW THE HERMIT EXPOUNDED THEIR VISION

THEN spake Nacien unto Ector: Sooth it is that Launcelot and ye come down off one chair: the chair betokeneth mastership and lordship which ye came down from. But ye two knights, said the hermit, ye go to seek that ye shall never find, that is the Sangreal; for it is the secret thing of our Lord Jesu Christ. What is to mean that Sir Launcelot fell down off his horse: he hath left pride and taken him to humility, for he had cried mercy loud for his sin, and sore repented him, and our Lord hath clothed him in his clothing which is full of knots, that is the hair that he weareth daily. And the ass that he rode upon is a beast of humility, for God would not ride upon no steed, nor upon no palfrey; so in ensample that an ass betokeneth meekness, that thou sawest Sir Launcelot ride on in thy sleep. And the well whereas the water sank from him when he should have taken thereof, and when he saw he might not have it, he returned thither from whence he came, for the well betokeneth the high grace of God, the more men desire it to take it, the more shall be their desire. So when he came nigh the Sangreal, he meeked him that he held him not a man worthy to be so nigh the holy vessel, for he had been so befouled in deadly sin by the space of many years; yet when he kneeled to drink of the well, there he saw great providence of the Sangreal. And for he had served so long the devil, he shall have vengeance four and twenty days long, for that he hath been the devil's servant four and twenty years. And then soon after he shall return unto Camelot out of this country, and he shall say a part of such things as he hath found. Now will I tell you what betokeneth the hand with the candle and the bridle: that is to understand the holy ghost where charity is ever, and the bridle signifieth abstinence. For when she is bridled in Christian man's heart she holdeth him so short that he falleth not in deadly sin. And the candle which sheweth clearness and sight signifieth the right way of Jesu Christ. And when he went and said: Knights of poor faith and of wicked belief, these three things failed, charity, abstinence, and truth; therefore ye may not attain that high adventure of the Sangreal.

CHAPTER V

OF THE GOOD COUNSEL THAT THE HERMIT GAVE TO HIM

CERTES, said Gawaine, soothly have ye said, that I see it openly. Now, I pray you, good man and holy father, tell me why we met not with so many adventures as we were wont to do, and commonly have the better. I shall tell you gladly, said the good man; the adventure of the Sangreal which ye and many other have undertaken the quest of it and find it not, the cause is for it appeareth not to sinners. Wherefore marvel not though ye fail thereof, and many other. For ye be an untrue knight, and a great murderer, and to good men signifieth other things than murder. For I dare say as sinful as Sir Launcelot hath been, sith that he went into the quest of the Sangreal he slew never man, nor nought shall, till that he come unto Camelot again, for he hath taken upon him for to forsake sin. And nere that he nys not stable, but by his thought he is likely to turn again, he should be next to achieve it save Galahad, his son. But God knoweth his thought and his unstableness, and yet shall he die right an holy man, and no doubt he hath no fellow of no earthly sinful man. Sir, said Gawaine, it seemeth me by your words that for our sins it will not avail us to travel in this quest. Truly, said the good man, there be an hundred such as ye be that never shall prevail, but to have shame. And when they had heard these voices they commended him unto God. Then the good man called Gawaine, and said: It is long time passed sith that ye were made knight, and never sithen thou servedst thy Maker, and now thou art so old a tree that in thee is neither life nor fruit; wherefore bethink thee that thou yield to Our Lord the bare rind, sith

the fiend hath the leaves and the fruit. Sir, said Gawaine,
an I had leisure I would speak with you, but my fellow here,
Sir Ector, is gone, and abideth me yonder beneath the hill.
Well, said the good man, thou were better to be counselled.
Then departed Gawaine and came to Ector, and so took
their horses and rode till they came to a forester's house,
which harboured them right well. And on the morn they
departed from their host, and rode long or they could find
any adventure.

CHAPTER VI

HOW SIR BORS MET WITH AN HERMIT, AND HOW
HE WAS CONFESSED TO HIM, AND OF HIS
PENANCE ENJOINED TO HIM

WHEN Bors was departed from Camelot he met with a
religious man riding on an ass, and Sir Bors saluted him.
Anon the good man knew him that he was one of the knights
errant that was in the quest of the Sangreal. What are ye?
said the good man. Sir, said he, I am a knight that fain
would be counselled in the quest of the Sangreal, for he shall
have much earthly worship that may bring it to an end.
Certes, said the good man, that is sooth, for he shall be the
best knight of the world, and the fairest of all the fellowship.
But wit you well there shall none attain it but by cleanness,
that is pure confession. So rode they together till that they
came to an hermitage. And there he prayed Bors to dwell
all that night with him. And so he alit and put away his
armour, and prayed him that he might be confessed; and so
they went into the chapel, and there he was clean confessed,
and they ate bread and drank water together. Now, said
the good man, I pray thee that thou eat none other till that
thou sit at the table where the Sangreal shall be. Sir, said
he, I agree me thereto, but how wit ye that I shall sit there.
Yes, said the good man, that know I, but there shall be but
few of your fellows with you. All is welcome, said Sir Bors,
that God sendeth me. Also, said the good man, instead of
a shirt, and in sign of chastisement, ye shall wear a garment;
therefore I pray you do off all your clothes and your shirt:

and so he did. And then he took him a scarlet coat, so that should be instead of his shirt till he had fulfilled the quest of the Sangreal; and the good man found in him so marvellous a life and so stable, that he marvelled and felt that he was never corrupt in fleshly lusts, but in one time that he begat Elian le Blank. Then he armed him, and took his leave, and so departed. And so a little from thence he looked up into a tree, and there he saw a passing great bird upon an old tree, and it was passing dry, without leaves; and the bird sat above, and had birds, the which were dead for hunger. So smote he himself with his beak, the which was great and sharp. And so the great bird bled till that he died among his birds. And the young birds took the life by the blood of the great bird. When Bors saw this he wist well it was a great tokening; for when he saw the great bird arose not, then he took his horse and yede his way. So by evensong, by adventure he came to a strong tower and an high, and there was he lodged gladly.

CHAPTER VII

HOW SIR BORS WAS LODGED WITH A LADY, AND HOW HE TOOK UPON HIM FOR TO FIGHT AGAINST A CHAMPION FOR HER LAND

AND when he was unarmed they led him into an high tower where was a lady, young, lusty, and fair. And she received him with great joy, and made him to sit down by her, and so was he set to sup with flesh and many dainties. And when Sir Bors saw that, he bethought him on his penance, and bad a squire to bring him water. And so he brought him, and he made sops therein and ate them. Ah, said the lady, I trow ye like not my meat. Yes, truly, said Sir Bors, God thank you, madam, but I may eat none other meat this day. Then she spake no more as at that time, for she was loth to displease him. Then after supper they spake of one thing and other. With that came a squire and said: Madam, ye must purvey you tomorn for a champion, for else your sister will have this castle and also your lands, except ye can find a knight that will fight tomorn in your quarrel against Pridam le Noire. Then she made sorrow and said: Ah, Lord God, wherefore granted ye to hold my land, whereof I should now be disherited without reason and right? And when Sir Bors had heard her say thus, he said: I shall comfort you. Sir, said she, I shall tell you there was here a king that hight Aniause, which held all this land in his keeping. So it mishapped he loved a gentlewoman a great deal elder than I. So took he her all this land to her keeping, and all his men to govern; and she brought up many evil customs whereby she put to death a great part of his kinsmen. And when he saw that, he let chase her out of this land, and betook it me, and all this land in my demesnes. But anon as that worthy king was dead, this other lady began to war upon me, and hath destroyed many of my men, and turned them against me, that I have wellnigh no man left me; and I have nought else but this high tower that she left me. And yet she hath promised me to have this tower, without I can find a knight to fight with her champion. Now tell me, said Sir Bors, what is that Pridam le Noire? Sir, said she, he is the most doubted man of this land. Now may ye send her word that ye have found a knight that shall fight with that Pridam le Noire in God's quarrel and yours. Then that lady was not a little glad, and sent word that she was purveyed, and that night Bors had good cheer; but in no bed he would come, but laid him on the floor, nor never would do otherwise till that he had met with the quest of the Sangreal.

CHAPTER VIII

OF A VISION WHICH SIR BORS HAD THAT NIGHT, AND HOW HE FOUGHT AND OVERCAME HIS ADVERSARY

AND anon as he was asleep him befel a vision, that there came to him two birds, the one as white as a swan, and the other was marvellous black; but it was not so great as the other, but in the likeness of a Raven. Then the white bird came to him, and said: An thou wouldst give me meat and serve me I should give thee all the riches of the world, and I shall make thee as fair and as white as I am. So the white bird departed, and there came the black bird to him, and said: An thou wolt, serve me to-morrow and have me in no despite though I be black, for wit thou well that more availeth my blackness than the other's whiteness. And then he departed. And he had another vision: him thought that he came to a great place which seemed a chapel, and there he found a chair set on the left side, which was wormeaten and feeble. And on the right hand were two flowers like a lily, and the one would have benome the other's whiteness, but a good man departed them that the one touched not the other; and then out of every flower came out many flowers, and fruit great plenty. Then him thought the good man said: Should not he do great folly that would let these two flowers perish for to succour the rotten tree, that it fell not to the earth? Sir, said he, it seemeth me that this wood might not avail. Now keep thee, said the good man, that thou never see such adventure befall thee. Then he awaked and made a sign of the cross in middes of the forehead, and so rose and clothed him. And there came the lady of the place, and she saluted him, and he her again, and so went to a chapel and heard their service. And there came a company of knights, that the lady had sent for, to lead Sir Bors unto battle. Then asked he his arms. And when he was armed she prayed him to take a little morsel to dine. Nay, madam, said he, that shall I not do till I have done my battle, by the grace of God. And so he lept upon his horse, and departed all the knights and men with him. And as soon as these two ladies met together, she which Bors should fight for complained her, and said: Madam, ye have done me wrong to bereave me of my lands that King Aniause gave me, and full loth I am there should be any battle. Ye shall not choose, said the other lady, or else your knight withdraw him. Then there was the cry made, which party had the better of the two knights, that his lady should rejoice all the land. Now departed the one knight here, and the other there. Then they came together with such a raundon that they pierced their shields and their hauberks, and the spears flew in pieces, and they wounded either other sore. Then hurtled they together, so that they fell both to the earth, and their horses betwixt their legs; and anon they arose, and set hands to their swords, and smote each one other upon the heads, that they made great wounds and deep, that the blood went out of their bodies. For there found Sir Bors greater defence in that knight more than he weened. For that Pridam was a passing good knight, and he wounded Sir Bors full evil, and he him again; but ever this Pridam held the stour in like hard. That perceived Sir Bors, and suffered him till he was nigh attaint. And then he ran upon him more and more, and the other went back for dread of death. So in his withdrawing he fell upright, and Sir Bors drew his helm so strongly that he rent it from his head, and gave him great strokes with the flat of his sword upon the visage, and bad him yield him or he should slay him. Then he cried him mercy and said: Fair knight, for God's love slay me not, and I shall ensure thee never to war against thy lady, but be alway toward her. Then Bors let him be; then the old lady fled with all her knights.

CHAPTER IX

HOW THE LADY WAS RETURNED TO HER LANDS BY THE BATTLE OF SIR BORS, AND OF HIS DEPARTING, AND HOW HE MET SIR LIONEL TAKEN AND BEATEN WITH THORNS, AND ALSO OF A MAID WHICH SHOULD HAVE BEEN DISHONOURED

So then came Bors to all those that held lands of his lady, and said he should destroy them but if they did such service unto her as longed to their lands. So they did their homage, and they that would not were chased out of their lands. Then befel that young lady to come to her estate again, by the mighty prowess of Sir Bors de Ganis. So when all the country was well set in peace, then Sir Bors took his leave and departed; and she thanked him greatly, and would have given him great riches, but he refused it. Then he rode all that day till night, and came to an harbour to a lady which knew him well enough, and made of him great joy. Upon the morn, as soon as the day appeared, Bors departed from thence, and so rode into a forest unto the hour of midday, and there befel him a marvellous adventure. So he met at the departing of the two ways two knights that led Lionel, his brother, all naked, bounden upon a strong hackney, and his hands bounden tofore his breast. And every each of them held in his hands thorns wherewith they went beating him so sore that the blood trailed down more than in an hundred places of his body, so that he was all blood tofore and behind, but he said never a word; as he which was great of heart he suffered all that ever they did to him as though he had felt none anguish. Anon Sir Bors dressed him to rescue him that was his brother; and so he looked upon the other side of him, and saw a knight which brought a fair gentlewoman, and would have set her in the thickest place of the forest for to have been the more surer out of the way from them that sought him. And she which was nothing assured cried with an high voice: Saint Mary succour your maid. And anon she espied where Sir Bors came riding. And when she came nigh him she deemed him a knight of the Round Table, whereof she hoped to have some comfort; and then she conjured him: By the faith that he ought unto him in whose service thou art entered in, and for the faith ye owe unto the high order of knighthood, and for the noble King Arthur's sake, that I suppose that made thee knight, that thou help me, and suffer me not to be shamed of this knight. When Bors heard her say thus he had so much sorrow there he nyst not what to do. For if I let my brother be in adventure he must be slain, and that would I not for all the earth. And if I help not the maid she is shamed for ever, and also she shall lose her virginity the which she shall never get again. Then lift he up his eyes and said weeping: Fair sweet Lord Jesu Christ, whose liege man I am, keep Lionel, my brother, that these knights slay him not, and for pity of you, and for Mary's sake, I shall succour this maid.

CHAPTER X

HOW SIR BORS LEFT TO RESCUE HIS BROTHER, AND RESCUED THE DAMOSEL; AND HOW IT WAS TOLD HIM THAT LIONEL WAS DEAD

THEN dressed he him unto the knight the which had the gentlewoman, and then he cried: Sir knight, let your hand off that maiden, or ye be but dead. And then he set down the maiden, and was armed at all pieces save he lacked his spear. Then he dressed his shield, and drew out his sword, and Bors smote him so hard that it went through his shield and habergeon on the left shoulder. And through great strength he beat him down to the earth, and at the pulling out of Bors' spear there he swooned. Then came Bors to the maid and said: How seemeth it you? of this knight ye be delivered at this time. Now sir, said she, I pray you lead me there as this knight had me. So shall I do gladly: and took the horse of the wounded knight, and set the gentlewoman upon him, and so brought her as she desired. Sir knight, said she, ye have better sped than ye weened, for an I had lost my maidenhead, five hundred men should have died for it. What knight was he that had you in the forest? By my faith, said she, he is my cousin. So wot I never with what engyn the fiend enchafed him, for yesterday he took me from my father privily; for I nor none of my father's men mistrusted him not, and if he had had my maidenhead he should have died for the sin, and his body shamed and dishonoured for ever. Thus as she stood talking with him there came twelve knights seeking after her, and anon she told them all how Bors had delivered her; then they made great joy, and besought him to come to her father, a great lord, and he should be right welcome. Truly, said Bors, that may not be at this time, for I have a great adventure to do in this country. So he commended them unto God and departed. Then Sir Bors rode after Lionel, his brother, by the trace of their horses, thus he rode seeking a great while. Then he overtook a man clothed in a religious clothing, and rode on a strong black horse blacker than a bear, and said: Sir knight, what seek you? Sir, said he, I seek my brother that I saw within a while beaten with two knights. Ah, Bors, discomfort you not, nor fall into no wanhope, for I shall tell you tidings such as they be, for truly he is dead. Then showed he him a new slain body lying in a bush, and it seemed him well that it was the body of Lionel; and then he made such a sorrow that he fell to the earth all in a swoon, and lay a great while there. And when he came to himself he said: Fair brother, sith the company of you and me is departed shall I never have joy in my heart, and now he which I have taken unto my master, He be my help. And when he had said thus he took his body lightly in his arms, and put it upon the arson of his saddle. And then he said to the man: Canst thou tell me unto some chapel where that I may bury this body? Come on, said he, here is one fast by; and so long they rode till they saw a fair tower, and afore it there seemed an old feeble chapel. And then they alit both, and put him into a tomb of marble.

CHAPTER XI

HOW SIR BORS TOLD HIS DREAM TO A PRIEST, WHICH HE HAD DREAMED, AND OF THE COUNSEL THAT THE PRIEST GAVE TO HIM

Now leave we him here, said the good man, and go we to our harbour till to-morrow; we will come here again to do him service. Sir, said Bors, be ye a priest? Yea forsooth, said he. Then I pray you tell me a dream that befell to me the last night. Say on, said he. Then he began so much to tell him of the great bird in the forest, and after told him of his birds, one white, another black, and of the rotten tree, and of the white flowers. Sir, I shall tell you a part now, and the other dele to-morrow. The white fowl betokeneth a gentlewoman, fair and rich, which loved thee paramours, and hath loved thee long; and if thou warne her love she shall go die anon, if thou have no pity on her. That signifieth the great bird, the which shall make thee to warne her. Now for no fear that thou hast, nor for no dread that thou hast of God, thou shalt not warne her, but thou wouldst not do it for to be holden chaste, for to conquer the loos of the vain glory of the world; for that shall befall thee now an thou warne her, that Launcelot, the good knight, thy cousin, shall die. And therefore men shall now say that thou art a manslayer, both of thy brother, Sir Lionel, and of thy cousin, Sir Launcelot du Lake, the which thou mightest have saved and rescued easily, but thou weenest to rescue a maid which pertaineth nothing to thee. Now look thou whether it had been greater harm of thy brother's death, or else to have suffered her to have lost her maidenhood. Then asked he him: Hast thou heard the tokens of thy dream the which I have told to you? Yea forsooth, said Sir Bors, all your exposition and declaring of my dream I have well understood and heard. Then said the man in this black clothing: Then is it in thy default if Sir Launcelot, thy cousin, die. Sir, said Bors, that were me loth, for wit ye well there is nothing in the world but I had lever do it than to see my lord Sir Launcelot du Lake, to die in my default. Choose ye now the one or the other, said the good man. And then he led Sir Bors into an high tower, and there he found knights and ladies: those ladies said he was welcome, and so they unarmed him. And when he was in his doublet men brought him a mantle furred with ermine, and put it about him; and then they made him such cheer that he had forgotten all his sorrow and anguish, and only set his heart in these delights and dainties, and took no thought more for his brother, Sir Lionel, neither of Sir Launcelot du Lake, his cousin. And anon came out of a chamber to him the fairest lady that ever he saw, and more richer bysene than ever he saw Queen Guenever or any other estate. Lo, said they, Sir Bors, here is the lady unto whom we owe all our service, and I trow she be the richest lady and the fairest of all the world, and the which loveth you best above all other knights, for she will have no knight but you. And when he understood that language he was abashed. Not for then she saluted him, and he her; and then they sat down together and spake of many things, in so much that she besought him to be her love, for she had loved him above all earthly men, and she should make him richer than ever was man of his age. When Bors understood her words he was right evil at ease, which in no manner would not break chasity, so wist not he how to answer her.

CHAPTER XII

HOW A DEVIL IN WOMAN'S LIKENESS WOULD HAVE TEMPTED SIR BORS, AND HOW BY GOD'S GRACE HE ESCAPED

ALAS, said she, Bors, shall ye not do my will? Madam, said Bors, there is no lady in the world whose will I will fulfill as of this thing, for my brother lieth dead which was slain right late. Ah Bors, said she, I have loved you long for the great beauty I have seen in you, and the great hardiness that I have heard of you, that needs ye must lie by me this night, and therefore I pray you grant it me. Truly, said he, I shall not do it in no manner wise. Then she made him such sorrow as though she would have died. Well Bors, said she, unto this have ye brought me, nigh to mine end. And therewith she took him by the hand, and bad him behold her. And ye shall see how I shall die for your love. Ah, said then he, that shall I never see. Then she departed and went up into an high battlement, and led with her twelve gentlewomen; and when they were above, one of the gentlewomen cried, and said: Ah, Sir Bors, gentle knight have mercy on us all, and suffer my lady to have her will, and if ye do not we must suffer death with our lady, for to fall down off this high tower, and if ye suffer us thus to die for so little a thing all ladies and gentlewomen will say of you dishonour. Then looked he upward, they seemed all ladies of great estate, and richly and well bisene. Then had he of them great pity; not for that he was uncounselled in himself that lever he had they all had lost their souls than he his, and with that they fell adown all at once unto the earth. And when he saw that, he was all abashed, and had thereof great marvel. With that he blessed his body and his visage. And anon he

heard a great noise and a great cry, as though all the fiends
of hell had been about him; and therewith he saw neither
tower nor lady, nor gentlewoman, nor no chapel where he
brought his brother to. Then held he up both his hands to
the heaven, and said: Fair Father God, I am grievously
escaped; and then he took his arms and his horse and rode
on his way. Then he heard a clock smite on his right
hand; and thither he came to an Abbey on his right hand,
closed with high walls, and there was let in. Then they
supposed that he was one of the quest of the Sangreal, so
they led him into a chamber and unarmed him. Sirs, said
Sir Bors, if there be any holy man in this house I pray you
let me speak with him. Then one of them led him unto
the Abbot, which was in a Chapel. And then Sir Bors
saluted him, and he him again. Sir, said Bors, I am a
knight errant; and told him all the adventure which he had
seen. Sir Knight, said the Abbot, I wot not what ye be, for
I weened never that a knight of your age might have been
so strong in the grace of our Lord Jesu Christ. Not for
then ye shall go unto your rest, for I will not counsel you
this day, it is too late, and to-morrow I shall counsel you as
I can.

CHAPTER XIII

OF THE HOLY COMMUNICATION OF AN ABBOT TO SIR BORS, AND HOW THE ABBOT COUNSELLED HIM

AND that night was Sir Bors served richly; and on the
morn early he heard mass, and the Abbot came to him, and
bad him good morrow, and Bors to him again. And then
he told him he was a fellow of the quest of the Sangreal,
and how he had charge of the holy man to eat bread and
water. Then said the Abbot: Our Lord Jesu Christ showed
him unto you in the likeness of a soul that suffered great
anguish for us, syne He was put upon the cross, and bled
His heart blood for mankind: there was the token and the
likeness of the Sangreal that appeared afore you, for the
blood that the great fowl bled revived the chickens from
death to life. And by the bare tree is betokened the world

which is naked and without fruit but if it come to Our Lord. Also the lady for whom ye fought for, and King Aniause which was lord there tofore, betokeneth Jesu Christ which is the King of the world. And that ye fought with the champion for the lady, this it betokeneth: for when ye took the battle for the lady, by her shall ye understand the new law of Jesu Christ and Holy Church; and by the other lady ye shall understand the old law and the fiend, which all day warreth against Holy Church, therefore ye did your battle with right. For ye be Jesu Christ's knights, therefore ye ought to be defenders of Holy Church. And by the black bird might ye understand Holy Church, which sayeth I am black, but he is fair. And by the white bird might men understand the fiend, and I shall tell you how the swan is white without forth, and black within: it is hypocrisy which is without yellow or pale, and seemeth without forth the servants of Jesu Christ, but they be within so horrible of filth and sin, and beguile the world evil. Also when the fiend appeared to thee in likeness of a man of religion, and blamed thee that thou left thy brother for a lady, so led thee where thou seemed thy brother was slain, but he is yet on live; and all was for to put thee in error, and bring thee unto wanhope and lechery, for he knew thou were tender hearted, and all was for thou shouldst not find the blessed adventure of the Sangreal. And the third fowl betokeneth the strong battle against the fair ladies which were all devils. Also the dry tree and the white lily: the dry tree betokeneth thy brother Lionel, which is dry without virtue, and therefore many men ought to call him the rotten tree, and the wormeaten tree, for he is a murderer and doth contrary to the order of knighthood. And the two white flowers signify two maidens, the one is a knight which was wounded the other day, and the other is the gentlewoman which ye rescued; and why the other flower drew nigh the other, that was the knight which would have befouled her and himself both. And Sir Bors, ye had been a great fool and in great peril for to have seen those two flowers perish for to succour the rotten tree, for and they had sinned together they had been damned; and for that ye rescued them both, men might call you a very knight and servant of Jesu Christ.

CHAPTER XIV

HOW SIR BORS MET WITH HIS BROTHER SIR LIONEL, AND HOW SIR LIONEL WOULD HAVE SLAIN SIR BORS

THEN went Sir Bors from thence and commended the abbot unto God. And then he rode all that day, and harboured with an old lady. And on the morn he rode to a castle in a valley, and there he met with a yeoman going a great pace toward a forest. Say me, said Sir Bors, canst thou tell me of any adventure? Sir, said he, here shall be under this castle a great and a marvellous tournament. Of what folks shall it be? said Sir Bors. The Earl of Plains shall be in the one party, and the lady's nephew of Hervin on the other party. Then Bors thought to be there if he might meet with his brother Sir Lionel, or any other of his fellowship, which were in the quest of the Sangreal. And then he turned to an hermitage that was in the entry of the forest. And when he was come thither he found there Sir Lionel, his brother, which sat all armed at the entry of the chapel door for to abide there harbour till on the morn that the tournament shall be. And when Sir Bors saw him he had great joy of him, that it were marvel to tell of his joy. And then he alit off his horse, and said: Fair sweet brother, when came ye hither? Anon as Lionel saw him he said: Ah Bors, ye may not make none avaunt, but as for you I might have been slain; when ye saw two knights leading me away beating me, ye left me for to succour a gentlewoman, and suffered me in peril of death; for never erst ne did no brother to another so great an untruth. And for that misdeed now I ensure you but death, for well have ye deserved it; therefore keep thee from henceforward, and that shall ye find as soon as I am armed. When Sir Bors understood his brother's wrath he kneeled down to the earth and cried him mercy, holding up both his hands, and prayed him to forgive him his evil will. Nay, said Lionel, that shall never be an I may have the higher hand, that I make mine avow to God, thou shalt have death for it, for it were pity ye lived any longer. Right so he went in and took his harness, and

mounted upon his horse, and came tofore him and said:
Bors, keep thee from me, for I shall do to thee as I would
to a felon or a traitor, for ye be the untruest knight that
ever came out of so worthy an house as was King Bors' de
Ganis which was our father, therefore start upon thy horse,
and so shall ye be most at your advantage. And but if ye
will I will run upon you there as ye stand upon foot, and
so the shame shall be mine and the harm yours, but of that
shame ne reck I nought. When Sir Bors saw that he must
fight with his brother or else to die, he nist what to do; then
his heart counselled him not thereto, inasmuch as Lionel was
born or he, wherefore he ought to bear him reverence; yet
kneeled he down afore Lionel's horse's feet, and said: Fair
sweet brother, have mercy upon me and slay me not, and
have in remembrance the great love which ought to be between us twain. What Sir Bors said to Lionel he recked not,
for the fiend had brought him in such a will that he should
slay him. Then when Lionel saw he would none other, and
that he would not have risen to give him battle, he rushed
over him so that he smote Bors with his horse, feet upward
to the earth, and hurt him so sore that he swooned of distress,
the which he felt in himself to have died without confession.
So when Lionel saw this, he alit off his horse to have smitten
off his head. And so he took him by the helm, and would
have rent it from his head. Then came the hermit running
unto him, which was a good man and of great age, and well
had heard all the words that were between them, and so fell
down upon Sir Bors.

CHAPTER XV

HOW SIR COLGREVANCE FOUGHT AGAINST SIR LIONEL FOR TO SAVE SIR BORS, AND HOW THE HERMIT WAS SLAIN

THEN he said to Lionel: Ah gentle knight, have mercy
upon me and on thy brother, for if thou slay him thou shalt
be dead of sin, and that were sorrowful, for he is one of the
worthiest knights of the world, and of the best conditions.
So God help me, said Lionel, sir priest, but if ye flee from
him I shall slay you, and he shall never the sooner be quit.

Certes, said the good man, I have lever ye slay me than him, for my death shall not be great harm, not half so much as of his. Well, said Lionel, I am agreed; and set his hand to his sword and smote him so hard that his head yede backward. Not for that he restrained him of his evil will, but took his brother by the helm, and unlaced it to have stricken off his head, and had slain him without fail. But so it happed, Colgrevance, a fellow of the Round Table, came at that time thither as Our Lord's will was. And when he saw the good man slain he marvelled much what it might be. And then he beheld Lionel would have slain his brother, and knew Sir Bors which he loved right well. Then start he down and took Lionel by the shoulders, and drew him strongly aback from Bors, and said: Lionel, will ye slay your brother, the worthiest knight of the world one? and that should no good man suffer. Why, said Lionel, will ye let me? therefore if ye intermit you in this I shall slay you, and him after. Why, said Colgrevance, is this sooth that ye will slay him? Slay him will I, said he, whoso say the contrary, for he hath done so much against me that he hath well deserved it. And so ran upon him, and would have smitten him through the head, and Sir Colgrevance ran betwixt them, and said: An ye be so hardy to do so more, we two shall meddle together. When Lionel understood his words he took his shield afore him, and asked him what that he was. And he told him, Colgrevance, one of his fellows. Then Lionel defied him, and gave him a great stroke through the helm. Then he drew his sword, for he was a passing good knight, and defended him right manfully. So long dured the battle that Bors rose up all anguishly, and beheld Colgrevance, the good knight, fought with his brother for his quarrel; then was he full sorry and heavy, and thought if Colgrevance slay him that was his brother he should never have joy; and if his brother slew Colgrevance the shame should ever be mine. Then would he have risen to have departed them, but he had not so much might to stand on foot; so he abode him so long till Colgrevance had the worse, for Lionel was of great chivalry and right hardy, for he had pierced the hauberk and the helm, that he abode but death, for he had lost much of his blood that it was

marvel that he might stand upright. Then beheld he Sir
Bors which sat dressing him upward and said: Ah, Bors,
why come ye not to cast me out of peril of death, wherein I
have put me to succour you which were right now nigh the
death? Certes, said Lionel, that shall not avail you, for
none of you shall bear others warrant, but that ye shall die
both of my hand. When Bors heard that, he did so much,
he rose and put on his helm. Then perceived he first the
hermit priest which was slain, then made he a marvellous
sorrow upon him.

CHAPTER XVI

HOW SIR LIONEL SLEW SIR COLGREVANCE, AND HOW
AFTER HE WOULD HAVE SLAIN SIR BORS

Then often Colgrevance cried upon Sir Bors: Why will
ye let me die here for your sake? if it please you that I die
for you the death, it will please me the better for to save a
worthy man. With that word Sir Lionel smote off the
helm from his head. Then Colgrevance saw that he might
not escape; then he said: Fair sweet Jesu, that I have
misdone have mercy upon my soul, for such sorrow that
my heart suffereth for goodness, and for alms deed that I
would have done here, be to me alygement of penance
unto my soul's health. At these words Lionel smote him
so sore that he bare him to the earth. So he had slain
Colgrevance he ran upon his brother as a fiendly man, and
gave him such a stroke that he made him stoop. And he
that was full of humility prayed him for God's love to leave
this battle: For an it befel, fair brother, that I slew you or
ye me, we should be dead of that sin. Never God me
help but if I have on you mercy, and I may have the better
hand. Then drew Bors his sword, all weeping, and said:
Fair brother, God knoweth mine intent. Ah, fair brother,
ye have done full evil this day to slay such an holy priest
the which never trespassed. Also ye have slain a gentle
knight, and one of our fellows. And well wot ye that I
am not afeared of you greatly, but I dread the wrath of
God, and this is an unkindly war, therefore God show miracle

upon us both. Now God have mercy upon me though I
defend my life against my brother; with that Bors lift up his
hand and would have smitten his brother.

CHAPTER XVII

HOW THERE CAME A VOICE WHICH CHARGED SIR BORS TO TOUCH HIM NOT, AND OF A CLOUD THAT CAME BETWEEN THEM

'AND then he heard a voice that said: Flee Bors, and
touch him not, or else thou shall slay him. Right so alit a
cloud betwixt them in likeness of a fire and a marvellous
flame, that both their two shields burnt. Then were they
sore afraid, that they fell both to the earth, and lay there a
great while in a swoon. And when they came to themself,
Bors saw that his brother had no harm; then he held up
both his hands, for he dread God had taken vengeance upon
him. With that he heard a voice say: Bors, go hence, and
bear thy brother no longer fellowship, but take thy way
anon right to the sea, for Sir Percivale abideth thee there.
Then he said to his brother: Fair sweet brother, forgive
me for God's love all that I have trespassed unto you.
Then he answered: God forgive it thee and I do gladly.
So Sir Bors departed from him and rode the next way to
the sea. And at the last by fortune he came to an Abbey
which was nigh the sea. That night Bors rested him there;
and in his sleep there came a voice to him and bad him go
to the sea. Then he start up and made a sign of the Cross
in the middes of his forehead, and took his harness, and
made ready his horse, and mounted upon him; and at a
broken wall he rode out, and rode so long till that he came
to the sea. And on the strand he found a ship covered all
with white samite, and he alit, and betook him to Jesu
Christ. And as soon as he entered into the ship, the ship
departed into the sea, and went so fast that him seemed
the ship went flying, but it was soon dark so that he might
know no man, and so he slept till it was day. Then he
awaked, and saw in middes of the ship a knight lie all armed

save his helm. Then knew he that it was Sir Percivale of Wales, and then he made of him right great joy; but Sir Percivale was abashed of him, and he asked him what he was. Ah, fair sir, said Bors, know ye me not? Certes, said he, I marvel how ye came hither, but if Our Lord brought ye hither Himself. Then Sir Bors smiled and did off his helm. Then Percivale knew him, and either made great joy of other, that it was marvel to hear. Then Bors told him how he came into the ship, and by whose admonishment; and either told other of their temptations, as ye have heard toforehand. So went they downward in the sea, one while backward, another while forward, and every each comforted other, and oft were in their prayers. Then said Sir Percivale: We lack nothing but Galahad, the good knight.

And thus endeth the syxteenth book, whiche is of syre Gawayne, Ector de marys, and syre Bors de ganys, and sir Percyval. And here foloweth the sevententh book, whiche is of the noble Knyghte syre Galahad.

THE SEVENTEENTH BOOK

CHAPTER I

HOW SIR GALAHAD FOUGHT AT A TOURNAMENT, AND HOW HE WAS KNOWN OF SIR GAWAINE AND SIR ECTOR DE MARIS

NOW saith this story, when Galahad had rescued Percivale from the twenty knights, he yede then into a waste forest wherein he rode many journeys; and he found many adventures the which he brought to an end, whereof the story maketh here no mention. Then he took his way to the sea on a day, and it befel as he passed by a castle where was a wonder tournament, but they without had

done so much that they within were put to the worse, yet
were they within good knights enough. When Galahad
saw that those within were at so great a mischief that men
slew them at the entry of the castle, then he thought to
help them, and put a spear forth and smote the first that
he fell to the earth, and the spear brake to pieces. Then
he drew his sword and smote there as they were thickest,
and so he did wonderful deeds of arms that all they marvelled.
Then it happed that Gawaine and Sir Ector de Maris were
with the knights without. But when they espied the white
shield with the red cross the one said to the other: Yonder
is the good knight, Sir Galahad, the haut prince: now he
should be a great fool which should meet with him to fight.
So by adventure he came by Sir Gawaine, and he smote
him so hard that he clave his helm and the coiffe of iron
unto his head, so that Gawaine fell to the earth; but the
stroke was so great that it slanted down to the earth and
carved the horse's shoulder in two. When Ector saw
Gawaine down he drew him aside, and thought it no
wisdom for to abide him, and also for natural love, that he
was his uncle. Thus through his great hardiness he beat
aback all the knights without. And then they within came
out and chased them all about. But when Galahad saw
there would none turn again he stole away privily so that
none wist where he was become. Now by my head, said
Gawaine to Ector, now are the wonders true that were said
of Launcelot du Lake, that the sword which stuck in the
stone should give me such a buffet that I would not have
it for the best castle in this world; and soothly now it is
proved true, for never ere had I such a stroke of man's
hand. Sir, said Ector, meseemeth your quest is done.
And yours is not done, said Gawaine, but mine is done, I
shall seek no further. Then Gawaine was borne into a castle
and unarmed him, and laid him in a rich bed, and a leech
found that he might live, and to be whole within a month.
Thus Gawaine and Ector abode together, for Sir Ector
would not away till Gawaine were whole. And the good
knight, Galahad, rode so long till he came that night to
the Castle of Carboneck; and it befel him thus that he
was benighted in an hermitage. So the good man was fain

when he saw he was a knight errant. Then when they were at rest there came a gentlewoman knocking at the door, and called Galahad, and so the good man came to the door to wit what she would. Then she called the hermit: Sir Ulfin, I am a gentlewoman that would speak with the knight which is with you. Then the good man awaked Galahad, and bad him: Arise, and speak with a gentlewoman that seemeth hath great need of you. Then Galahad went to her and asked her what she would. Galahad, said she, I will that ye arm you, and mount upon your horse and follow me, for I shall show you within these three days the highest adventure that ever any knight saw. Anon Galahad armed him, and took his horse, and commended him to God, and bad the gentlewoman go, and he would follow there as she liked.

CHAPTER II

HOW SIR GALAHAD RODE WITH A DAMOSEL, AND CAME TO THE SHIP WHEREAS SIR BORS AND SIR PERCIVALE WERE IN

So she rode as fast as her palfrey might bear her, till that she came to the sea, the which was called Collibe. And at the night they came unto a castle in a valley, closed with a running water, and with strong walls and high; and so she entered into the castle with Galahad, and there had he great cheer, for the lady of that castle was the damosel's lady. So when he was unarmed, then said the damosel: Madam, shall we abide here all this day? Nay, said she, but till he hath dined and till he hath slept a little. So he ate and slept a while till that the maid called him, and armed him by torchlight. And when the maid was horsed and he both, the lady took Galahad a fair child and rich; and so they departed from the castle till they came to the seaside; and there they found the ship where Bors and Percivale were in, the which cried on the ship's board: Sir Galahad, ye be welcome, we have abiden you long. And when he heard them he asked them what they were. Sir, said she, leave your horse here, and I shall leave mine;

and took their saddles and their bridles with them, and
made a cross on them, and so entered into the ship. And
the two knights received them both with great joy, and
every each knew other; and so the wind arose, and drove
them through the sea in a marvellous place. And within a
while it dawned. Then did Galahad off his helm and his
sword, and asked of his fellows from whence came that fair
ship. Truly, said they, ye wot as well as we but of God's
grace; and then they told every each to other of all their
hard adventures, and of their great temptations. Truly,
said Galahad, ye are much bounden to God, for ye have
escaped great adventures; and had not the gentlewoman
been I had not come here, for as for you I weened never
to have found you in these strange countries. Ah Galahad,
said Bors, if Launcelot, your father, were here then were we
well at ease, for then meseemed we failed nothing. That
may not be, said Galahad, but if it pleased Our Lord. By
then the ship went from the land of Logris, and by
adventure it arrived up betwixt two rocks passing great and
marvellous; but there they might not land, for there was a
swallow of the sea, save there was another ship, and upon
it they might go without danger. Go we thither, said the
gentlewoman, and there shall we see adventures, for so is
Our Lord's will. And when they came thither they found
the ship rich enough, but they found neither man nor
woman therein. But they found in the end of the ship
two fair letters written, which said a dreadful word and a
marvellous: Thou man, which shall enter into this ship,
beware thou be in steadfast belief, for I am Faith, and
therefore beware how thou enterest, for an thou fail I
shall not help thee. Then said the gentlewoman: Percivale,
wot ye what I am? Certes, said he, nay, to my witing.
Wit ye well, said she, that I am thy sister, which am
daughter of King Pellinore, and therefore wit ye well ye
are the man in the world that I most love; and if ye
be not in perfect belief of Jesu Christ enter not in no
manner of wise, for then should ye perish the ship, for he
is so perfect he will suffer no sinner in him. When
Percivale understood that she was his very sister he was
inwardly glad, and said: Fair sister, I shall enter there-

in, for if I be a miscreature or an untrue knight there shall I perish.

CHAPTER III

HOW SIR GALAHAD ENTERED INTO THE SHIP, AND OF A FAIR BED THEREIN, WITH OTHER MARVELLOUS THINGS, AND OF A SWORD

IN the meanwhile Galahad blessed him, and entered therein; and then next the gentlewoman, and then Sir Bors and Sir Percivale. And when they were in, it was so marvellous fair and rich that they marvelled; and in middes of the ship was a fair bed, and Galahad went thereto, and found there a crown of silk. And at the feet was a sword, rich and fair, and it was drawn out of the sheath half a foot and more; and the sword was of divers fashions, and the pommel was of stone, and there was in him all manner of colours that any man might find, and every each of the colours had divers virtues; and the scales of the haft were of two ribs of divers beasts, the one beast was a serpent which was conversant in Calidone, and is called the serpent of the fiend; and the bone of him is of such a virtue that there is no hand that handleth him shall never be weary nor hurt. And the other beast is a fish which is not right great, and haunteth the flood of Euphrates; and that fish is called Ertanax, and his bones be of such a manner of kind that who that handleth them shall have so much will that he shall never be weary, and he shall not think on joy nor sorrow that he hath had, but only that thing that he beholdeth before him. And as for this sword there shall never man begrip him at the handles but one, but he shall pass all other. In the name of God, said Percivale, I shall essay to handle it. So he set his hand to the sword, but he might not begrip it. By my faith, said he, now have I failed. Bors set his hand thereto and failed. Then Galahad beheld the sword and saw letters like blood that said: Let see who shall essay to draw me out of my sheath, but if he be more hardier than any other; and who that draweth me, wit ye well he shall never fail of shame of his body, or to be wounded to the death. By my faith, said Galahad, I would draw this sword out of the sheath, but the offending is so great that I shall not set my hand thereto. Now sirs, said the gentlewoman, wit ye well that the drawing of this sword is warned to all men save all only to you. Also this ship arrived in the realm of Logris; and that time was deadly war between King Labor, which was father unto the maimed king, and King Hurlame, which was a Saracen. But then was he newly christened, so that men held him afterward one of the wyttyest men of the world. And so upon a day it befel that King Labor and King Hurlame had assembled their folk upon the sea where this ship was arrived; and there King Hurlame was discomfit, and his men slain; and he was afeard to be dead, and fled to his ship, and there found this sword and drew it, and came out and found King Labor, the man in the world of all Christendom in whom was then the greatest faith. And when King Hurlame saw King Labor he dressed this sword, and smote him upon the helm so hard that he clave him and his horse to the earth with the first stroke of his sword. And it was in the realm of Logris; and so befel great pestilence and great harm to both realms. For sithen increased neither corn, nor grass, nor well-nigh no fruit, nor in the water was no fish; wherefore men call it the lands of the two marches, the waste land, for that dolorous stroke. And when King Hurlame saw this sword so carving, he turned again to fetch the scabbard, and so came into this ship and entered, and put up the sword in the sheath. And as soon as he had done it he fell down dead afore the bed. Thus was the sword proved, that none ne drew it but he were dead or maimed. So lay he there till a maiden came into the ship and cast him out, for there was no man so hardy of the world to enter into that ship for the defence.

CHAPTER IV

OF THE MARVELS OF THE SWORD AND OF THE SCABBARD

AND then beheld they the scabbard, it seemed to be of a serpent's skin, and thereon were letters of gold and silver. And the girdle was but poorly to come to, and not able to sustain such a rich sword. And the letters said: He which shall wield me ought to be more harder than any other, if he bear me as truly as me ought to be borne. For the body of him which I ought to hang by, he shall not be shamed in no place while he is girt with this girdle, nor never none be so hardy to do away this girdle; for it ought not to be done away but by the hands of a maid, and that she be a king's daughter and queen's, and she must be a maid all the days of her life, both in will and in deed. And if she break her virginity she shall die the most villainous death that ever died any woman. Sir, said Percivale, turn this sword that we may see what is on the other side. And it was red as blood, with black letters as any coal, which said: He that shall praise me most, most shall he find me to blame at a great need; and to whom I should be most debonair shall I be most felon, and that shall be at one time. Fair brother, said she to Percivale, it befell after a forty year after the passion of Jesu Christ that Nacien, the brother-in-law of King Mordrains, was borne into a town more than fourteen days' journey from his country, by the commandment of Our Lord, into an isle, into the parts of the West, that men clepyd the isle of Turnance. So befell it that he found this ship at the entry of a rock, and he found the bed and this sword as we have heard now. Not for then he had not so much hardiness to draw it; and there he dwelled an eight days, and at the ninth day there fell a great wind which departed him out of the isle, and brought him to another isle by a rock, and there he found the greatest giant that ever man might see. Therewith came that horrible giant to slay him; and then he looked about him and might not flee, and he had nothing to defend him with. So he ran to his sword, and when he saw it naked he praised it much, and then he shook it, and therewith he brake it in the middes. Ah, said Nacien, the thing that I most praised ought I now most to blame, and therewith he threw the pieces of his sword over his bed. And after he leapt over the board to fight with the giant, and slew him. And anon he entered into the ship again, and the wind arose, and drove him through the sea, that by adventure he came to another ship where King Mordrains was, which had been tempted full evil with a fiend in the port of perilous rock. And when that one saw the other they made great joy of other, and either told other of their adventure, and how the sword failed him at his most need. When Mordrains saw the sword he praised it much: But the breaking was not to do but by wickedness of thy self ward, for thou art in some sin. And there he took the sword, and set the pieces together, and they soldered as fair as ever they were tofore; and there put he the sword in the sheath, and laid it down on the bed. Then heard they a voice that said: Go out of this ship a little while, and enter into the other, for dread ye fall in deadly sin, for and ye be found in deadly sin ye may not escape but perish: and so they went into the other ship. And as Nacien went over the board he was smitten with a sword on the right foot, that he fell down noseling to the ship's board; and therewith he said: O God, how am I hurt. And then there came a voice and said: Take thou that for thy forfeit that thou didst in drawing of this sword, therefore thou receivest a wound, for thou were never worthy to handle it, as the writing maketh mention. In the name of God, said Galahad, ye are right wise of these works.

CHAPTER V

HOW KING PELLES WAS SMITTEN THROUGH BOTH THIGHS BECAUSE HE DREW THE SWORD, AND OTHER MARVELLOUS HISTORIES

SIR, said she, there was a king that hight Pelles, the maimed king. And while he might ride he supported much

Christendom and Holy Church. So upon a day he hunted
in a wood of his which lasted unto the sea; and at the last
he lost his hounds and his knights save only one: and there
he and his knight went till that they came toward Ireland,
and there he found the ship. And when he saw the letters
and understood them, yet he entered, for he was right
perfect of his life, but his knight had none hardiness to
enter; and there found he this sword, and he drew it out as
much as ye may see. So therewith entered a spear wherewith he was smitten him through both the thighs, and never
sith might he be healed, nor nought shall tofore we come to
him. Thus, said she, was not King Pelles, your grandsire,
maimed for his hardiness? In the name of God, damosel,
said Galahad. So they went toward the bed to behold all
about it, and above the head there hung two swords. Also
there were two spindles which were as white as any snow,
and other that were as red as blood, and other above green
as any emerald: of these three colours were the spindles,
and of natural colour within, and without any painting.
These spindles, said the damosel, were when sinful Eve
came to gather fruit, for which Adam and she were put out
of paradise, she took with her the bough on which the
apple hung on. Then perceived she that the branch was
fair and green, and she remembered her the loss which
came from the tree. Then she thought to keep the branch
as long as she might. And for she had no coffer to keep it
in, she put it in the earth. So by the will of Our Lord the
branch grew to a great tree within a little while, and was as
white as any snow, branches, boughs, and leaves: that was
a token a maiden planted it. But after God came to Adam,
and bad him know his wife fleshly as nature required. So
lay Adam with his wife under the same tree; and anon the
tree which was white was full green as any grass, and all
that came out of it; and in the same time that they medled
together there was Abel begotten: thus was the tree long
of green colour. And so it befell many days after, under
the same tree Cain slew Abel, whereof befel great marvel.
For anon as Abel had received the death under the green
tree, it lost the green colour and became red; and that was
in tokening of the blood. And anon all the plants died

thereof, but the tree grew and waxed marvellously fair, and it was the fairest tree and the most delectable that any man might behold and see; and so died the plants that grew out of it tofore that Abel was slain under it. So long dured the tree till that Solomon, King David's son, reigned, and held the land after his father. This Solomon was wise, and knew all the virtues of stones and trees, and so he knew the course of the stars, and many other divers things. This Solomon had an evil wife, wherethrough he weened that there had been no good women, and so he despised them in his books. So answered a voice him once: Solomon, if heaviness come to a man by a woman, ne reck thou never; for yet shall there come a woman whereof there shall come greater joy to man an hundred times more than this heaviness giveth sorrow; and that woman shall be born of thy lineage. Then when Solomon heard these words he held himself but a fool, and the truth he perceived by old books. Also the Holy Ghost showed him the coming of the glorious Virgin Mary. Then asked he of the voice, if it should be in the yerde of his lineage. Nay, said the voice, but there shall come a man which shall be a maid, and the last of your blood, and he shall be as good a knight as Duke Josua, thy brother-in-law.

CHAPTER VI

HOW SOLOMON TOOK DAVID'S SWORD BY THE COUNSEL OF HIS WIFE, AND OF OTHER MATTERS MARVELLOUS

Now have I certified thee of that thou stoodest in doubt. Then was Solomon glad that there should come any such of his lineage; but ever he marvelled and studied who that should be, and what his name might be. His wife perceived that he studied, and thought she would know it at some season; and so she waited her time, and asked of him the cause of his studying, and there he told her all together how the voice told him. Well, said she, I shall let make a ship of the best wood and most durable that men may find. So Solomon sent for all the carpenters of the land, and the best. And when they had made the ship the lady said to Solomon:

Sir, said she, syne it is so that this knight ought to pass all knights of chivalry which have been tofore him and shall come after him, moreover I shall tell you, said she, ye shall go into Our Lord's temple, where is King David's sword, your father, the which is the marvelloust and the sharpest that ever was taken in any knight's hand. Therefore take that, and take off the pommel, and thereto make ye a pommel of precious stones, that it be so subtilely made that no man perceive it but that they be all one; and after make there an hilt so marvellously and wonderly that no man may know it; and after make a marvellous sheath. And when ye have made all this I shall let make a girdle thereto such as shall please me. All this King Solomon did let make as she devised, both the ship and all the remnant. And when the ship was ready in the sea to sail, the lady let make a great bed and marvellous rich, and set her upon the bed's head, covered with silk, and laid the sword at the feet, and the girdles were of hemp, and therewith the king was angry. Sir, wit ye well, said she, that I have none so high a thing which were worthy to sustain so high a sword, and a maid shall bring other knights thereto, but I wot not when it shall be, nor what time. And there she let make a covering to the ship, of cloth of silk that should never rot for no manner of weather. Yet went that lady and made a carpenter to come to the tree which Abel was slain under. Now, said she, carve me out of this tree as much wood as will make me a spindle. Ah madam, said he, this is the tree the which our first mother planted. Do it, said she, or else I shall destroy thee. Anon as he began to work there came out drops of blood: and then would he have left, but she would not suffer him, and so he took away as much wood as might make a spindle: and so she made him to take as much of the green tree and of the white tree. And when these three spindles were shapen she made them to be fastened upon the selar of the bed. When Solomon saw this, he said to his wife: Ye have done marvellously, for though all the world were here right now, he could not devise wherefore all this was made, but Our Lord Himself; and thou that hast done it wotest not what it shall betoken. Now let it be, said she, for ye shall hear tidings sooner than

ye ween. Now shall ye hear a wonderful tale of King
Solomon and his wife.

CHAPTER VII

A WONDERFUL TALE OF KING SOLOMON AND HIS WIFE

THAT night lay Solomon before the ship with little fellowship. And when he was on sleep him thought there come
from heaven a great company of angels, and alit into the
ship, and took water which was brought by an angel, in a
vessel of silver, and sprente all the ship. And after he came
to the sword, and drew letters on the hilt. And after went
to the ship's board, and wrote there other letters which
said: Thou man that wilt enter within me, beware that thou
be full within the faith, for I ne am but Faith and Belief.
When Solomon espied these letters he was abashed, so that
he durst not enter, and so drew him aback; and the ship
was anon shoven in the sea, and he went so fast that he
lost sight of him within a little while. And then a little
voice said: Solomon, the last knight of thy lineage shall
rest in this bed. Then went Solomon and awaked his wife,
and told her of the adventures of the ship. Now saith the
history that a great while the three fellows beheld the bed
and the three spindles. Then they were at certain that
they were of natural colours without painting. Then they
lift up a cloth which was above the ground, and there found
a rich purse by seeming. And Percivale took it, and found
therein a writ and so he read it, and devised the manner of
the spindles and of the ship, whence it came, and by whom
it was made. Now, said Galahad, where shall we find the
gentlewoman that shall make new girdles to the sword?
Fair sir, said Percivale's sister, dismay you not, for by the
leave of God I shall let make a girdle to the sword, such
one as shall long thereto. And then she opened a box, and
took out girdles which were seemly wrought with golden
threads, and upon that were set full precious stones, and a
rich buckle of gold. Lo, lords, said she, here is a girdle
that ought to be set about the sword. And wit ye well the
greatest part of his girdle was made of my hair, which I

loved well while that I was a woman of the world. But as soon as I wist that this adventure was ordained me I clipped off my hair, and made this girdle in the name of God. Ye be well found, said Sir Bors, for certes ye have put us out of great pain, wherein we should have entered ne had your tidings been. Then went the gentlewoman and set it on the girdle of the sword. Now, said the fellowship, what is the name of the sword, and what shall we call it? Truly, said she, the name of the sword is the Sword with the strange girdles; and the sheath, mover of blood; for no man that hath blood in him ne shall never see the one part of the sheath which was made of the tree of life. Then they said to Galahad: In the name of Jesu Christ, and pray you that ye gird you with this sword which hath been desired so much in the realm of Logris. Now let me begin, said Galahad, to grip this sword for to give you courage; but wit ye well it longeth no more to me than it doth to you. And then he gripped about it with his fingers a great deal; and then she girt him about the middle with the sword. Now reck I not though I die, for now I hold me one of the blessed maidens of the world, which hath made the worthiest knight of the world. Damosel, said Galahad, ye have done so much that I shall be your knight all the days of my life. Then they went from that ship, and went to the other. And anon the wind drove them into the sea a great pace, but they had no victuals: but it befell that they came on the morn to a castle that men call Carteloise, that was in the marches of Scotland. And when they had passed the port, the gentlewoman said: Lords, here be men arriven that, an they wist that ye were of King Arthur's court, ye should be assailed anon. Damosel, said Galahad, He that cast us out of the rock shall deliver us from them.

CHAPTER VIII

HOW GALAHAD AND HIS FELLOWS CAME TO A CASTLE,
AND HOW THEY WERE FOUGHT WITHAL, AND
HOW THEY SLEW THEIR ADVERSARIES,
AND OTHER MATTERS

So it befell as they spoke thus there came a squire by them, and asked what they were; and they said they were of King Arthur's house. Is that sooth? said he. Now by my head, said he, ye be ill arrayed; and then turned he again unto the cliff fortress. And within a while they heard an horn blow. Then a gentlewoman came to them, and asked them of whence they were; and they told her. Fair lords, said she, for God's love turn again if ye may, for ye be come unto your death. Nay, they said, we will not turn again, for He shall help us in whose service we be entered in. Then as they stood talking there came knights well armed, and bad them yield them or else die. That yielding, said they, shall be noyous to you. And therewith they let their horses run, and Sir Percivale smote the foremost to the earth, and took his horse, and mounted thereupon, and the same did Galahad. Also Bors served another so, for they had no horses in that country, for they left their horses when they took their ship in other countries. And so when they were horsed then began they to set upon them; and they of the castle fled into the strong fortress, and the three knights after them into the castle, and so alit on foot, and with their swords slew them down, and gat into the hall. Then when they beheld the great multitude of people that they had slain, they held themself great sinners. Certes, said Bors, I ween an God had loved them that we should not have had power to have slain them thus. But they have done so much against Our Lord that He would not suffer them to reign no longer. Say ye not so, said Galahad, for if they misdid against God, the vengeance is not ours, but to Him which hath power thereof. So came there out of a chamber a good man which was a priest, and bare God's body in a cup. And when he saw them which lay dead in the hall he was all abashed; and

Galahad did off his helm and kneeled down, and so did his two fellows. Sir, said they, have ye no dread of us, for we be of King Arthur's court. Then asked the good man how they were slain so suddenly, and they told it him. Truly, said the good man, an ye might live as long as the world might endure, ne might ye have done so great an alms deed at this. Sir, said Galahad, I repent me much, inasmuch as they were christened. Nay, repent you not, said he, for they were not christened, and I shall tell you how that I wot of this castle. Here was Lord Earl Hernox not but one year, and he had three sons, good knights of arms, and a daughter, the fairest gentlewoman that men knew. So those three knights loved their sister so sore that they brent in love, and so they lay by her, maugre her head. And for she cried to her father they slew her, and took their father and put him in prison, and wounded him nigh to death, but a cousin of hers rescued him. And then did they great untruth: they slew clerks and priests, and made beat down chapels, that Our Lord's service might not be served nor said. And this same day her father sent to me for to be confessed and houseld; but such shame had never man as I had this day with the three brethren, but the earl bad me suffer, for he said they should not long endure, for three servants of Our Lord should destroy them, and now it is brought to an end. And by this may ye wit that Our Lord is not displeased with your deeds. Certes, said Galahad, an it had not pleased Our Lord, never should we have slain so many men in so little a while. And then they brought the Earl Hernox out of prison into the middes of the hall, that knew Galahad anon, and yet he saw him never afore but by revelation of Our Lord.

CHAPTER IX

HOW THE THREE KNIGHTS, WITH PERCIVALE'S SISTER,
CAME UNTO THE SAME FOREST, AND OF AN
HART AND FOUR LIONS, AND
OTHER THINGS

THEN began he to weep right tenderly, and said: Long
have I abiden your coming, but for God's love hold me in
your arms, that my soul may depart out of my body in so
good a man's arms as ye be. Gladly, said Galahad. And
then one said on high, that all heard: Galahad, well hast
thou avenged me on God's enemies. Now behoveth thee
to go to the maimed king as soon as thou mayest, for he
shall receive by thee health which he hath abiden so long.
And therewith the soul departed from the body, and Galahad
made him to be buried as him ought to be. Right so departed the three knights, and Percivale's sister with them.
And so they came into a waste forest, and there they saw
afore them a white hart which four lions led. Then they
took them to assent for to follow after for to know whither
they repaired; and so they rode after a great pace till that
they came to a valley, and thereby was an hermitage where a
good man dwelled, and the hart and the lions entered also.
So when they saw all this they turned to the chapel, and saw
the good man in a religious weed and in the armour of Our
Lord, for he would sing mass of the Holy Ghost; and so
they entered in and heard mass. And at the secrets of the
mass they three saw the hart become a man, the which
marvelled them, and set him upon the altar in a rich siege;
and saw the four lions were changed, the one to the form of
a man, the other to the form of a lion, and the third to an
eagle, and the fourth was changed unto an ox. Then took
they their siege where the hart sat, and went out through a
glass window, and there was nothing perished nor broken;
and they heard a voice say: In such a manner entered the
Son of God in the womb of a maid Mary, whose virginity ne
was perished ne hurt. And when they heard these words they
fell down to the earth and were astonied; and therewith was

a great clereness. And when they were come to theirself
again they went to the good man and prayed him that he
would say them truth. What thing have ye seen? said he.
And they told him all that they had seen. Ah lords, said he,
ye be welcome; now wot I well ye be the good knights the
which shall bring the Sangreal to an end; for ye be they
unto whom Our Lord shall shew great secrets. And well
ought Our Lord be signified to an hart, for the hart when
he is old he waxeth young again in his white skin. Right
so cometh again Our Lord from death to life, for He lost
earthly flesh that was the deadly flesh, which He had taken
in the womb of the blessed Virgin Mary; and for that cause
appeared Our Lord as a white hart without spot. And the
four that were with Him is to understand the four evangelists which set in writing a part of Jesu Christ's deeds that
He did sometime when He was among you an earthly man;
for wit ye well never erst ne might no knight know the
truth, for ofttimes or this Our Lord showed Him unto good
men and unto good knights, in likeness of an hart, but I
suppose from henceforth ye shall see no more. And then
they joyed much, and dwelled there all that day. And upon the
morrow when they had heard mass they departed and commended the good man to God: and so they came to a castle
and passed by. So there came a knight armed after them
and said: Lords, hark what I shall say to you.

CHAPTER X

HOW THEY WERE DESIRED OF A STRANGE CUSTOM, THE WHICH THEY WOULD NOT OBEY; AND HOW THEY FOUGHT AND SLEW MANY KNIGHTS

THIS gentlewoman that ye lead with you is a maid? Sir,
said she, a maid I am. Then he took her by the bridle and
said: By the Holy Cross, ye shall not escape me tofore ye
have yolden the custom of this castle. Let her go, said
Percivale, ye be not wise, for a maid in what place she
cometh is free. So in the meanwhile there came out a ten
or twelve knights armed, out of the castle, and with them

came gentlewomen which held a dish of silver. And then they said: This gentlewoman must yield us the custom of this castle. Sir, said a knight, what maid passeth hereby shall give this dish full of blood of her right arm. Blame have ye, said Galahad, that brought up such customs, and so God me save, I ensure you of this gentlewoman ye shall fail while that I live. So God me help, said Percivale, I had lever be slain. And I also, said Sir Bors. By my troth, said the knight, then shall ye die, for ye may not endure against us though ye were the best knights of the world. Then let them run each to other, and the three fellows beat the ten knights, and then set their hands to their swords and beat them down and slew them. Then there came out of the castle a three score knights armed. Fair lords, said the three fellows, have mercy on yourself and have not ado with us. Nay, fair lords, said the knights of the castle, we counsel you to withdraw you, for ye be the best knights of the world, and therefore do no more, for ye have done enough. We will let you go with this harm, but we must needs have the custom. Certes, said Galahad, for nought speak ye. Well, said they, will ye die? We be not yet come thereto, said Galahad. Then began they to meddle together, and Galahad, with the strange girdles, drew his sword, and smote on the right hand and on the left hand, and slew what that ever abode him, and did such marvels that there was none that saw him but weened he had been none earthly man, but a monster. And his two fellows halp him passing well, and so they held the journey every each in like hard till it was night; then must they needs depart. So came in a good knight, and said to the three fellows: If ye will come in to-night and take such harbour as here is ye shall be right welcome, and we shall ensure you by the faith of our bodies, and as we be true knights, to leave you in such estate to-morrow as we find you, without any falsehood. And as soon as ye know of the custom we dare say ye will accord. Therefore for God's love, said the gentlewoman, go thither and spare not for me. Go we, said Galahad; and so they entered into the chapel. And when they were alit they made great joy of them. So within a while the three knights asked the custom of the castle and wherefore it was. What it is, said they, we will say you sooth.

CHAPTER XI

HOW SIR PERCIVALE'S SISTER BLED A DISH FULL OF BLOOD FOR TO HEAL A LADY, WHEREFORE SHE DIED; AND HOW THAT THE BODY WAS PUT IN A SHIP

THERE is in this castle a gentlewoman which we and this castle is hers, and many other. So it befell many years agone there fell upon her a malady; and when she had lain a great while she fell unto a measle, and of no leech she could have no remedy. But at the last an old man said an she might have a dish full of blood of a maid and a clene virgin in will and in work, and a king's daughter, that blood should be her health, and for to anoint her withal; and for this thing was this custom made. Now, said Percivale's sister, fair knights, I see well that this gentlewoman is but dead. Certes, said Galahad, an ye bleed so much ye may die. Truly, said she, an I die for to heal her I shall get me great worship and soul's health, and worship to my lineage, and better is one harm than twain. And therefore there shall be no more battle, but tomorn I shall yield you your custom of this castle. And then there was great joy more than there was tofore, for else had there been mortal war upon the morn; notwithstanding she would none other, whether they would or nold. That night were the three fellows eased with the best; and on the morn they heard mass, and Sir Percivale's sister bad bring forth the sick lady. So she was, the which was evil at ease. Then said she: Who shall let me blood? So one came forth and let her blood, and she bled so much that the dish was full. Then she lift up her hand and blessed her; and then she said to the lady: Madam, I am come to the death for to make you whole, for God's love pray for me. With that she fell in a swoon. Then Galahad and his two fellows start up to her, and lift her up and staunched her, but she had bled so much that she might not live. Then she said when she was awaked: Fair brother Percivale, I die for the healing of this lady, so I require you that ye bury me not in this country, but as soon as I am dead put me in a boat at the next haven, and let me go as adventure will lead me; and as soon as ye three come to the City of Sarras, there to achieve the Holy Grail, ye shall find me under a tower arrived, and there bury me in the spiritual place; for I say you so much, there Galahad shall be buried, and ye also, in the same place. Then Percivale understood these words, and granted it her, weeping. And then said a voice: Lords and fellows, to-morrow at the hour of prime ye three shall depart every each from other, till the adventure bring you to the maimed king. Then asked she her Saviour; and as soon as she had received it the soul departed from the body. So the same day was the lady healed, when she was anointed withal. Then Sir Percivale made a letter of all that she had holpen them as in strange adventures, and put it in her right hand, and so laid her in a barge, and covered it with black silk; and so the wind arose, and drove the barge from the land, and all knights beheld it till it was out of their sight. Then they drew all to the castle, and so forthwith there fell a sudden tempest and a thunder, lightning, and rain, as all the earth would have broken. So half the castle turned up so down. So it passed evensong or the tempest was ceased. Then they saw afore them a knight armed and wounded hard in the body and in the head, that said: O God, succour me for now it is need. After this knight came another knight and a dwarf, which cried to them afar: Stand, ye may not escape. Then the wounded knight held up his hands to God that he should not die in such tribulation. Truly, said Galahad, I shall succour him for His sake that he calleth upon. Sir, said Bors, I shall do it, for it is not for you, for he is but one knight. Sir, said he, I grant. So Sir Bors took his horse, and commended him to God, and rode after, to rescue the wounded knight. Now turn we to the two fellows.

CHAPTER XII

HOW GALAHAD AND PERCIVALE FOUND IN A CASTLE MANY
TOMBS OF MAIDENS THAT HAD BLED TO DEATH

Now saith the story that all night Galahad and Percivale were in a chapel in their prayers, for to save Sir Bors. So on the morrow they dressed them in their harness toward the castle, to wit what was fallen of them therein. And when they came there they found neither man nor woman that he ne was dead by the vengeance of Our Lord. With that they heard a voice that said: This vengeance is for blood shedding of maidens. Also they found at the end of the chapel a churchyard, and therein might they see a three score fair tombs, and that place was so fair and so delectable that it seemed them there had been none tempest, for there lay the bodies of all the good maidens which were martyred for the sick lady's sake. Also they found the names of every each, and of what blood they were come, and all were of kings' blood, and twelve of them were kings' daughters. Then they departed and went into a forest. Now, said Percivale unto Galahad, we must depart, so pray we Our Lord that we may meet together in short time: then they did off their helms and kissed together, and wept at their departing.

CHAPTER XIII

HOW SIR LAUNCELOT ENTERED INTO THE SHIP WHERE
SIR PERCIVALE'S SISTER LAY DEAD, AND HOW
HE MET WITH SIR GALAHAD, HIS SON

Now saith the history, that when Launcelot was come to the water of Mortoise, as it is rehearsed before, he was in great peril, and so he laid him down and slept, and took the adventure that God would send him. So when he was asleep there came a vision unto him and said: Launcelot, arise up and take thine armour, and enter into the first ship that thou shalt find. And when he heard these words he

start up and saw great clereness about him. And then he
lift up his hand and blessed him, and so took his arms and
made him ready; and so by adventure he came by a strand,
and found a ship the which was without sail or oar. And as
soon as he was within the ship there he felt the most sweetness that ever he felt, and he was fulfilled with all thing
that he thought on or desired. Then he said: Fair sweet
Father, Jesu Christ, I wot not in what joy I am, for this joy
passeth all earthly joys that ever I was in. And so in this
joy he laid him down to the ship's board, and slept till day.
And when he awoke he found there a fair bed, and therein
lying a gentlewoman dead, the which was Sir Percivale's
sister. And as Launcelot devised her, he espied in her right
hand a writ, the which he read, the which told him all the
adventures that ye have heard tofore, and of what lineage
she was come. So with this gentlewoman Sir Launcelot was
a month and more. If ye would ask how he lived, He that
fed the people of Israel with manna in the desert, so was he
fed; for every day when he had said his prayers he was sustained with the grace of the Holy Ghost. So on a night he
went to play him by the water side, for he was somewhat
weary of the ship. And then he listened and heard an
horse come, and one riding upon him. And when he came
nigh he seemed a knight. And so he let him pass, and
went thereas the ship was; and there he alit, and took the
saddle and the bridle and put the horse from him, and went
into the ship. And then Launcelot dressed unto him, and
said: Ye be welcome. And he answered and saluted him
again, and asked him: What is your name? for much my
heart giveth unto you. Truly, said he, my name is Launcelot
du Lake. Sir, said he, then be ye welcome, for ye were the
beginning of me in this world. Ah, said he, are ye Galahad?
Yea, forsooth, said he; and so he kneeled down and asked
him his blessing, and after took off his helm and kissed him.
And there was great joy between them, for there is no tongue
can tell the joy that they made either of other, and many
a friendly word spoken between, as kin would, the which is
no need here to be rehearsed. And there every each told
other of their adventures and marvels that were befallen to
them in many journeys sith that they departed from the

court. Anon, as Galahad saw the gentlewoman dead in the
bed, he knew her well enough, and told great worship of
her, that she was the best maid living, and it was great pity
of her death. But when Launcelot heard how the marvellous
sword was gotten, and who made it, and all the marvels
rehearsed afore, then he prayed Galahad, his son, that he
would show him the sword, and so he did; and anon he
kissed the pommel, and the hilt, and the scabbard. Truly,
said Launcelot, never erst knew I of so high adventures
done, and so marvellous and strange. So dwelt Launcelot
and Galahad within that ship half a year, and served God
daily and nightly with all their power; and often they
arrived in isles far from folk, where there repaired none but
wild beasts, and there they found many strange adventures
and perillous, which they brought to an end; but for those
adventures were with wild beasts, and not in the quest of the
Sangreal, therefore the tale maketh here no mention thereof,
for it would be too long to tell of all those adventures that
befell them.

CHAPTER XIV

HOW A KNIGHT BROUGHT UNTO SIR GALAHAD A HORSE, AND BAD HIM COME FROM HIS FATHER, SIR LAUNCELOT

So after, on a Monday, it befell that they arrived in
the edge of a forest tofore a cross; and then saw they
a knight armed all in white, and was richly horsed, and
led in his right hand a white horse; and so he came to
the ship, and saluted the two knights on the High Lord's
behalf, and said: Galahad, sir, ye have been long enough
with your father, come out of the ship, and start upon
this horse, and go where the adventures shall lead thee
in the quest of the Sangreal. Then he went to his father
and kissed him sweetly, and said: Fair sweet father, I wot
not when I shall see you more till I see the body of Jesu
Christ. I pray you, said Launcelot, pray ye to the High
Father that He hold me in His service. And so he took
his horse, and there they heard a voice that said: Think

for to do well, for the one shall never see the other before the dreadful day of doom. Now, son Galahad, said Launcelot, syne we shall depart, and never see other, I pray to the High Father to conserve me and you both. Sir, said Galahad, no prayer availeth so much as yours. And therewith Galahad entered into the forest. And the wind arose, and drove Launcelot more than a month throughout the sea, where he slept but little, but prayed to God that he might see some tidings of the Sangreal. So it befell on a night, at midnight, he arrived afore a castle, on the back side, which was rich and fair, and there was a postern opened toward the sea, and was open without any keeping, save two lions kept the entry; and the moon shone clear. Anon Sir Launcelot heard a voice that said: Launcelot, go out of this ship and enter into the castle, where thou shalt see a great part of thy desire. Then he ran to his arms, and so armed him, and so went to the gate and saw the lions. Then set he hand to his sword and drew it. Then there came a dwarf suddenly, and smote him on the arm so sore that the sword fell out of his hand. Then heard he a voice say: O man of evil faith and poor belief, wherefore trowest thou more on thy harness than in thy Maker, for He might more avail thee than thine armour, in whose service that thou art set. Then said Launcelot: Fair Father Jesu Christ, I thank thee of Thy great mercy that Thou reprovest me of my misdeed; now see I well that ye hold me for your servant. Then took he again his sword and put it up in his sheath, and made a cross in his forehead, and came to the lions, and they made semblant to do him harm. Notwithstanding he passed by them without hurt, and entered into the castle to the chief fortress, and there were they all at rest. Then Launcelot entered in so armed, for he found no gate nor door but it was open. And at the last he found a chamber whereof the door was shut, and he set his hand thereto to have opened it, but he might not.

CHAPTER XV

HOW SIR LAUNCELOT WAS AFORE THE DOOR OF THE CHAMBER WHEREIN THE HOLY SANGREAL WAS

THEN he enforced him mickle to undo the door. Then he listened and heard a voice which sang so sweetly that it seemed none earthly thing; and him thought the voice said: Joy and honour be to the Father of Heaven. Then Launcelot kneeled down tofore the chamber, for well wist he that there was the Sangreal within that chamber. Then said he: Fair sweet Father, Jesu Christ, if ever I did thing that pleased Thee, Lord for Thy pity never have me not in despite for my sins done aforetime, and that Thou show me something of that I seek. And with that he saw the chamber door open, and there came out a great clereness, that the house was as bright as all the torches of the world had been there. So came he to the chamber door, and would have entered. And anon a voice said to him, Flee, Launcelot, and enter not, for thou oughtest not to do it; and if thou enter thou shalt forethink it. Then he withdrew him aback right heavy. Then looked he up in the middes of the chamber, and saw a table of silver, and the holy vessel, covered with red samite, and many angels about it, whereof one held a candle of wax burning, and the other held a cross, and the ornaments of an altar. And before the holy vessel he saw a good man clothed as a priest. And it seemed that he was at the sacring of the mass. And it seemed to Launcelot that above the priest's hands were three men, whereof the two put the youngest by likeness between the priest's hands; and so he lift it up right high, and it seemed to show so to the people. And then Launcelot marvelled not a little, for him thought the priest was so greatly charged of the figure that him seemed that he should fall to the earth. And when he saw none about him that would help him, then came he to the door a great pace, and said: Fair Father Jesu Christ, ne take it for no sin though I help the good man which hath great need of help. Right so entered he into the chamber, and

came toward the table of silver; and when he came nigh
he felt a breath, that him thought it was intermeddled with
fire, which smote him so sore in the visage that him thought
it brent his visage; and therewith he fell to the earth, and
had no power to arise, as he that was so araged, that had
lost the power of his body, and his hearing, and his seeing.
Then felt he many hands about him, which took him up
and bare him out of the chamber door, without any amend-
ing of his swoon, and left him there, seeming dead to
all people. So upon the morrow when it was fair day
they within were arisen, and found Launcelot lying afore
the chamber door. All they marvelled how that he came
in, and so they looked upon him, and felt his pulse to wit
whether there were any life in him; and so they found life
in him, but he might not stand nor stir no member that he
had. And so they took him by every part of the body,
and bare him into a chamber, and laid him in a rich bed,
far from all folk; and so he lay four days. Then the one
said he was on live, and the other said, Nay. In the name
of God, said an old man, for I do you verily to wit he is
not dead, but he is so full of life as the mightiest of you
all; and therefore I counsel you that he be well kept till
God send him life again.

CHAPTER XVI

HOW SIR LAUNCELOT HAD LAIN FOUR AND TWENTY
DAYS AND AS MANY NIGHTS AS A DEAD MAN,
AND OTHER DIVERS MATTERS

In such manner they kept Launcelot four and twenty
days and all so many nights, that ever he lay still as a dead
man; and at the twenty-fifth day befell him after midday
that he opened his eyes. And when he saw folk he made
great sorrow, and said: Why have ye awaked me, for I
was more at ease than I am now. O Jesu Christ, who
might be so blessed that might see openly thy great marvels
of secretness there where no sinner may be! What have
ye seen? said they about him. I have seen, said he, so
great marvels that no tongue may tell, and more than any

heart can think, and had not my son been here afore me
I had seen much more. Then they told him how he had lain
there four and twenty days and nights. Then him thought
it was punishment for the four and twenty years that
he had been a sinner, wherefore Our Lord put him in penance four and twenty days and nights. Then looked
Sir Launcelot afore him, and saw the hair which
he had borne nigh a year, for that he forethought him
right much that he had broken his promise unto the
hermit, which he had avowed to do. Then they asked
how it stood with him. For sooth, said he, I am whole
of body, thanked be Our Lord; therefore, sirs, for God's
love tell me where I am. Then said they all that he
was in the castle of Carbonek. Therewith came a gentlewoman and brought him a shirt of small linen cloth, but
he changed not there, but took the hair to him again.
Sir, said they, the quest of the Sangreal is achieved now
right in you, that never shall ye see of the Sangreal no
more than ye have seen. Now I thank God, said Launcelot,
of His great mercy of that I have seen, for it sufficeth me;
for as I suppose no man in this world hath lived better
than I have done to achieve that I have done. And
therewith he took the hair and clothed him in it, and above
that he put a linen shirt, and after a robe of scarlet, fresh
and new. And when he was so arrayed they marvelled
all, for they knew him that he was Launcelot, the good
knight. And then they said all: O my lord Sir Launcelot,
be that ye? And he said: Truly I am he. Then came
word to King Pelles that the knight that had lain so long
dead was Sir Launcelot. Then was the king right glad,
and went to see him. And when Launcelot saw him
come he dressed him against him, and there made the
king great joy of him. And there the king told him tidings
that his fair daughter was dead. Then Launcelot was right
heavy of it, and said: Sir, me forthinketh the death of
your daughter, for she was a full fair lady, fresh and young.
And well I wot she bare the best knight that is now on
the earth, or that ever was sith God was born. So the
king held him there four days, and on the morrow he took
his leave at King Pelles and at all the fellowship, and

thanked them of their great labour. Right so as they sat at their dinner in the chief hall, then was it so that the Sangreal had fulfilled the table with all manner of meats that any heart might think. So as they sat they saw all the doors and the windows of the place were shut without man's hand, whereof they were all abashed, and none wist what to do. And then it happened suddenly that a knight came to the chief door and knocked, and cried: Undo the door. But they would not. And ever he cried: Undo; but they would not. And at last it annoyed him so much that the king himself arose and came to a window where the knight called. Then he said: Sir knight, ye shall not enter at this time while the Sangreal is here, and therefore go into another; for certes ye be none of the knights of the quest, but one of them which hath served the fiend, and hast left the service of Our Lord: and he was passing wroth at the king's words. Sir knight, said the king, sith ye would so fain enter, say me of what country ye be. Sir, said he, I am of the realm of Logris, and my name is Ector de Maris, and brother unto my lord, Sir Launcelot. In the name of God, said the king, me forthinketh of what I have said, for your brother is here within. And when Ector de Maris understood that his brother was there, for he was the man in the world that he most dread and loved, and then he said: Ah God, now doubleth my sorrow and shame. Full truly said the good man of the hill unto Gawaine and to me of our dreams. Then went he out of the court as fast as his horse might, and so throughout the castle.

CHAPTER XVII

HOW SIR LAUNCELOT RETURNED TOWARDS LOGRIS, AND OF OTHER ADVENTURES WHICH HE SAW IN THE WAY

THEN King Pelles came to Sir Launcelot and told him tidings of his brother, whereof he was sorry, that he wist not what to do. So Sir Launcelot departed, and took his arms, and said he would go see the realm of Logris, which I have not seen these twelve months. And therewith he commended the king to God, and so rode through many realms. And at the last he came to a white abbey, and there they made him that night great cheer; and on the morn he rose and heard mass. And afore an altar he found a rich tomb, the which was newly made; and then he took heed, and saw the sides written with gold which said: Here lieth King Bagdemagus of Gore, which King Arthur's nephew slew; and named him, Sir Gawaine. Then was he not a little sorry, for Launcelot loved him much more than any other, and had it been any other than Gawaine he should not have escaped from death to life; and said to himself: Ah Lord God, this is a great hurt unto King Arthur's court, the loss of such a man. And then he departed and came to the abbey where Galahad did the adventure of the tombs, and won the white shield with the red cross; and there had he great cheer all that night. And on the morn he turned unto Camelot, where he found King Arthur and the queen. But many of the knights of the Round Table were slain and destroyed, more than half. And so three were come home again, that were Sir Gawaine, Sir Ector, and Sir Lionel, and many other that need not to be rehearsed. Then all the court was passing glad of Sir Launcelot, and the king asked him many tidings of his son Galahad. And there Launcelot told the king of his adventures that had befallen him syne he departed. And also he told him of the adventures of Galahad, Percivale, and Bors, which that he knew by the letter of the dead damosel, and as Galahad had told him. Now God would, said the king, that they were all three here. That shall never be, said Launcelot, for two of them shall ye never see, but one of them shall come again.

CHAPTER XVIII

HOW GALAHAD CAME TO KING MORDRAINS, AND OF OTHER MATTERS AND ADVENTURES

Now saith the story that Galahad rode many journeys in vain. And at the last he came to the Abbey where King

Mordrains was, and when he heard that, he thought he would abide to see him. And upon the morn, when he had heard mass, Galahad came unto King Mordrains, and anon the king saw him, which had lain blind a long time. And then he dressed him against him, and said: Galahad, the servant of Jesu Christ, whose coming I have abiden so long, now embrace me and let me rest on thy breast, so that I may rest between thine arms, for thou art a clene virgin above all knights, as the flower of the lily in whom virginity is signified, and thou art the rose the which is the flower of all good virtues, and in colour of fire. For the fire of the Holy Ghost is taken so in thee that my flesh which was of dead oldness is become young again. When Galahad heard his words, then he embraced him and all his body. Then said he: Fair Lord Jesu Christ, now I have my will. Now I require thee, in this point that I am in, thou come and visit me. And anon Our Lord heard his prayer: therewith the soul departed from the body. And then Galahad put him in the earth as a king ought to be, and so departed and came into a perilous forest where he found the well the which boileth with great waves, as the tale telleth tofore. And as soon as Galahad set his hand thereto it ceased, so that it burnt no more, and the heat departed. For that it brent it was a sign of lechery, the which was that time much used. But that heat might not abide his pure virginity. And this was taken in the country for a miracle. And so ever after was it called Galahad's well. Then by adventure he came into the country of Gore, and into the Abbey where Launcelot had been toforehand, and found the tomb of King Bagdemagus, but Joseph of Aramathie's son was founder thereof; and the tomb of Simeon where Launcelot had failed. Then he looked into a croft under the minster, and there he saw a tomb which burnt full marvellously. Then asked he the brethren what it was. Sir, said they, a marvellous adventure that may not be brought unto none end but by him that passeth of bounty and of knighthood all the knights of the Round Table. I would, said Galahad, that ye would lead me thereto. Gladly, said they. And so they led him unto a cave. And he went down upon gretys, and came nigh the tomb. And then the flaming failed, and the fire stanched, the which many a day had been great. Then came there a voice that said: much are ye beholden to thank Our Lord, the which hath given you a good hour, that ye may draw out the souls of earthly pain, and to put them into the joys of paradise. I am of your kindred, the which hath dwelled in this heat this three hundred four and fifty winter to be purged of the sin that I did against Joseph of Aramathie. Then Galahad took the body in his arms and bare it into the minster. And that night lay Galahad in the abbey; and on the morn he gave him service, and put him in the earth afore the high altar.

CHAPTER XIX

HOW SIR PERCIVALE AND SIR BORS MET WITH SIR GALAHAD, AND HOW THEY CAME TO THE CASTLE OF CARBONEK, AND OTHER MATTERS

So departed he from thence, and commended the brethren to God; and so he rode five days till that he came to the maimed king. And ever followed Percivale the five days, asking where he had been; and so one told him how the adventures of Logris were achieved. So on a day it befell that they came out of a great forest, and there they met at traverse with Sir Bors, the which rode alone. It is none need to tell if they were glad; and them he saluted, and they yielded him honour and good adventure, and every each told other. Then said Bors: It is more than a year and an half that I ne lay ten times where men dwelled, but in wild forests and in mountains, but God was ever my comfort. Then rode they a great while till that they came to the castle of Carbonek. And when they were entered within the castle King Pelles knew them; then there was great joy, for they wist well by their coming that they had fulfilled the quest of the Sangreal. Then Eliazar, King Pelles' son, brought tofore them the broken sword wherewith Joseph was stricken through the thigh. Then Bors set his hand thereto, if that he might have soldered it again; but

it would not be. Then he took it to Percivale, but he had
no more power thereto than he. Now have ye it again, said
Percivale to Galahad, for an it be ever achieved by any bodily
man ye must do it. And then he took the pieces and set
them together, and they seemed that they had never been
broken, and as well as it had been first forged. And when
they within espied that the adventure of the sword was
achieved, then they gave the sword to Bors, for it might not
be better set; for he was a good knight and a worthy man.
And a little afore even the sword arose great and marvellous,
and was full of great heat that many men fell for dread.
And anon alit a voice among them, and said: They that
ought not to sit at the table of Jesu Christ arise, for now
shall very knights be fed. So they went thence, all save
King Pelles and Eliazar, his son, the which were holy men,
and a maid which was his niece; and so these three fellows
and they three were there, no more. Anon they saw knights
all armed come in at the hall door, and did off their helms
and their arms, and said unto Galahad: Sir, we have hied
right much for to be with you at this table where the holy
meat shall be departed. Then said he: Ye be welcome,
but of whence be ye? So three of them said they were of
Gaul, and other three said they were of Ireland, and the
other three said they were of Denmark. So as they sat
thus there came out a bed of tree, of a chamber, the which
four gentlewomen brought; and in the bed lay a good man
sick, and a crown of gold upon his head; and there in the
middes of the place they set him down, and went again their
way. Then he lift up his head, and said: Galahad, Knight,
ye be welcome, for much have I desired your coming, for in
such anguish I have been long. But now I trust to God the
term is come that my pain shall be allayed, that I shall pass
out of this world so as it was promised me long ago. Therewith a voice said: There be two among you that be not in
the quest of the Sangreal, and therefore depart ye.

CHAPTER XX

HOW GALAHAD AND HIS FELLOWS WERE FED OF THE HOLY SANGREAL, AND HOW OUR LORD APPEARED TO THEM, AND OTHER THINGS

THEN King Pelles and his son departed. And therewithal beseemed them that there came a man, and four angels from heaven, clothed in likeness of a bishop, and had a cross in his hand; and there four angels bare him in a chair, and set him down before the table of silver whereupon the Sangreal was; and it seemed that he had in middes of his forehead letters the which said: See ye here Joseph, the first bishop of Christendom, the same which Our Lord succoured in the city of Sarras in the spiritual place. Then the knights marvelled, for that bishop was dead more than three hundred years tofore. O knights, said he, marvel not, for I was sometime an earthly man. With that they heard the chamber door open, and there they saw angels; and two bare candles of wax, and the third a towel, and the fourth a spear which bled marvellously, that three drops fell within a box which he held with his other hand. And they set the candles upon the table, and the third the towel upon the vessel, and the fourth the holy spear even upright upon the vessel. And then the bishop made semblant as though he would have gone to the sacring of the mass. And then he took an ubblye which was made in likeness of bread. And at the lifting up there came a figure in likeness of a child, and the visage was as red and as bright as any fire, and smote himself into the bread, so that they all saw it that the bread was formed of a fleshly man; and then he put it into the holy vessel again, and then he did that longed to a priest to do to a mass. And then he went to Galahad and kissed him, and bad him go and kiss his fellows: and so he did anon. Now, said he, servants of Jesu Christ, ye shall be fed afore this table with sweetmeats that never knights tasted. And when he had said, he vanished away. And they set them at the table in great dread and made their prayers. Then looked they and saw a man come out of the holy vessel, that had all the signs of the passion of Jesu Christ, bleeding all openly, and said: My knights, and my servants, and my true children, which be come out of deadly life into spiritual life, I will now no longer hide me from you, but ye shall see now a part of my secrets and of my hidden things: now hold and receive the high meat which ye have so much desired. Then took he himself the holy vessel and came to Galahad; and he kneeled down, and there he received his Saviour, and after him so received all his fellows; and they thought it so sweet that it was marvellous to tell. Then said he to Galahad: Son, wotest thou what I hold betwixt my hands? Nay, said he, but if ye will tell me. This is, said he, the holy dish wherein I ate the lamb on Sher-Thursday. And now hast thou seen that thou most desired to see, but yet hast thou not seen it so openly as thou shalt see it in the city of Sarras in the spiritual place. Therefore thou must go hence and bear with thee this holy vessel; for this night it shall depart from the realm of Logris, that it shall never be seen more here. And wotest thou wherefore? For he is not served nor worshipped to his right by them of this land, for they be turned to evil living; therefore I shall disherit them of the honour which I have done them. And therefore go ye three to-morrow unto the sea, where ye shall find your ship ready and with you take the sword with the strange girdles, and no more with you but Sir Percivale and Sir Bors. Also I will that ye take with you of the blood of this spear for to anoint the maimed king, both his legs and all his body, and he shall have his health. Sir, said Galahad, why shall not these other fellows go with us? For this cause: for right as I departed my apostles one here and another there, so I will that ye depart; and two of you shall die in my service, but one of you shall come again and tell tidings. Then gave he them his blessing and vanished away.

CHAPTER XXI

HOW GALAHAD ANOINTED WITH THE BLOOD OF THE SPEAR THE MAIMED KING, AND OTHER ADVENTURES

AND Galahad went anon to the spear which lay upon the table, and touched the blood with his fingers, and came after to the maimed king and anointed his legs. And therewith he clothed him anon, and start upon his feet out of his bed as an whole man, and thanked Our Lord that He had healed him. And that was not to the world ward, for anon he yielded him to a place of religion of white monks, and was a full holy man. That same night about midnight came a voice among them which said: My sons and not my chief sons, my friends and not my warriors, go ye hence where ye hope best to do and as I bad you. Ah, thanked be Thou, Lord, that Thou wilt vouchsafe to call us, Thy sinners. Now may we well prove that we have not lost our pains. And anon in all haste they took their harness and departed. But the three knights of Gaul, one of them hight Claudine, King Claudas' son, and the other two were great gentlemen. Then prayed Galahad to every each of them, that if they come to King Arthur's court that they should salute my lord, Sir Launcelot, my father, and of them of the Round Table; and prayed them if that they came on that part that they should not forget it. Right so departed Galahad, Percivale and Bors with him; and so they rode three days, and then they came to a rivage and found the ship whereof the tale speaketh of tofore. And when they came to the board they found in the middes the table of silver which they had left with the maimed king, and the Sangreal which was covered with red samite. Then were they glad to have such things in their fellowship; and so they entered and made great reverence thereto; and Galahad fell in his prayer long time to Our Lord, that at what time he asked, that he should pass out of this world. So much he prayed till a voice said to him: Galahad, thou shalt have thy request; and when thou askest the death of thy body thou shalt have it, and then shalt thou find the life of the soul.

Percivale heard this, and prayed him, of fellowship that was between them, to tell him wherefore he asked such things. That shall I tell you, said Galahad; the other day when we saw a part of the adventures of the Sangreal I was in such a joy of heart, that I trow never man was that was earthly. And therefore I wot well, when my body is dead my soul shall be in great joy to see the blessed Trinity every day, and the Majesty of Our Lord, Jesu Christ. So long were they in the ship that they said to Galahad: Sir, in this bed ought ye to lie, for so saith the scripture. And so he laid him down and slept a great while; and when he awaked he looked afore him and saw the city of Sarras. And as they would have landed they saw the ship wherein Percivale had put his sister in. Truly, said Percivale, in the name of God, well hath my sister holden us covenant. Then took they out of the ship the table of silver, and he took it to Percivale and to Bors, to go tofore, and Galahad came behind. And right so they went to the city, and at the gate of the city they saw an old man crooked. Then Galahad called him and bad him help to bear this heavy thing. Truly, said the old man, it is ten year ago that I might not go but with crutches. Care thou not, said Galahad, and arise up and shew thy good will. And so he essayed, and found himself as whole as ever he was. Then ran he to the table, and took one part against Galahad. And anon arose there great noise in the city, that a cripple was made whole by knights marvellous that entered into the city. Then anon after, the three knights went to the water, and brought up into the palace Percivale's sister, and buried her as richly as a king's daughter ought to be. And when the king of the city, which was cleped Estorause, saw the fellowship, he asked them of whence they were, and what thing it was that they had brought upon the table of silver. And they told him the truth of the Sangreal, and the power which that God had set there. Then the king was a tyrant, and was come of the line of paynims, and took them and put them in prison in a deep hole.

CHAPTER XXII

HOW THEY WERE FED WITH THE SANGREAL WHILE
THEY WERE IN PRISON, AND HOW
GALAHAD WAS MADE KING

BUT as soon as they were there Our Lord sent them the Sangreal, through whose grace they were alway fulfilled while that they were in prison. So at the year's end it befel that this King Estorause lay sick, and felt that he should die. Then he sent for the three knights, and they came afore him; and he cried them mercy of that he had done to them, and they forgave it him goodly; and he died anon. When the king was dead all the city was dismayed, and wist not who might be their king. Right so as they were in counsel there came a voice among them, and bad them choose the youngest knight of them three to be their king: For he shall well maintain you and all yours. So they made Galahad king by all the assent of the holy city, and else they would have slain him. And when he was come to behold the land, he let make above the table of silver a chest of gold and of precious stones, that hylled the holy vessel. And every day early the three fellows would come afore it, and make their prayers. Now at the year's end, and the self day after Galahad had borne the crown of gold, he arose up early and his fellows, and came to the palace, and saw tofore them the holy vessel, and a man kneeling on his knees in likeness of a bishop, that had about him a great fellowship of angels as it had been Jesu Christ himself; and then he arose and began a mass of Our Lady. And when he came to the sacrament of the mass, and had done, anon he called Galahad, and said to him: Come forth the servant of Jesu Christ, and thou shalt see that thou hast much desired to see. And then he began to tremble right hard when the deadly flesh began to behold the spiritual things. Then he held up his hands toward heaven and said: Lord, I thank thee, for now I see that that hath been my desire many a day. Now, blessed Lord, would I not longer live, if it might please thee, Lord. And therewith the good man

took Our Lord's body betwixt his hands, and proffered it to
Galahad, and he received it right gladly and meekly. Now
wotest thou what I am? said the good man. Nay, said
Galahad. I am Joseph of Aramathie, the which Our Lord
hath sent here to thee to bear thee fellowship; and wotest
thou wherefore that he hath sent me more than any other?
For thou hast resembled me in two things; in that thou
hast seen the marvels of the Sangreal, in that thou hast been
a clene maiden, as I have been and am. And when he had
said these words Galahad went to Percivale and kissed him,
and commended him to God; and so he went to Sir Bors
and kissed him, and commended him to God, and said:
Fair lord, salute me to my lord, Sir Launcelot, my father,
and as soon as ye see him, bid him remember of this unstable
world. And therewith he kneeled down tofore the table
and made his prayers, and then suddenly his soul departed
to Jesu Christ, and a great multitude of angels bare his
soul up to heaven, that the two fellows might well behold
it. Also the two fellows saw come from heaven an hand,
but they saw not the body. And then it came right to the
Vessel, and took it and the spear, and so bare it up to
heaven. Sithen was there never man so hardy to say that
he had seen the Sangreal.

CHAPTER XXIII

OF THE SORROW THAT PERCIVALE AND BORS MADE WHEN
GALAHAD WAS DEAD: AND OF PERCIVALE HOW
HE DIED, AND OTHER MATTERS

WHEN Percivale and Bors saw Galahad dead they made
as much sorrow as ever did two men. And if they had not
been good men they might lightly have fallen in despair. And
the people of the country and of the city were right heavy.
And then he was buried; and as soon as he was buried Sir
Percivale yielded him to an hermitage out of the city, and
took a religious clothing. And Bors was alway with him,
but never changed he his secular clothing, for that he purposed him to go again into the realm of Logris. Thus a
year and two months lived Sir Percivale in the hermitage

a full holy life, and then passed out of this world; and Bors let bury him by his sister and by Galahad in the spiritualities. When Bors saw that he was in so far countries as in the parts of Babylon he departed from Sarras, and armed him and came to the sea, and entered into a ship; and so it befell him in good adventure he came into the realm of Logris; and he rode so fast till he came to Camelot where the king was. And then was there great joy made of him in the court, for they weened all he had been dead, forasmuch as he had been so long out of the country. And when they had eaten, the king made great clerks to come afore him, that they should chronicle of the high adventures of the good knights. When Bors had told him of the adventures of the Sangreal, such as had befallen him and his three fellows, that was Launcelot, Percivale, Galahad, and himself, there Launcelot told the adventures of the Sangreal that he had seen. All this was made in great books, and put up in almeryes at Salisbury. And anon Sir Bors said to Sir Launcelot: Galahad, your own son, saluted you by me, and after you King Arthur and all the Court, and so did Sir Percivale, for I buried them with mine own hands in the city of Sarras. Also, Sir Launcelot, Galahad prayed you to remember of this unsyker world as ye behight him when ye were together more than half a year. This is true, said Launcelot; now I trust to God his prayer shall avail me. Then Launcelot took Sir Bors in his arms, and said: Gentle cousin, ye are right welcome to me, and all that ever I may do for you and for yours ye shall find my poor body ready at all times, while the spirit is in it, and that I promise you faithfully, and never to fail. And wit ye well, gentle cousin, Sir Bors, that ye and I will never depart in sunder whilst our lives may last. Sir, said he, I will as ye will.

Thus endeth thistory of the Sancgreal, that was brevely drawen oute of Frensshe in to Englysshe, the whiche is a story cronycled for one of the truest and the holyest that is in thys world, the which is the xvii. book.

A DESCRIPTION OF ELIZABETHAN ENGLAND

WRITTEN BY
WILLIAM HARRISON

FOR
HOLINSHED CHRONICLES

INTRODUCTORY NOTE

NEAR *the beginning of Elizabeth's reign, Reginald Wolfe, the Queen's Printer, with the splendid audacity characteristic of that age, planned to publish a "universal Cosmography of the whole world, and therewith also certain particular histories of every known nation." Raphael Holinshed had charge of the histories of England, Scotland, and Ireland, the only part of the work ever published; and these were issued in 1577, and have since been known as "Holinshed's Chronicles." From them Shakespeare drew most of the material for his historical plays.*

Among Holinshed's collaborators was one William Harrison, chaplain to Lord Cobham, and later Rector of Radwinter in Essex and Canon of Windsor. To him was allotted the task of writing the "Descriptions of Britain and England" from which the following chapters are drawn. He gathered his facts from books, letters, maps, conversations, and, most important of all, his own observation and experience; and he put them loosely together into what he calls "this foul frizzled treatise." Yet, with all his modesty, he claims to "have had an especial eye to the truth of things"; and as a result we have in his pages the most vivid and detailed picture in existence of the England into which Shakespeare was born.

In 1876 Dr. Furnivall condensed Harrison's chapters for the New Shakspere Society, and these have since been reprinted by Mr. Lothrop Withington in the modern dress in which the most interesting of them appear here. No apology is needed for thus selecting and rearranging, since in their original form they were without unity, and formed part of a vast compilation.

Harrison's merit does not lie in the rich interest of his matter alone. He wrote a racy style with a strong individual as well as Elizabethan flavor; and his personal comment upon the manners of his time serves as a piquant sauce to the solid meat of his historical information.

A DESCRIPTION OF ELIZABETHAN ENGLAND

CHAPTER I

OF DEGREES OF PEOPLE IN THE COMMONWEALTH OF ELIZABETHAN ENGLAND

[1577, Book III., Chapter 4; 1587, Book II., Chapter 5.][1]

WE in England, divide our people commonly into four sorts, as gentlemen, citizens or burgesses, yeomen, and artificers or labourers. Of gentlemen the first and chief (next the king) be the prince, dukes, marquesses, earls, viscounts, and barons; and these are called gentlemen of the greater sort, or (as our common usage of speech is) lords and noblemen: and next unto them be knights, esquires, and, last of all, they that are simply called gentlemen. So that in effect our gentlemen are divided into their conditions, whereof in this chapter I will make particular rehearsal.

The title of prince doth peculiarly belong with us to the king's eldest son, who is called Prince of Wales, and is the heir-apparent to the crown; as in France the king's eldest son hath the title of Dauphin, and is named peculiarly *Monsieur*. So that the prince is so termed of the Latin word *Princeps*, since he is (as I may call him) the chief or principal next the king. The king's younger sons be but gentlemen by birth (till they have received creation or donation from their father of higher estate, as to be either viscounts, earls, or dukes) and called after their names, as Lord Henry, or Lord Edward, with the addition of the word Grace, properly assigned to the king and prince, and

[1] These references are to the first two editions of Holinshed's *Chronicles*. The modernization of the spelling, etc., follows that of Mr. L. Wilkington, whose notes are signed W.

now also by custom conveyed to dukes, archbishops, and (as some say) to marquesses and their wives.[2] . . .

Unto this place I also refer our bishops, who are accounted honourable, called lords, and hold the same room in the Parliament house with the barons, albeit for honour sake the right hand of the prince is given unto them, and whose countenances in time past were much more glorious than at this present it is, because those lusty prelates sought after earthly estimation and authority with far more diligence than after the lost sheep of Christ, of which they had small regard, as men being otherwise occupied and void of leisure to attend upon the same. Howbeit in these days their estate remaineth no less reverend than before, and the more virtuous they are that be of this calling the better are they esteemed with high and low. They retain also the ancient name ("lord") still, although it be not a little impugned by such as love either to hear of change of all things or can abide no superiors. For notwithstanding it be true that in respect of function the office of the eldership[3] is equally distributed between the bishop and the minister, yet for civil government's sake the first have more authority given unto them by kings and princes, to the end that the rest may thereby be with more ease retained within a limited compass of uniformity than otherwise they would be if each one were suffered to walk in his own course. This also is more to be marvelled at, that very many call for an alteration of their estate, crying to have the word "lord" abolished, their civil authority taken from them, and the present condition of the church in other things reformed; whereas, to say truly, few of them do agree upon form of discipline and government of the church succeedent, wherein they resemble the Capuans (of whom Livy doth speak) in the slaughter of their senate. Neither is it possible to frame a whole monarchy after the pattern of one town or city, or to stir up such an exquisite face of the church as we imagine or desire, sith our corruption is such that it will never yield to so great perfection; for that which is not able to be performed in a private house will be much less be brought to

[2] Here follow etymologies of the terms "Duke," "Marquess," and "Baron."—W.
[3] 1 Sam. ii. 15; 1 Kings i. 7.—H.

pass in a commonwealth and kingdom, before such a prince be found as Xenophon describeth, or such an orator as Tully hath devised.[4] . . .

Dukes, marquesses, earls, viscounts, and barons either be created of the prince or come to that honour by being the eldest sons or highest in succession to their parents. For the eldest son of a duke during his father's life is an earl, the eldest son of an earl is a baron, or sometimes a viscount, according as the creation is. The creation I call the original donation and condition of the honour given by the prince for good service done by the first ancestor, with some advancement, which, with the title of that honour, is always given to him and his heirs males only. The rest of the sons of the nobility by the rigour of the law be but esquires; yet in common speech all dukes' and marquesses' sons and earls' eldest sons be called lords, the which name commonly doth agree to none of lower degree than barons, yet by law and use these be not esteemed barons.

The barony or degree of lords doth answer to the degree of senators of Rome (as I said) and the title of nobility (as we used to call it in England) to the Roman *Patricii*. Also in England no man is commonly created baron except he may dispend of yearly revenues a thousand pounds, or so much as may fully maintain and bear out his countenance and port. But viscounts, earls, marquesses, and dukes exceed them according to the proportion of their degree and honour. But though by chance he or his son have less, yet he keepeth this degree: but if the decay be excessive, and not able to maintain the honour (as *Senatores Romani* were *amoti à senatu*), so sometimes they are not admitted to the upper house in the parliament, although they keep the name of " lord " still, which cannot be taken from them upon any such occasion.

The most of these names have descended from the French invention, in whose histories we shall read of them eight hundred years past.[5] . . .

Knights be not born, neither is any man a knight by succession, no, not the king or prince: but they are made either

[4] Here follows a long paragraph on the character of the clergy which is more appropriate to the chapter on " The Church."—W.
[5] Here follows a learned disquisition upon " Valvasors."—W.

before the battle, to encourage them the more to adventure and try their manhood; or after the battle ended, as an advancement for their courage and prowess already shewed, and then are they called *Milites;* or out of the wars for some great service done, or for the singular virtues which do appear in them, and then are they named *Equites Aurati,* as common custom intendeth. They are made either by the king himself, or by his commission and royal authority given for the same purpose, or by his lieutenant in the wars.[6] . . .

Sometime diverse ancient gentlemen, burgesses, and lawyers are called unto knighthood by the prince, and nevertheless refuse to take that state upon them, for which they are of custom punished by a fine, that redoundeth unto his coffers, and (to say truth) is oftentimes more profitable unto him than otherwise their service should be, if they did yield unto knighthood. And this also is a cause wherefore there be many in England able to dispend a knight's living, which never come unto that countenance, and by their own consents. The number of the knights in Rome was also uncertain: and so is it of knights likewise, with us, as at the pleasure of the prince. And whereas the *Equites Romani* had *Equum Publicum* of custom bestowed upon them, the knights of England have not so, but bear their own charges in that also, as in other kind of furniture, as armour meet for their defence and service. This nevertheless is certain, that whoso may dispend forty pounds by the year of free land, either at the coronation of the king, or marriage of his daughter, or time of his dubbing, may be informed unto the taking of that degree, or otherwise pay the revenues of his land for one year, which is only forty pounds by an old proportion, and so for a time be acquitted of that title.[7] . . .

At the coronation of a king or queen, there be other knights made with longer and more curious ceremonies, called "knights of the bath." But howsoever one be dubbed or made knight, his wife is by-and-by called "Madam," or "Lady," so well as the baron's wife: he himself having added to his name in common appellation this syllable "Sir," which is the title whereby we call our knights in

[6] Here follows a discourse upon *Equites Aurati.*—W.
[7] Here is a description of dubbing a knight.—W.

England. His wife also of courtesy so long as she liveth
is called " my lady," although she happen to marry with a
gentleman or man of mean calling, abeit that by the common
law she hath no such prerogative. If her first husband
also be of better birth than her second, though this latter
likewise be a knight, yet in that she pretendeth a privilege
to lose no honour through courtesy yielded to her sex, she
will be named after the most honourable or worshipful of
both, which is not seen elsewhere.

The other order of knighthood in England, and the most
honourable, is that of the garter, instituted by King Edward
the Third, who, after he had gained many notable victories,
taken King John of France, and King James of Scotland
(and kept them both prisoners in the Tower of London at
one time), expelled King Henry of Castille, the bastard,
out of his realm, and restored Don Pedro unto it (by the
help of the Prince of Wales and Duke of Aquitaine, his
eldest son, called the Black Prince), he then invented this
society of honour, and made a choice out of his own realm
and dominions, and throughout all Christendom of the best,
most excellent, and renowned persons in all virtues and
honour, and adorned them with that title to be knights of his
order, giving them a garter garnished with gold and precious
stones, to wear daily on the left leg only; also a kirtle, gown,
cloak, chaperon, collar, and other solemn and magnificent
apparel, both of stuff and fashion exquisite and heroical to
wear at high feasts, and as to so high and princely an order
appertaineth. . . .

The order of the garter therefore was devised in the time
of King Edward the Third, and (as some write) upon this
occasion. The queen's majesty then living, being departed
from his presence the next way toward her lodging, he following soon after happened to find her garter, which slacked
by chance and so fell from her leg, unespied in the throng
by such as attended upon her. His grooms and gentlemen
also passed by it, as disdaining to stoop and take up such a
trifle: but he, knowing the owner, commanded one of them
to stay and reach it up to him. " Why, and like your grace,"
saith a gentleman, " it is but some woman's garter that hath
fallen from her as she followed the queen's majesty."

"Whatsoever it be," quoth the king, "take it up and give
it me." So when he had received the garter, he said to such
as stood about him: "You, my masters, do make small
account of this bule garter here," and therewith held it out,
"but, if God lend me life for a few months, I will make
the proudest of you all to reverence the like." And even
upon this slender occasion he gave himself to the devising
of this order. Certes, I have not read of anything that
having had so simple a beginning hath grown in the end
to so great honour and estimation.[8] . . .

There is yet another order of knights in England called
knights bannerets, who are made in the field with the ceremony of cutting away the point of his pennant of arms, and
making it as it were a banner, so that, being before but a
bachelor knight, he is now of an higher degree, and allowed
to display his arms in a banner, as barons do. Howbeit
these knights are never made but in the wars, the king's
standard being unfolded.[9] . . .

Moreover, as the king doth dub knights, and createth the
barons and higher degrees, so gentlemen whose ancestors
are not known to come in with William Duke of Normandy
(for of the Saxon races yet remaining we now make none
accounted, much less of the British issue) do take their
beginning in England, after this manner in our times.

Whosoever studieth the laws of the realm, whoso abideth
in the university (giving his mind to his book), or pro-
fesseth physic and the liberal sciences, or beside his service
in the room of a captain in the wars, or good counsel given
at home, whereby his commonwealth is benefited, can live
without manual labour, and thereto is able and will bear the
port, charge, and countenance of a gentleman, he shall for
money have a coat and arms bestowed upon him by heralds
(who in the charter of the same do of custom pretend antiquity and service, and many gay things), and thereunto,
being made so good cheap, be called master (which is the
title that men give to esquires and gentlemen), and reputed
for a gentleman ever after, which is so much less to be
disallowed of for that the prince doth lose nothing by it, the

[8] Long details are given of Garter history, very inaccurate, both here and
in the last omitted passage.—W.
[9] Derivations of "Esquire" and "Gentleman" are given.—W.

gentleman being so much subject to taxes and public payments as is the yeoman or husbandman, which he likewise
doth bear the gladlier for the saving of his reputation.
Being called also to the wars (for with the government of
the commonwealth he meddleth little), whatsoever it cost
him, he will both array and arm himself accordingly, and
shew the more manly courage, and all the tokens of the
person which he representeth. No man hath hurt by it but
himself, who peradventure will go in wider buskins than
his legs will bear, or, as our proverb saith, " now and then
bear a bigger sail than his boat is able to sustain."

Certes the making of new gentlemen bred great strife
sometimes amongst the Romans, I mean when those which
were *Novi homines* were more allowed of for their virtues
newly seen and shewed than the old smell of ancient race,
lately defaced by the cowardice and evil life of their nephews
and descendants, could make the other to be. But as envy
hath no affinity with justice and equity, so it forceth not
what language the malicious do give out, against such as
are exalted for their wisdoms. This nevertheless is generally to be reprehended in all estates of gentility, and which
in short time will turn to the great ruin of our country, and
that is, the usual sending of noblemen's and mean gentlemen's sons into Italy, from whence they bring home nothing
but mere atheism, infidelity, vicious conversation, and ambitious and proud behaviour, whereby it cometh to pass that
they return far worse men than they went out. A gentleman at this present is newly come out of Italy, who went
thither an earnest Protestant; but coming home he could say
after this manner: " Faith and truth is to be kept where no
loss or hindrance of a future purpose is sustained by holding
of the same; and forgiveness only to be shewed when full
revenge is made." Another no less forward than he, at his
return from thence, could add thus much: " He is a fool
that maketh account of any religion, but more fool that will
lose any part of his wealth or will come in trouble for constant leaning to any; but if he yield to lose his life for his
possession, he is stark mad, and worthy to be taken for most
fool of all the rest." This gay booty got these gentlemen
by going into Italy; and hereby a man may see what fruit

is afterward to be looked for where such blossoms do appear. "I care not," saith a third, "what you talk to me of God, so as I may have the prince and the laws of the realm on my side." Such men as this last are easily known; for they have learned in Italy to go up and down also in England with pages at their heels finely apparelled, whose face and countenance shall be such as sheweth the master not to be blind in his choice. But lest I should offend too much, I pass over to say any more of these Italianates and their demeanour, which, alas! is too open and manifest to the world, and yet not called into question.

Citizens and burgesses have next place to gentlemen, who be those that are free within the cities, and are of some likely substance to bear office in the same. But these citizens or burgesses are to serve the commonwealth in their cities and boroughs, or in corporate towns where they dwell, and in the common assembly of the realm wherein our laws are made (for in the counties they bear but little sway), which assembly is called the High Court of Parliament: the ancient cities appoint four and the borough two burgesses to have voices in it, and give their consent or dissent unto such things as pass, to stay there in the name of the city or borough for which they are appointed.

In this place also are our merchants to be installed as amongst the citizens (although they often change estate with gentlemen, as gentlemen do with them, by a mutual conversion of the one into the other), whose number is so increased in these our days that their only maintenance is the cause of the exceeding prices of foreign wares, which otherwise, when every nation was permitted to bring in her own commodities, were far better, cheaper, and more plentifully to be had. Of the want of our commodities here at home, by their great transportation of them into other countries, I speak not, sith the matter will easily betray itself. Certes among the Lacedæmonians it was found out that great numbers of merchants were nothing to the furtherance of the state of the commonwealth: wherefore it is to be wished that the huge heap of them were somewhat restrained, as also of our lawyers, so should the rest live more easily upon their own, and few honest chapmen be brought to decay by breaking of the bankrupt. I do not deny but that the navy of the land is in part maintained by their traffic, and so are the high prices of wares kept up, now they have gotten the only sale of things upon pretence of better furtherance of the commonwealth into their own hands: whereas in times past, when the strange bottoms were suffered to come in, we had sugar for fourpence the pound, that now at the writing of this Treatise is well worth half-a-crown; raisins or currants for a penny that now are holden at sixpence, and sometimes at eightpence and ten-pence the pound; nutmegs at twopence halfpenny the ounce, ginger at a penny an ounce, prunes at halfpenny farthing, great raisins three pounds for a penny, cinnamon at four-pence the ounce, cloves at twopence, and pepper at twelve and sixteen pence the pound. Whereby we may see the sequel of things not always, but very seldom, to be such as is pretended in the beginning. The wares that they carry out of the realm are for the most part broad clothes and carsies[10] of all colours, likewise cottons, friezes, rugs, tin, wool, our best beer, baize, bustian, mockadoes (tufted and plain), rash, lead, fells, etc.: which, being shipped at sundry ports of our coasts, are borne from thence into all quarters of the world, and there either exchanged for other wares or ready money, to the great gain and commodity of our merchants. And whereas in times past their chief trade was into Spain, Portugal, France, Flanders, Danske [Den-mark], Norway, Scotland, and Ireland only, now in these days, as men not contented with these journeys, they have sought out the East and West Indies, and made now and then suspicious voyages, not only unto the Canaries and New Spain, but likewise into Cathay, Muscovy, and Tartaria, and the regions thereabout, from whence (as they say) they bring home great commodities. But alas! I see not by all their travel that the prices of things are any whit abated. Certes this enormity (for so I do account of it) was suffi-ciently provided for (Ann. 9 Edward III.) by a noble statute made in that behalf, but upon what occasion the general execution thereof is stayed or not called on, in good sooth, I cannot tell. This only I know, that every function

[10] Kerseys.

and several vocation striveth with other, which of them should have all the water of commodity run into her own cistern.

Yeomen are those which by our law are called *Legales homines,* free men born English, and may dispend of their own free land in yearly revenue to the sum of forty shillings sterling, or six pounds as money goeth in our times. Some are of the opinion, by Cap. 2 Rich. 2 Ann. 20, that they are the same which the Frenchmen call varlets, but, as that phrase is used in my time, it is very unlikely to be so. The truth is that the word is derived from the Saxon term *Zeoman,* or *Geoman,* which signifieth (as I have read) a settled or staid man, such I mean as, being married and of some years, betaketh himself to stay in the place of his abode for the better maintenance of himself and his family, whereof the single sort have no regard, but are likely to be still fleeting now hither now thither, which argueth want of stability in determination and resolution of judgment, for the execution of things of any importance. This sort of people have a certain pre-eminence, and more estimation than labourers and the common sort of artificers, and these commonly live wealthily, keep good houses, and travel to get riches. They are also for the most part farmers to gentlemen (in old time called *Pagani, et opponuntur militibus,* and therefore Persius calleth himself *Semipaganus*), or at the leastwise artificers, and with grazing, frequenting of markets, and keeping of servants (not idle servants, as the gentlemen do, but such as get both their own and part of their masters' living), do come to great wealth, insomuch that many of them are able and do buy the lands of unthrifty gentlemen, and often setting their sons to the schools, to the universities, and to the Inns of the Court, or, otherwise leaving them sufficient lands whereupon they may live without labour, do make them by those means to become gentlemen. These were they that in times past made all France afraid. And albeit they be not called " Master," as gentlemen are, or " Sir," as to knights appertaineth, but only " John " and " Thomas," etc., yet have they been found to have done very good service.

The kings of England in foughten battles were wont to

remain among them (who were their footmen) as the
French kings did amongst their horsemen, the prince thereby shewing where his chief strength did consist.

The fourth and last sort of people in England are day-
labourers, poor husbandmen, and some retailers (which have
no free land) copyholders, and all artificers, as tailors,
shoemakers, carpenters, brickmakers, masons, etc.[11]

As for slaves and bondmen, we have none; nay, such is
the privilege of our country by the especial grace of God
and bounty of our princes, that if any come hither from
other realms, so soon as they set foot on land they become
so free of condition as their masters, whereby all note of
servile bondage is utterly removed from them, wherein we
resemble (not the Germans, who had slaves also, though
such as in respect of the slaves of other countries might well
be reputed free, but) the old Indians and the Taprobanes,[12]
who supposed it a great injury to Nature to make or suffer
them to be bond, whom she in her wonted course doth pro-
duct and bring forth free. This fourth and last sort of people
therefore have neither voice nor authority in the commonwealth, but are to be ruled and not to rule other: yet they are
not altogether neglected, for in cities and corporate towns,
for default of yeomen, they are fain to make up their in-
quests of such manner of people. And in villages they are
commonly made churchwardens, sidesmen, aleconners, now
and then constables, and many times enjoy the name of
head boroughs. Unto this sort also may our great swarms
of idle serving-men be referred, of whom there runneth a
proverb, " Young servingmen, old beggars," because service
is none heritage. These men are profitable to none; for, if
their condition be well perused, they are enemies to their masters, to their friends, and to themselves: for by them oftentimes their masters are encouraged unto unlawful exactions of
their tenants, their friends brought unto poverty by their
rents enhanced, and they themselves brought to confusion by
their own prodigality and errors, as men that, having not
wherewith of their own to maintain their excesses, do search
in highways, budgets, coffers, mails, and stables, which way

[11] Capite censi, or Proletarii.—H.
[12] The Ceylonese. The Greek name for the island of Ceylon was Taprobane, which Harrison used merely as a classical scholar.—W.

to supply their wants. How divers of them also, coveting to bear an high sail, do insinuate themselves with young gentlemen and noblemen newly come to their lands, the case is too much apparent, whereby the good natures of the parties are not only a little impaired, but also their livelihoods and revenues so wasted and consumed that, if at all, yet not in many years, they shall be able to recover themselves. It were very good therefore that the superfluous heaps of them were in part diminished. And since necessity enforceth to have some, yet let wisdom moderate their numbers, so shall their masters be rid of unnecessary charge, and the commonwealth of many thieves. No nation cherisheth such store of them as we do here in England, in hope of which maintenance many give themselves to idleness that otherwise would be brought to labour, and live in order like subjects. Of their whoredoms I will not speak anything at all, more than of their swearing; yet is it found that some of them do make the first a chief pillar of their building, consuming not only the goods but also the health and welfare of many honest gentlemen, citizens, wealthy yeomen, etc., by such unlawful dealings. But how far have I waded in this point, or how far may I sail in such a large sea? I will therefore now stay to speak any more of those kind of men. In returning therefore to my matter, this furthermore among other things I have to say of our husbandmen and artificers, that they were never so excellent in their trades as at this present. But as the workmanship of the latter sort was newer, more fine, and curious to the eye, so was it never less strong and substantial for continuance and benefit of the buyers. Neither is there anything that hurteth the common sort of our artificers more than haste, and a barbarous or slavish desire to turn the penny, and, by ridding their work, to make speedy utterance of their wares: which enforceth them to bungle up and despatch many things they care not how so they be out of their hands, whereby the buyer is often sore defrauded, and findeth to his cost that haste maketh waste, according to the proverb.

Oh, how many trades and handicrafts are now in England whereof the commonwealth hath no need! How many needful commodities have we which are perfected with great cost, etc., and yet may with far more ease and less cost be provided from other countries if we could use the means! I will not speak of iron, glass, and such like, which spoil much wood, and yet are brought from other countries better cheap than we can make them here at home; I could exemplify also in many other. But to leave these things and proceed with our purpose, and herein (as occasion serveth) generally, by way of conclusion, to speak of the commonwealth of England, I find that it is governed and maintained by three sorts of persons—

1. The prince, monarch, and head governor, which is called the king, or (if the crown fall to a woman) the queen: in whose name and by whose authority all things are administered.

2. The gentlemen which be divided into two sorts, as the barony or estate of lords (which containeth barons and all above that degree), and also those that be no lords, as knights, esquires, and simple gentlemen, as I have noted already. Out of these also are the great deputies and high presidents chosen, of which one serveth in Ireland, as another did some time in Calais, and the captain now at Berwick, as one lord president doth govern in Wales, and the other the north parts of this island, which later, with certain counsellors and judges, were erected by King Henry the Eighth. But, for so much as I have touched their conditions elsewhere, it shall be enough to have remembered them at this time.

3. The third and last sort is named the yeomanry, of whom and their sequel, the labourers and artificers, I have said somewhat even now. Whereto I add that they may not be called *masters* and *gentlemen*, but *goodmen*, as Goodman Smith, Goodman Coot, Goodman Cornell, Goodman Mascall, Goodman Cockswet, etc., and in matters of law these and the like are called thus, *Giles Jewd, yeoman; Edward Mountford, yeoman; James Cocke, yeoman; Harry Butcher, yeoman*, etc.; by which addition they are exempt from the vulgar and common sorts. Cato calleth them "*Aratores et optimos cives rei publicæ*," of whom also you may read more in the book of commonwealth which Sir Thomas Smith some time penned of this land.

CHAPTER II

OF CITIES AND TOWNS IN ENGLAND

[1577, Book II., Chapter 7; 1587, Book II., Chapter 13.]

AS in old time we read that there were eight-and-twenty flamines and archflamines in the south part of this isle, and so many great cities under their jurisdiction, so in these our days there is but one or two fewer, and each of them also under the ecclesiastical regiment of some one bishop or archbishop, who in spiritual cases have the charge and oversight of the same. So many cities therefore are there in England and Wales as there be bishoprics and arch-bishoprics.[1] For, notwithstanding that Lichfield and Coventry and Bath and Wells do seem to extend the aforesaid number unto nine-and-twenty, yet neither of these couples are to be accounted but as one entire city and see of the bishop, sith one bishopric can have relation but unto one see, and the said see be situate but in one place, after which the bishop doth take his name.[2] . . .

Certes I would gladly set down, with the names and number of the cities, all the towns and villages in England and Wales with their true longitudes and latitudes, but as yet I cannot come by them in such order as I would; howbeit the tale of our cities is soon found by the bishoprics, sith every see hath such prerogative given unto it as to bear the name of a city and to use *Regaleius* within her own limits. Which privilege also is granted to sundry ancient towns in England, especially northward, where more plenty of

[1] If Harrison means to give us the impression that a city has any direct connection with episcopal affairs, he is quite in error. Cities are distinctly royal and imperial institutions. The accident of the number of cities and sees being the same comes from the natural tendency of the two institutions to drift together, though of distinct origin.—W.

[2] Here follows a long and learned disquisition upon the Roman and other early towns, especially about St. Albans, a portion of which will be found in the Appendix.—W.

242

them is to be found by a great deal than in the south. The names therefore of our cities are these: London, York, Canterbury, Winchester, Carlisle, Durham, Ely, Norwich, Lincoln, Worcester, Gloucester, Hereford, Salisbury, Exeter, Bath, Lichfield, Bristol, Rochester, Chester, Chichester, Oxford, Peterborough, Llandaff, St. Davids, Bangor, St. Asaph, whose particular plots and models, with their descriptions, shall ensue, if it may be brought to pass that the cutters can make despatch of them before this history be published.

Of towns and villages likewise thus much will I say, that there were greater store in old time (I mean within three or four hundred years passed) than at this present. And this I note out of divers records, charters, and donations (made in times past unto sundry religious houses, as Glastonbury, Abingdon, Ramsey, Ely, and such like), and whereof in these days I find not so much as the ruins. Leland, in sundry places, complaineth likewise of the decay of parishes in great cities and towns, missing in some six or eight or twelve churches and more, of all which he giveth particular notice. For albeit that the Saxons built many towns and villages, and the Normans well more at their first coming, yet since the first two hundred years after the latter conquest, they have gone so fast again to decay that the ancient number of them is very much abated. Ranulph, the monk of Chester, telleth of general survey made in the fourth, sixteenth, and nineteenth of the reign of William Conqueror, surnamed the Bastard, wherein it was found that (notwithstanding the Danes had overthrown a great many) there were to the number of 52,000 towns, 45,002 parish churches, and 75,000 knights' fees, whereof the clergy held 28,015. He addeth moreover that there were divers other builded since that time, within the space of a hundred years after the coming of the Bastard, as it were in lieu or recompense of those that William Rufus pulled down for the erection of his New Forest. For by an old book which I have, and some time written as it seemeth by an under-sheriff of Nottingham, I find even in the time of Edward IV. 45,120 parish churches, and but 60,216 knights' fees, whereof the clergy held as before 28,015, or at the least 28,000; for so small is the difference which he doth seem to use. Howbeit, if the assertions of such as write in our time concerning this matter either are or ought to be of any credit in this behalf, you shall not find above 17,000 towns and villages, and 9210 in the whole, which is little more than a fourth part of the aforesaid number, if it be thoroughly scanned.[3] . . .

In time past in Lincoln (as the same goeth) there have been two-and-fifty parish churches, and good record appeareth for eight-and-thirty; but now, if there be four-and-twenty, it is all. This inconvenience hath grown altogether to the church by appropriations made unto monasteries and religious houses—a terrible canker and enemy to religion.

But to leave this lamentable discourse of so notable and grievous an inconvenience, growing as I said by encroaching and joining of house to house and laying land to land, whereby the inhabitants of many places of our country are devoured and eaten up, and their houses either altogether pulled down or suffered to decay little by little, although some time a poor man peradventure doth dwell in one of them, who, not being able to repair it, suffereth it to fall down—and thereto thinketh himself very friendly dealt withal, if he may have an acre of ground assigned unto him, wherein to keep a cow, or wherein to set cabbages, radishes, parsnips, carrots, melons, pompons,[4] or such like stuff, by which he and his poor household liveth as by their principal food, sith they can do no better. And as for wheaten bread, they eat it when they can reach unto the price of it, contenting themselves in the meantime with bread made of oats or barley: a poor estate, God wot! Howbeit, what care our great encroachers? But in divers places where rich men dwelled some time in good tenements, there be now no houses at all, but hop-yards, and sheds for poles, or peradventure gardens, as we may see in Castle Hedingham, and divers other places. But to proceed.

It is so that, our soil being divided into champaign ground and woodland, the houses of the first lie uniformly builded in every town together, with streets and lanes; whereas in the woodland countries (except here and there in great

[3] Here follows an allusion to the decay of Eastern cities.—W.
[4] The old and proper form of the modern pumpkin.—W.

market towns) they stand scattered abroad, each one dwelling in the midst of his own occupying. And as in many and most great market towns, there are commonly three hundred or four hundred families or mansions, and two thousand communicants (or peradventure more), so in the other, whether they be woodland or champaign, we find not often above forty, fifty, or three score households, and two or three hundred communicants, whereof the greatest part nevertheless are very poor folks, oftentimes without all manner of occupying, sith the ground of the parish is gotten up into a few men's hands, yea sometimes into the tenure of one or two or three, whereby the rest are compelled either to be hired servants unto the other or else to beg their bread in misery from door to door.

There are some (saith Leland) which are not so favourable, when they have gotten such lands, as to let the houses remain upon them to the use of the poor; but they will compound with the lord of the soil to pull them down for altogether, saying that " if they did let them stand, they should but toll beggars to the town, thereby to surcharge the rest of the parish, and lay more burden upon them." But alas! these pitiful men see not that they themselves hereby do lay the greatest log upon their neighbours' necks. For, sith the prince doth commonly loose nothing of his duties accustomable to be paid, the rest of the parishioners that remain must answer and bear them out: for they plead more charge other ways, saying: " I am charged already with a light horse; I am to answer in this sort, and after that matter." And it is not yet altogether out of knowledge that, where the king had seven pounds thirteen shillings at a task gathered of fifty wealthy householders of a parish in England, now, a gentleman having three parts of the town in his own hands, four households do bear all the aforesaid payment, or else Leland is deceived in his *Commentaries,* lib. 13, lately come to my hands, which thing he especially noted in his travel over this isle. A common plague and enormity, both in the heart of the land and likewise upon the coasts. Certes a great number complain of the increase of poverty, laying the cause upon God, as though he were in fault for sending such increase of people, or want of wars that should

consume them, affirming that the land was never so full,
etc.; but few men do see the very root from whence it
doth proceed. Yet the Romans found it out, when they
flourished, and therefore prescribed limits to every man's
tenure and occupying. Homer commendeth Achilles for
overthrowing of five-and-twenty cities: but in mine opinion
Ganges is much better preferred by Suidas for building of
three score in India, where he did plant himself. I could
(if need required) set down in this place the number of
religious houses and monasteries, with the names of their
founders, that have been in this island: but, sith it is a
thing of small importance, I pass it over as impertinent to my
purpose. Yet herein I will commend sundry of the monastical votaries, especially monks, for that they were authors of
many goodly borowes and endwares,[5] near unto their dwellings although otherwise they pretended to be men separated
from the world. But alas! their covetous minds, one way in
enlarging their revenues, and carnal intent another, appeared
herein too, too much. For, being bold from time to time to
visit their tenants, they wrought oft great wickedness, and
made those endwares little better than brothel-houses, especially where nunneries were far off, or else no safe access
unto them. But what do I spend my time in the rehearsal of
these filthinesses? Would to God the memory of them
might perish with the malefactors! My purpose was also
at the end of this chapter to have set down a table of the
parish churches and market towns throughout all England
and Wales; but, sith I cannot perform the same as I would,
I am forced to give over my purpose; yet by these few
that ensue you shall easily see what I would have used
according to the shires, if I might have brought it to
pass.

Shires.	Market Towns.	Parishes.
Middlesex	3	73
London within the walls and without		120
Surrey	6	140
Sussex	18	312
Kent	17	398
Cambridge	4	163

[5] The first is a variant on a Keltic, the second on a Saxon, word, both
relating to matters sufficiently indicated in the text.—W.

Shires.	Market Towns.	Parishes.
Bedford	9	13
Huntingdon	5	78
Rutland	2	47
Berkshire	11	150
Northampton	10	326
Buckingham	11	196
Oxford	10	216
Southampton	18	248
Dorset	19	279
Norfolk	26	625
Suffolk	25	575
Essex	18	415

And these I had of a friend of mine, by whose travel and his master's excessive charges I doubt not but my countrymen ere long shall see all England set forth in several shires after the same manner that Ortelius hath dealt with other countries of the main, to the great benefit of our nation and everlasting fame of the aforesaid parties.

CHAPTER III

OF GARDENS AND ORCHARDS

[1587, Book II., Chapter 20.]

AFTER such time as Calais was won from the French, and that our countrymen had learned to trade into divers countries (whereby they grew rich), they began to wax idle also, and thereupon not only left off their former painfulness and frugality, but in like sort gave themselves to live in excess and vanity, whereby many goodly commodities failed, and in short time were not to be had amongst us. Such strangers also as dwelled here with us, perceiving our sluggishness, and espying that this idleness of ours might redound to their great profit, forthwith employed their endeavors to bring in the supply of such things as we lacked continually from foreign countries, which yet more augmented our idleness. For, having all things at reasonable prices (as we supposed) by such means from them, we thought it mere madness to spend either time or cost about the same here at home. And thus we became enemies to our own welfare, as men that in those days reposed our felicity in following the wars, wherewith we were often exercised both at home and other places. Besides this, the natural desire that mankind hath to esteem of things far sought, because they be rare and costly, and the irksome contempt of things near hand, for that they are common and plentiful, hath borne no small sway also in this behalf amongst us. For hereby we have neglected our own good gifts of God, growing here at home, as vile and of no value, and had every trifle and toy in admiration that is brought hither from far countries, ascribing I wot not what great forces and solemn estimation unto them, until they also have waxen old, after which they have been so little regarded, if not more despised, amongst us than our own. Examples hereof I could set down many and in many things; but, sith my purpose is to deal at this time with gardens and orchards, it shall suffice that I touch them only, and show our inconstancy in the same, so far as shall seem and be convenient for my turn. I comprehend therefore under the word " garden " all such grounds as are wrought with the spade by man's hand, for so the case requireth.

Of wine I have written already elsewhere sufficiently, which commodity (as I have learned further since the penning of that book) hath been very plentiful in this island, not only in the time of the Romans, but also since the Conquest, as I have seen by record; yet at this present have we none at all (or else very little to speak of) growing in this island, which I impute not unto the soil, but the negligence of my countrymen. Such herbs, fruits, and roots also as grow yearly out of the ground, of seed, have been very plentiful in this land, in the time of the first Edward, and after his days; but in process of time they grew also to be neglected, so that from Henry the Fourth till the latter end of Henry the Seventh and beginning of Henry the Eighth, there was little or no use of them in England, but they remained either unknown or supposed as food more meet for hogs and savage beasts to feed upon than mankind. Whereas in my time their use is not only resumed among the poor commons, I mean of melons, pompons, gourds, cucumbers, radishes, skirets,[1] parsnips, carrots, cabbages, navews,[2] turnips, and all kinds of salad herbs—but also fed upon as dainty dishes at the tables of delicate merchants, gentlemen, and the nobility, who make their provision yearly for new seeds out of strange countries, from whence they have them abundantly. Neither do they now stay with such of these fruits as are wholesome in their kinds, but adventure further upon such as are very dangerous and hurtful, as the verangenes, mushrooms, etc., as if nature had ordained all for the belly, or that all things were to be eaten for whose mischievous operation the Lord in some measure hath given and provided a remedy.

[1] A vegetable something like a carrot.   [2] A kind of turnip.

Hops in time past were plentiful in this land. Afterwards also their maintenance did cease. And now, being revived, where are any better to be found? Where any greater commodity to be raised by them? Only poles are accounted to be their greatest charge. But, sith men have learned of late to sow ashen kexes in ashyards by themselves, that inconvenience in short time will be redressed.

Madder hath grown abundantly in this island, but of long time neglected, and now a little revived, and offereth itself to prove no small benefit unto our country, as many other things else, which are now fetched from us: as we before time, when we gave ourselves to idleness, were glad to have them other.

If you look into our gardens annexed to our houses, how wonderfully is their beauty increased, not only with flowers, which Columella calleth *Terrena sydera*,[3] saying,

> *"Pingit et in varios terrestria sydera flores,"*[4]

and variety of curious and costly workmanship, but also with rare and medicinable herbs sought up in the land within these forty years: so that, in comparison of this present, the ancient gardens were but dunghills and laistowes,[5] to such as did possess them. How art also helpeth nature in the daily colouring, doubling, and enlarging the proportion of our flowers, it is incredible to report: for so curious and cunning are our gardeners now in these days that they presume to do in manner what they list with nature, and moderate her course in things as if they were her superiors. It is a world also to see how many strange herbs, plants, and annual fruits are daily brought unto us from the Indies, Americans, Taprobane, Canary Isles, and all parts of the world: the which, albeit that in respect of the constitutions of our bodies they do not grow for us (because that God hath bestowed sufficient commodities upon every country for her own necessity), yet, for delectation sake unto the eye and their odoriferous savours unto the nose, they are to be cherished, and God to be glorified also in them, because they are his good gifts, and created to do man help

[3] Earthly stars.
[4] "And paints terrestrial constellations with varied flowers."
[5] Refuse-heaps.

and service. There is not almost one nobleman, gentleman, or merchant that hath not great store of these flowers, which now also do begin to wax so well acquainted with our soils that we may almost account of them as parcel of our own commodities. They have no less regard in like sort to cherish medicinable herbs fetched out of other regions nearer hand, insomuch that I have seen in some one garden to the number of three hundred or four hundred of them, if not more, of the half of whose names within forty years past we had no manner of knowledge. But herein I find some cause of just complaint, for that we extol their uses so far that we fall into contempt of our own, which are in truth more beneficial and apt for us than such as grow elsewhere, sith (as I said before) every region hath abundantly within her own limits whatsoever is needful and most convenient for them that dwell therein. How do men extol the use of tobacco in my time, whereas in truth (whether the cause be in the repugnancy of our constitution unto the operation thereof, or that the ground doth alter her force, I cannot tell) it is not found of so great efficacy as they write. And beside this, our common germander or thistle benet is found and known to be so wholesome and of so great power in medicine as any other herb, if they be used accordingly. I could exemplify after the like manner in sundry other, as the *Salsa parilla, Mochoacan,* etc., but I forbear so to do, because I covet to be brief. And truly, the estimation and credit that we yield and give unto compound medicines made with foreign drugs is one great cause wherefore the full knowledge and use of our own simples hath been so long raked up in the embers. And as this may be verified so to be one sound conclusion, for, the greater number of simples that go unto any compound medicine, the greater confusion is found therein, because the qualities and operations of very few of the particulars are thoroughly known. And even so our continual desire of strange drugs, whereby the physician and apothecary only hath the benefit, is no small cause that the use of our simples here at home doth go to loss, and that we tread those herbs under our feet, whose forces if we knew, and could apply them to our necessities, we would honour and have in rever-

ence as to their case behoveth. Alas! what have we to do
with such Arabian and Grecian stuff as is daily brought from
those parties which lie in another clime? And therefore
the bodies of such as dwell there are of another constitution
than ours are here at home. Certes they grow not for us,
but for the Arabians and Grecians. And albeit that they
may by skill be applied unto our benefit, yet to be more
skilful in them than in our own is folly; and to use foreign
wares, when our own may serve the turn, is more folly;
but to despise our own, and magnify above measure the
use of them that are sought and brought from far, is most
folly of all: for it savoureth of ignorance, or at the leastwise of negligence, and therefore worthy of reproach.

Among the Indians, who have the most present cures
for every disease of their own nation, there is small regard
of compound medicines, and less of foreign drugs, because
they neither know them nor can use them, but work wonders even with their own simples. With them also the
difference of the clime doth show her full effect. For,
whereas they will heal one another in short time with
application of one simple, etc., if a Spaniard or Englishman
stand in need of their help, they are driven to have a
longer space in their cures, and now and then also to use
some addition of two or three simples at the most, whose
forces unto them are thoroughly known, because their
exercise is only in their own, as men that never sought or
heard what virtue was in those that came from other
countries. And even so did Marcus Cato, the learned
Roman, endeavour to deal in his cures of sundry diseases,
wherein he not only used such simples as were to be had
in his own country, but also examined and learned the forces
of each of them, wherewith he dealt so diligently that in
all his lifetime he could attain to the exact knowledge but
of a few, and thereto wrote of those most learnedly, as
would easily be seen if those his books were extant. For
the space also of six hundred years the colewort only was
a medicine in Rome for all diseases, so that his virtues
were thoroughly known in those parts. * * *

For my part, I doubt not if the use of outlandish drugs
had not blinded our physicians of England in times past,

but that the virtues of our simples here at home would have been far better known, and so well unto us as those of India are to the practitioners of those parts, and thereunto be found more profitable for us than the foreign either are or may be. This also will I add, that even those which are most common by reason of their plenty, and most vile because of their abundance, are not without some universal and special efficacy, if it were known, for our benefit: sith God in nature hath so disposed his creatures that the most needful are the most plentiful and serving for such general diseases as our constitution most commonly is affected withal. Great thanks therefore be given unto the physicians of our age and country, who not only endeavour to search out the use of such simples as our soil doth yield and bring forth, but also to procure such as grow elsewhere, upon purpose so to acquaint them with our clime that they in time, through some alteration received from the nature of the earth, may likewise turn to our benefit and commodity and be used as our own.

The chief workman (or, as I may call him, the founder of this device) is Carolus Clusius, the noble herbarist whose industry hath wonderfully stirred them up into this good act. For albeit that Matthiolus, Rembert, Lobell, and others have travelled very far in this behalf, yet none hath come near to Clusius, much less gone further in the finding and true descriptions of such herbs as of late are brought to light. I doubt not but, if this man were in England but one seven years, he would reveal a number of herbs growing with us whereof neither our physicians nor apothecaries as yet have any knowledge. And even like thanks be given unto our nobility, gentlemen, and others, for their continual nutriture and cherishing of such homeborne and foreign simples in their gardens: for hereby they shall not only be had at hand and preserved, but also their forms made more familiar to be discerned and their forces better known than hitherto they have been.

And even as it fareth with our gardens, so doth it with our orchards, which were never furnished with so good fruit nor with such variety as at this present. For, beside that we have most delicate apples, plums, pears, walnuts, filberts, etc., and those of sundry sorts, planted within forty years past, in comparison of which most of the old trees are nothing worth, so have we no less store of strange fruit, as apricots, almonds, peaches, figs, corn-trees[6] in noblemen's orchards. I have seen capers, oranges, and lemons, and heard of wild olives growing here, beside other strange trees, brought from far, whose names I know not. So that England for these commodities was never better furnished, neither any nation under their clime more plentifully endued with these and other blessings from the most high God, who grant us grace withal to use the same to his honour and glory! And not as instruments and provocations into further excess and vanity, wherewith his displeasure may be kindled, lest these his benefits do turn unto thorns and briers unto us for our annoyance and punishment, which he hath bestowed upon us for our consolation and comfort.

We have in like sort such workmen as are not only excellent in grafting the natural fruits, but their artificial mixtures, whereby one tree bringeth forth sundry fruits, and one and the same fruit of divers colours and tastes, dallying as it were with nature and her course, as if her whole trade were perfectly known unto them: of hard fruits they will make tender, of sour sweet, of sweet yet more delicate, bereaving also some of their kernels, other of their cores, and finally enduing them with the savour of musk, amber, or sweet spices, at their pleasures. Divers also have written at large of these several practices, and some of them how to convert the kernels of peaches into almonds, of small fruit to make far greater, and to remove or add superfluous or necessary moisture to the trees, with other things belonging to their preservation, and with no less diligence than our physicians do commonly show upon our own diseased bodies, which to me doth seem right strange. And even so do our gardeners with their herbs, whereby they are strengthened against noisome blasts, and preserved from putrefaction and hindrance: whereby some such as were annual are now made perpetual, being yearly taken up, and either reserved in the house, or, having the ross pulled from their roots, laid again

[6] Probably *cornels.*

into the earth, where they remain in safety. With choice
they make also in their waters, and wherewith some of
them do now and then keep them moist, it is a world to see,
insomuch that the apothecaries' shops may seem to be needful also to our gardens and orchards, and that in sundry
wise: nay, the kitchen itself is so far from being able to be
missed among them that even the very dish-water is not
without some use amongst our finest plants. Whereby, and
sundry other circumstances not here to be remembered, I
am persuaded that, albeit the gardens of the Hesperides
were in times past so greatly accounted of, because of their
delicacy, yet, if it were possible to have such an equal
judge as by certain knowledge of both were able to pronounce upon them, I doubt not but he would give the prize
unto the gardens of our days, and generally over all Europe,
in comparison of those times wherein the old exceeded.
Pliny and others speak of a rose that had three score leaves
growing upon one button: but if I should tell of one which
bare a triple number unto that proportion, I know I shall not
be believed, and no great matter though I were not; howbeit
such a one was to be seen in Antwerp, 1585, as I have
heard, and I know who might have had a slip or stallon
thereof, if he would have ventured ten pounds upon the
growth of the same, which should have been but a tickle
hazard, and therefore better undone, as I did always imagine. For mine own part, good reader, let me boast a
little of my garden, which is but small, and the whole area
thereof little above 300 foot of ground, and yet, such hath
been my good luck in purchase of the variety of simples,
that, notwithstanding my small ability, there are very near
three hundred of one sort and other contained therein, no
one of them being common or usually to be had. If therefore my little plot, void of all cost in keeping, be so well
furnished, what shall we think of those of Hampton Court,
Nonsuch, Tibaults, Cobham Garden, and sundry others
appertaining to divers citizens of London, whom I could
particularly name, if I should not seem to offend them by
such my demeanour and dealing.

CHAPTER IV

OF FAIRS AND MARKETS

[1577, Book II., Chapter 11; 1587, Book II., Chapter 18.]

THERE are (as I take it) few great towns in England that have not their weekly markets, one or more granted from the prince, in which all manner of provision for household is to be bought and sold, for ease and benefit of the country round about. Whereby, as it cometh to pass that no buyer shall make any great journey in the purveyance of his necessities, so no occupier shall have occasion to travel far off with his commodities, except it be to seek for the highest prices, which commonly are near unto great cities, where round[1] and speediest utterance[2] is always to be had. And, as these have been in times past erected for the benefit of the realm, so are they in many places too, too much abused: for the relief and ease of the buyer is not so much intended in them as the benefit of the seller. Neither are the magistrates for the most part (as men loath to displease their neighbours for their one year's dignity) so careful in their offices as of right and duty they should be. For, in most of these markets, neither assizes of bread nor orders for goodness and sweetness of grain and other commodities that are brought thither to be sold are any whit looked unto, but each one suffered to sell or set up what and how himself listeth: and this is one evident cause of dearth and scarcity in time of great abundance.

I could (if I would) exemplify in many, but I will touch no one particularly, sith it is rare to see in any country town (as I said) the assize of bread well kept according to the statute; and yet, if any country baker happen to come in among them on the market day with bread of better

¹ Direct.   ² Market.

quantity, they find fault by-and-by with one thing or other in his stuff, whereby the honest poor man (whom the law of nations do commend, for that he endeavoureth to live by any lawful means) is driven away, and no more to come there, upon some round penalty, by virtue of their privileges. Howbeit, though they are so nice in the proportion of their bread, yet, in lieu of the same, there is such heady ale and beer in most of them as for the mightiness thereof among such as seek it out is commonly called " huffcap," " the mad dog," " Father Whoreson," " angels' food," " dragon's milk," " go-by-the-wall," " stride wide," and " lift leg," etc. And this is more to be noted, that when one of late fell by God's providence into a troubled conscience, after he had considered well of his reachless life and dangerous estate, another, thinking belike to change his colour and not his mind, carried him straight away to the strongest ale, as to the next physician. It is incredible to say how our malt-bugs lug at this liquor, even as pigs should lie in a row lugging at their dame's teats, till they lie still again and be not able to wag. Neither did Romulus and Remus suck their she-wolf or shepherd's wife Lupa with such eager and sharp devotion as these men hale at " huffcap," till they be red as cocks and little wiser than their combs. But how am I fallen from the market into the ale-house? In returning therefore unto my purpose, I find that in corn great abuse is daily suffered, to the great prejudice of the town and country, especially the poor artificer and householder, which tilleth no land, but, labouring all the week to buy a bushel or two of grain on the market day, can there have none for his money: because bodgers, loaders, and common carriers of corn do not only buy up all, but give above the price, to be served of great quantities. Shall I go any further? Well, I will say yet a little more, and somewhat by mine own experience.

At Michaelmas time poor men must make money of their grain, that they may pay their rents. So long then as the poor man hath to sell, rich men bring out none, but rather buy up that which the poor bring, under pretence of seed corn or alteration of grain, although they bring none of their own, because one wheat often sown without change of seed will soon decay and be converted into darnel. For this cause therefore they must needs buy in the markets, though they be twenty miles off, and where they be not known, promising there, if they happen to be espied (which, God wot, is very seldom), to send so much to their next market, to be performed I wot not when.

If this shift serve not (neither doth the fox use always one track for fear of a snare), they will compound with some one of the town where the market is holden, who for a pot of "huffcap" or "merry-go-down," will not let to buy it for them, and that in his own name. Or else they wage one poor man or other to become a bodger, and thereto get him a licence upon some forged surmise, which being done, they will feed him with money to buy for them till he hath filled their lofts, and then, if he can do any good for himself, so it is; if not, they will give him somewhat for his pains at this time, and reserve him for another year. How many of the like providers stumble upon blind creeks at the sea coast, I wot not well; but that some have so done and yet do under other men's wings, the case is too, too plain. But who dare find fault with them, when they have once a licence? yes, though it be but to serve a mean gentleman's house with corn, who hath cast up all his tillage, because he boasteth how he can buy his grain in the market better cheap than he can sow his land, as the rich grazier often doth also upon the like device, because grazing requireth a smaller household and less attendance and charge. If any man come to buy a bushel or two for his expenses unto the market cross, answer is made: "Forsooth, here was one even now that bade me money for it, and I hope he will have it." And to say the truth, these bodgers are fair chapmen; for there are no more words with them, but "*Let me see it! What shall I give you? Knit it up! I will have it—go carry it to such a chamber, and if you bring in twenty* seme[3] *more in the weekday to such an inn or sollar*[4] *where I lay my corn, I will have it, and give you* ( ) *pence or more in every bushel for six weeks' day of payment than another will.*" Thus the bodgers bear away all, so that the poor artificer and la-

[3] Horse-loads.   [4] Loft.

bourer cannot make his provision in the markets. sith
they will hardly nowadays sell by the bushel, nor break
their measure; and so much the rather for that the buyer
will look (as they say) for so much over measure in the
bushel as the bodger will do in a quarter. Nay, the poor
man cannot oft get any of the farmer at home, because he
provideth altogether to serve the bodger, or hath an hope,
grounded upon a greedy and insatiable desire of gain, that
the sale will be better in the market, so that he must give
twopence or a groat more in the bushel at his house than the
last market craved, or else go without it, and sleep with
a hungry belly. Of the common carriage of corn over unto
the parts beyond the seas I speak not; or at the leastwise,
if I should, I could not touch it alone, but needs must join
other provision withal, whereby not only our friends abroad,
but also many of our adversaries and countrymen, the papists, are abundantly relieved (as the report goeth); but sith
I see it not, I will not so trust mine ears as to write it for a
truth. But to return to our markets again.

By this time the poor occupier hath sold all his crop for
need of money, being ready peradventure to buy again ere
long. And now is the whole sale of corn in the great occupiers' hands, who hitherto have threshed little or none
of their own, but bought up of other men as much as they
could come by. Henceforth also they begin to sell, not by
the quarter or load at the first (for marring the market),
but by the bushel or two, or a horseload at the most, thereby
to be seen to keep the cross, either for a show, or to make
men eager to buy, and so, as they may have it for money, not
to regard what they pay. And thus corn waxeth dear; but
it will be dearer the next market day. It is possible also
that they mislike the price in the beginning for the whole
year ensuing, as men supposing that corn will be little worth
for this, and of better price the next year. For they have
certain superstitious observations whereby they will give a
guess at the sale of corn for the year following. And our
countrymen do use commonly for barley, where I dwell,
to judge after the price at Baldock upon St. Matthew's day;
and for wheat, as it is sold in seed time. They take in like
sort experiment by sight of the first flocks of cranes that

flee southward in winter, the age of the moon in the beginning of January, and such other apish toys as by laying twelve corns upon the hot hearth for the twelve months, etc., whereby they shew themselves to be scant good Christians; but what care they, so that they come by money? Hereupon also will they thresh out three parts of the old corn, towards the latter end of the summer, when new cometh apace to hand, and cast the same in the fourth unthreshed, where it shall lie until the next spring, or peradventure till it must and putrify. Certes it is not dainty to see musty corn in many of our great markets of England which these great occupiers bring forth when they can keep it no longer. But as they are enforced oftentimes upon this one occasion somewhat to abate the price, so a plague is not seldom engendered thereby among the poorer sort that of necessity must buy the same, whereby many thousands of all degrees are consumed, of whose death (in mine opinion) these farmers are not unguilty. But to proceed. If they lay not up their grain or wheat in this manner, they have yet another policy, whereby they will seem to have but small store left in their barns: for else they will gird their sheaves by the band, and stack it up anew in less room, to the end it may not only seem less in quantity, but also give place to the corn that is yet to come into the barn or growing in the field. If there happen to be such plenty in the market on any market day that they cannot sell it at their own price, then will they set it up in some friend's house, against another on the third day, and not bring it forth till they like of the sale. If they sell any at home, beside harder measure, it shall be dearer to the poor man that buyeth it by twopence or a groat in a bushel than they may sell it in the market. But, as these things are worthy redress, so I wish that God would once open their eyes that deal thus to see their own errors: for as yet some of them little care how many poor men suffer extremity, so that they fill their purses and carry away the gain.

It is a world also to see how most places of the realm are pestered with purveyors, who take up eggs, butter, cheese, pigs, capons, hens, chickens, hogs, bacon, etc., in one market under pretence of their commissions, and suffer their wives to sell the same in another, or to poulterers of London. If these chapmen be absent but two or three market days then we may perfectly see these wares to be more reasonably sold, and thereunto the crosses sufficiently furnished of all things. In like sort, since the number of buttermen have so much increased, and since they travel in such wise that they come to men's houses for their butter faster than they can make it, it is almost incredible to see how the price of butter is augmented: whereas when the owners were enforced to bring it to the market towns, and fewer of these butter buyers were stirring, our butter was scarcely worth eighteen pence the gallon that now is worth three shillings fourpence and perhaps five shillings. Whereby also I gather that the maintenance of a superfluous number of dealers in most trades, tillage always excepted, is one of the greatest causes why the prices of things became excessive: for one of them do commonly use to outbid another. And whilst our country commodities are commonly bought and sold at our private houses, I never look to see this enormity redressed or the markets well furnished.

I could say more, but this is even enough, and more peradventure than I shall be well thanked for: yet true it is, though some think it no trespass. This moreover is to be lamented, that one general measure is not in use throughout all England, but every market town hath in manner a several bushel; and the lesser it be, the more sellers it draweth to resort unto the same. Such also is the covetousness of many clerks of the market, that in taking a view of measures they will always so provide that one and the same bushel shall be either too big or too little at their next coming, and yet not depart without a fee at the first, so that what by their mending at one time, and impairing the same at another, the country is greatly charged, and few just measures to be had in any steed. It is oft found likewise that divers unconscionable dealers have one measure to sell by and another to buy withal; the like is also in weights, and yet all sealed and branded. Wherefore it were very good that these two were reduced unto one standard, that is, one bushel, one pound, one quarter, one hundred, one tale, one number: so should things in time fall into better order and fewer causes of contention be moved in this land. Of the complaint of such poor tenants as pay rent corn unto their landlords, I speak not, who are often dealt withal very hardly. For, beside that in measuring of ten quarters for the most part they lose one through the iniquity of the bushel (such is the greediness of the appointed receivers thereof), fault is found also with the goodness and cleanness of the grain. Whereby some piece of money must needs pass unto their purses to stop their mouths withal, or else " My lord will not like of the corn," " Thou art worthy to lose thy lease," etc. Or, if it be cheaper in the market than the rate allowed for it is in their rents, then must they pay money and no corn, which is no small extremity. And thereby we may see how each one of us endeavoureth to fleece and eat up another.

Another thing there is in our markets worthy to be looked into, and that is the recarriage of grain from the same into lofts and cellars, of which before I gave some intimation; wherefore if it were ordered that every seller should make his market by an hour, or else the bailey or clerk of the said market to make sale thereof, according to his discretion, without liberty to the farmers to set up their corn in houses and chambers, I am persuaded that the prices of our grain would soon be abated. Again, if it were enacted that each one should keep his next market with his grain (and not to run six, eight, ten, fourteen, or twenty miles from home to sell his corn where he doth find the highest price, and thereby leaveth his neighbours unfurnished), I do not think but that our markets would be far better served than at this present they are. Finally, if men's barns might be indifferently viewed immediately after harvest, and a note gathered by an estimate, and kept by some appointed and trusty person for that purpose, we should have much more plenty of corn in our town crosses than as yet is commonly seen: because each one hideth and hoardeth what he may, upon purpose either that it will be dearer, or that he shall have some privy vein by bodgers, who do accustomably so deal that the sea doth load away no small part thereof into other countries and our enemies, to the great hindrance of our commonwealth at home, and more likely yet to be, except some remedy be found. But what do I talk of these things, or desire the suppression of bodgers, being a minister? Certes I may speak of them right well as feeling the harm in that I am a buyer, nevertheless I speak generally in each of them.

To conclude therefore, in our markets all things are to be sold necessary for man's use; and there is our provision made commonly for all the week ensuing. Therefore, as there are no great towns without one weekly market at least, so there are very few of them that have not one or two fairs or more within the compass of the year, assigned unto them by the prince. And albeit that some of them are not much better than Louse fair,[5] or the common kirkemesses,[6] beyond the sea, yet there are divers not inferior to the greatest marts in Europe, as Stourbridge fair near to Cambridge, Bristow fair, Bartholomew fair at London, Lynn mart, Cold fair at Newport pond for cattle, and divers other, all which, or at leastwise the greatest part of them (to the end I may with the more ease to the reader and less travel to myself fulfil my task in their recital), I have set down according to the names of the months wherein they are holden at the end of this book, where you shall find them at large as I borrowed the same from J. Stow and the reports of others.

[5] The ancient London counterpart of the more modern " Rag Fair " known to literary fame.—W.
[6] The Kermess, or literally, " Church mass," so famous in " Faust."—W.

CHAPTER V

OF THE ANCIENT AND PRESENT ESTATE OF THE CHURCH OF ENGLAND

[1577, Book II., Chapter 5; 1585, Book II., Chapter 1.]

THERE are now two provinces only in England, of which the first and greatest is subject to the see of Canterbury, comprehending a part of Lhoegres, whole Cambria, and also Ireland, which in time past were several, and brought into one by the archbishop of the said see, and assistance of the pope, who, in respect of meed, did yield unto the ambitious desires of sundry archbishops of Canterbury, as I have elsewhere declared. The second province is under the see of York. And, of these, each hath her archbishop resident commonly within her own limits, who hath not only the chief dealing in matters appertaining to the hierarchy and jurisdiction of the church, but also great authority in civil affairs touching the government of the commonwealth, so far forth as their commissions and several circuits do extend.

In old time there were three archbishops, and so many provinces in this isle, of which one kept at London, another at York, and the third at Caerleon upon Usk. But as that of London was translated to Canterbury by Augustine, and that of York remaineth (notwithstanding that the greatest part of his jurisdiction is now bereft him and given to the Scottish archbishop), so that of Caerleon is utterly extinguished, and the government of the country united to that of Canterbury in spiritual cases, after it was once before removed to St. David's in Wales, by David, successor to Dubritius, and uncle to King Arthur, in the 519 of Grace, to the end that he and his clerks might be further off from the cruelty of the Saxons, where it remained till the time of the Bastard, and for a season after, before it was annexed to the see of Canterbury.

The Archbishop of Canterbury is commonly called the Primate of all England; and in the coronations of the kings of this land, and all other times wherein it shall please the prince to wear and put on his crown, his office is to set it upon their heads. They bear also the name of their high chaplains continually, although not a few of them have presumed (in time past) to be their equals, and void of subjection unto them. That this is true, it may easily appear by their own acts yet kept in record, beside their epistles and answers written or in print, wherein they have sought not only to match but also to mate [1] them with great rigour and more than open tyranny. Our adversaries will peradventure deny this absolutely, as they do many other things apparent, though not without shameless impudence, or at the leastwise defend it as just and not swerving from common equity, because they imagine every archbishop to be the king's equal in his own province. But how well their doing herein agreeth with the saying of Peter and examples of the primitive church it may easily appear. Some examples also of their demeanour—I mean in the time of popery—I will not let to remember, lest they should say I speak of malice, and without all ground of likelihood.

Of their practices with mean persons I speak not, neither will I begin at Dunstan, the author of all their pride and presumption here in England. . . .

Wherefore I refer you to those reports of Anselm and Becket sufficiently penned by other, the which Anselm also making a shew as if he had been very unwilling to be placed in the see of Canterbury, gave this answer to the letters of such his friends as did make request unto him to take the charge upon him—

"Secularia negotia nescio, quia scire nolo, eorum námque occupationes horreo, liberum affectans animum. Voluntati sacrarum intendo scripturarum, vos dissonantiam facitis, verendúmque est nè aratrum sanctæ ecclesiæ, quod in Anglia duo boves validi et pari fortitudine, ad bonum certantes, id est, rex et archiepiscopus, debeant trahere, nunc ove vetula cum tauro indomito jugata, distorqueatur à recto. Ego ovis vetula, qui si quietus essem, verbi Dei lacte, et operimento

[1] Overcome.

lanæ, aliquibus possèm fortassis non ingratus esse, sed si me cum hoc tauro coniungitis, videbitis pro disparilitate trahentium, aratrum non rectè procedere," etc.

Which is in English thus—

" Of secular affairs I have no skill, because I will not know them; for I even abhor the troubles that rise about them, as one that desireth to have his mind at liberty. I apply my whole endeavour to the rule of the Scriptures; you lead me to the contrary; and it is to be feared lest the plough of holy church, which two strong oxen of equal force, and both like earnest to contend unto that which is good (that is, the king and the archbishop), ought to draw, should thereby now swerve from the right furrow, by matching of an old sheep with a wild, untamed bull. I am that old sheep, who, if I might be quiet, could peradventure shew myself not altogether ungrateful to some, by feeding them with the milk of the Word of God, and covering them with wool: but if you match me with this bull, you shall see that, through want of equality in draught, the plough will not go to right," etc.

As followeth in the process of his letters. The said Thomas Becket was so proud that he wrote to King Henry the Second, as to his lord, to his king, and to his son, offering him his counsel, his reverence, and due correction, etc. Others in like sort have protested that they owed nothing to the kings of this land, but their council only, reserving all obedience unto the see of Rome, whereby we may easily see the pride and ambition of the clergy in the blind time of ignorance.

And as the old cock of Canterbury did crow in this behalf, so the young cockerels of other sees did imitate his demeanour, as may be seen by this one example also in King Stephen's time, worthy to be remembered; unto whom the Bishop of London would not so much as swear to be true subject: wherein also he was maintained by the pope. . . .

Thus we see that kings were to rule no further than it pleased the pope to like of; neither to challenge more obedience of their subjects than stood also with their good will and pleasure. He wrote in like sort unto Queen Maud about the same matter, making her " Samson's calf"[2] (the better to bring his purpose to pass). . . .

Is it not strange that a peevish order of religion (devised

[2] A fool or dupe.

by man) should break the express law of God, who commandeth all men to honour and obey their kings and princes, in whom some part of the power of God is manifest and laid open unto us? And even unto this end the cardinal of Hostia also wrote to the canons of Paul's after this manner, covertly encouraging them to stand to their election of the said Robert, who was no more willing to give over his new bishopric than they careful to offend the king, but rather imagined which way to keep it still, maugre his displeasure, and yet not to swear obedience unto him for all that he should be able to do or perform unto the contrary. . . .

Hereby you see how King Stephen was dealt withal. And albeit the Archbishop of Canterbury is not openly to be touched herewith, yet it is not to be doubted but he was a doer in it, so far as might tend to the maintenance of the right and prerogative of holy church. And even no less unquietness had another of our princes with Thomas of Arundel, who fled to Rome for fear of his head, and caused the pope to write an ambitious and contumelious letter unto his sovereign about his restitution. But when (by the king's letters yet extant, and beginning thus: "*Thomas proditionis non expers nostræ regiæ majestati insidias fabricavit*"[3]) the pope understood the bottom of the matter, he was contented that Thomas should be deprived, and another archbishop chosen in his stead.

Neither did this pride stay at archbishops and bishops, but descended lower, even to the rake-hells of the clergy and puddles of all ungodliness. For, beside the injury received of their superiors, how was King John dealt withal by the vile Cistertians at Lincoln in the second of his reign? Certes when he had (upon just occasion) conceived some grudge against them for their ambitious demeanour, and upon denial to pay such sums of money as were allotted unto them, he had caused seizure to be made of such horses, swine, neat, and other things of theirs as were maintained in his forests, they denounced him as fast amongst themselves with bell, book, and candle, to be accursed and excommunicated. Thereunto they so handled the matter with

[3] "Thomas, not innocent of treason, has intrigued against the majesty of our court."

the pope and their friends that the king was fain to yield
to their good graces, insomuch that a meeting for paci-
fication was appointed between them at Lincoln, by means
of the present Archbishop of Canterbury, who went off
between him and the Cistertian commissioners before the
matter could be finished. In the end the king himself came
also unto the said commissioners as they sat in their chapter-
house, and there with tears fell down at their feet, craving
pardon for his trespasses against them, and heartily requiring
that they would (from henceforth) commend him and his
realm in their prayers unto the protection of the Almighty,
and receive him into their fraternity, promising moreover
full satisfaction of their damages sustained, and to build
an house of their order in whatsoever place of England
it should please them to assign. And this he confirmed by
charter bearing date the seven-and-twentieth of November,
after the Scottish king was returned into Scotland, and departed from the king. Whereby (and by other the like, as
between John Stratford and Edward the Third, etc.) a man
may easily conceive how proud the clergymen have been in
former times, as wholly presuming upon the primacy of their
pope. More matter could I allege of these and the like broils,
not to be found among our common historiographers. Howbeit, reserving the same unto places more convenient, I will
cease to speak of them at this time, and go forward with such
other things as my purpose is to speak of. At the first,
therefore, there was like and equal authority in both our
archbishops, but as he of Canterbury hath long since obtained the prerogative above York (although I say not
without great trouble, suit, some bloodshed, and contention),
so the Archbishop of York is nevertheless written Primate
of England, as one contenting himself with a piece of a
title at the least, when all could not be gotten. And as he
of Canterbury crowneth the king, so this of York doth the
like to the queen, whose perpetual chaplain he is, and
hath been from time to time, since the determination of this
controversy, as writers do report. The first also hath under
his jurisdiction to the number of one-and-twenty inferior
bishops; the other hath only four, by reason that the
churches of Scotland are now removed from his obedience

unto an archbishop of their own, whereby the greatness and circuit of the jurisdiction of York is not a little diminished. In like sort, each of these seven-and-twenty sees have their cathedral churches, wherein the deans (a calling not known in England before the Conquest) do bear the chief rule, being men especially chosen to that vocation, both for their learning and godliness, so near as can be possible. These cathedral churches have in like manner other dignities and canonries still remaining unto them, as heretofore under the popish regiment. Howbeit those that are chosen to the same are no idle and unprofitable persons (as in times past they have been when most of these livings were either furnished with strangers, especially out of Italy, boys, or such idiots as had least skill of all in discharging of those functions whereunto they were called by virtue of these stipends), but such as by preaching and teaching can and do learnedly set forth the glory of God, and further the overthrow of anti-Christ to the uttermost of their powers.

These churches are called cathedral, because the bishops dwell or lie near unto the same, as bound to keep continual residence within their jurisdictions for the better oversight and governance of the same, the word being derived *a cathedra*—that is to say, a chair or seat where he resteth, and for the most part abideth. At the first there was but one church in every jurisdiction, whereinto no man entered to pray but with some oblation or other toward the maintenance of the pastor. For as it was reputed an infamy to pass by any of them without visitation, so it was no less reproach to appear empty before the Lord. And for this occasion also they were builded very huge and great; for otherwise they were not capable to such multitude as came daily unto them to hear the Word and receive the sacraments.

But as the number of Christians increased, so first monasteries, then finally parish churches, were builded in every jurisdiction: from whence I take our deanery churches to have their original (now called "mother churches," and their incumbents, archpriests), the rest being added since the Conquest, either by the lords of every town, or zealous men,

loth to travel far, and willing to have some ease by building
them near hand. Unto these deanery churches also the
clergy in old time of the same deanery were appointed to
repair at sundry seasons, there to receive wholesome ordinances, and to consult upon the necessary affairs of the
whole jurisdiction if necessity so required; and some image
hereof is yet to be seen in the north parts. But as the
number of churches increased, so the repair of the faithful
unto the cathedrals did diminish; whereby they now become,
especially in their nether parts, rather markets and shops
for merchandise than solemn places of prayer, whereunto
they were first erected. Moreover, in the said cathedral
churches upon Sundays and festival days the canons do make
certain ordinary sermons by course, whereunto great numbers
of all estates do orderly resort; and upon the working days,
thrice in the week, one of the said canons (or some other in
his stead) doth read and expound some piece of holy
Scripture, whereunto the people do very reverently repair.
The bishops themselves in like sort are not idle in their
callings; for, being now exempt from court and council,
which is one (and a no small) piece of their felicity (although Richard Archbishop of Canterbury thought otherwise, as yet appeareth by his letters to Pope Alexander,
Epistola 44, Petri Blesensis, where he saith, because the
clergy of his time were somewhat narrowly looked unto,
"*Supra dorsum ecclesiæ fabricant peccatores,*" etc.),[4] they
so apply their minds to the setting forth of the Word that
there are very few of them which do not every Sunday or
oftener resort to some place or other within their jurisdictions where they expound the Scriptures with much gravity
and skill, and yet not without the great misliking and contempt of such as hate the Word. Of their manifold translations from one see to another I will say nothing, which
is not now done for the benefit of the flock as the preferment of the party favoured and advantage unto the prince,
a matter in time past much doubted of—to wit, whether a
bishop or pastor might be translated from one see to another,
and left undecided till prescription by royal authority made
it good. For, among princes, a thing once done is well done,

[4] " Sinners build on the back of the church."

and to be done oftentimes, though no warrant be to be found therefore.

They have under them also their archdeacons, some one, divers two, and many four or more, as their circuits are in quantity, which archdeacons are termed in law the bishops' eyes; and these (beside their ordinary courts, which are holden within so many or more of their several deaneries by themselves or their officials once in a month at the least) do keep yearly two visitations or synods (as the bishop doth in every third year, wherein he confirmeth some children, though most care but a little for that ceremony), in which they make diligent inquisition and search, as well for the doctrine and behaviour of the ministers as the orderly dealing of the parishioners in resorting to their parish churches and conformity unto religion. They punish also with great severity all such trespassers, either in person or by the purse (where permutation of penance is thought more grievous to the offender), as are presented unto them; or, if the cause be of the more weight, as in cases of heresy, pertinacy, contempt, and such like, they refer them either to the bishop of the diocese, or his chancellor, or else to sundry grave persons set in authority, by virtue of an high commission directed unto them from the prince to that end, who in very courteous manner do see the offenders gently reformed or else severely punished if necessity so enforce.

Beside this, in many of our archdeaconries, we have an exercise lately begun which for the most part is called a *prophecy* or *conference,* and erected only for the examination or trial of the diligence of the clergy in their study of holy Scriptures. Howbeit, such is the thirsty desire of the people in these days to hear the Word of God that they also have as it were with zealous violence intruded themselves among them (but as hearers only) to come by more knowledge through their presence at the same. Herein also (for the most part) two of the younger sort of ministers do expound each after other some piece of the Scriptures ordinarily appointed unto them in their courses (wherein they orderly go through with some one of the Evangelists, or of the Epistles, as it pleaseth the whole assembly to choose at the first in every of these conferences); and when they

have spent an hour or a little more between them, then
cometh one of the better learned sort, who, being a graduate
for the most part, or known to be a preacher sufficiently
authorised and of a sound judgment, supplieth the room of
a moderator, making first a brief rehearsal of their dis-
courses, and then adding what him thinketh good of his
own knowledge, whereby two hours are thus commonly
spent at this most profitable meeting. When all is done, if
the first speakers have shewed any piece of diligence, they
are commended for their travel, and encouraged to go forward. If they have been found to be slack, or not sound
in delivery of their doctrine, their negligence and error is
openly reproved before all their brethren, who go aside of
purpose from the laity after the exercise ended to judge of
these matters, and consult of the next speakers and quantity
of the text to be handled in that place. The laity never
speak, of course (except some vain and busy head will
now and then intrude themselves with offence), but are only
hearers; and, as it is used in some places weekly, in other
once in fourteen days, in divers monthly, and elsewhere
twice in a year, so is it a notable spur unto all the ministers
thereby to apply their books, which otherwise (as in times
past) would give themselves to hawking, hunting, tables,
cards, dice, tippling at the alehouse, shooting of matches,
and other like vanities, nothing commendable in such as
should be godly and zealous stewards of the good gifts of
God, faithful distributors of his Word unto the people, and
diligent pastors according to their calling.

But alas! as Sathan, the author of all mischief, hath in
sundry manners heretofore hindered the erection and maintenance of many good things, so in this he hath stirred up
adversaries of late unto this most profitable exercise, who,
not regarding the commodity that riseth thereby so well to
the hearers as speakers, but either stumbling (I cannot tell
how) at words and terms, or at the leastwise not liking to
hear of the reprehension of vice, or peradventure taking a
misliking at the slender demeanours of such negligent
ministers as now and then in their course do occupy the
rooms, have either by their own practice, their sinister information, or suggestions made upon surmises unto other,

procured the suppression of these conferences, condemning them as hurtful, pernicious, and daily breeders of no small hurt and inconvenience. But hereof let God be judge, unto the cause belongeth.

Our elders or ministers and deacons (for subdeacons and the other inferior orders sometime used in popish church we have not) are made according to a certain form of consecration concluded upon in the time of King Edward the Sixth by the clergy of England, and soon after confirmed by the three estates of the realm in the high court of parliament. And out of the first sort—that is to say, of such as are called to the ministry (without respect whether they be married or not)—are bishops, deans, archdeacons, and such as have the higher places in the hierarchy of the church elected; and these also, as all the rest, at the first coming unto any spiritual promotion do yield unto the prince the entire tax of that their living for one whole year, if it amount in value unto ten pounds and upwards, and this under the name and title of first fruits.

With us also it is permitted that a sufficient man may (by dispensation from the prince) hold two livings, not distant either from other above thirty miles; whereby it cometh to pass that, as her Majesty doth reap some commodity by the faculty, so that the unition of two in one man doth bring oftentimes more benefit to one of them in a month (I mean for doctrine) than they have had before peradventure in many years.

Many exclaim against such faculties, as if there were more good preachers that want maintenance than livings to maintain them. Indeed when a living is void there are so many suitors for it that a man would think the report to be true, and most certain; but when it cometh to the trial (who are sufficient and who not, who are staid men in conversation, judgment, and learning), of that great number you shall hardly find one or two such as they ought to be, and yet none more earnest to make suit, to promise largely, bear a better shew, or find fault with the stage of things than they. Nevertheless I do not think that their exclamations, if they were wisely handled, are altogether grounded upon rumours or ambitious minds, if you respect the state

of the thing itself, and not the necessity growing through
want of able men to furnish out all the cures in England,
which both our universities are never able to perform. For
if you observe what numbers of preachers Cambridge and
Oxford do yearly send forth, and how many new compositions are made in the Court of First Fruits by the deaths of
the last incumbents, you shall soon see a difference. Wherefore, if in country towns and cities, yea even in London
itself, four or five of the little churches were brought into
one, the inconvenience would in great part be redressed and
amended.

And, to say truth, one most commonly of those small
livings is of so little value that it is not able to maintain a
mean scholar, much less a learned man, as not being above
ten, twelve, sixteen, seventeen, twenty, or thirty pounds at
the most, toward their charges, which now (more than before time) do go out of the same. I say more than before,
because every small trifle, nobleman's request, or courtesy
craved by the bishop, doth impose and command a twentieth
part, a three score part, or twopence in the pound, etc., out
of the livings, which hitherto hath not been usually granted,
but by the consent of a synod, wherein things were decided
according to equity, and the poorer sort considered of,
which now are equally burdened.

We pay also the tenths of our livings to the prince yearly,
according to such valuation of each of them as hath been
lately made: which nevertheless in time past were not annual,
but voluntary, and paid at request of king or pope.[5] . . .

But to return to our tenths, a payment first as devised by
the pope, and afterward taken up as by the prescription of
the king, whereunto we may join also our first fruits, which
is one whole year's commodity of our living, due at our
entrance into the same, the tenths abated unto the prince's
coffers, and paid commonly in two years. For the receipt
also of these two payments an especial office or court is
erected, which beareth name of First Fruits and Tenths,
whereunto, if the party to be preferred do not make his
dutiful repair by an appointed time after possession taken,

[5] Here follows a story about the bootless errand of a pope's legate in
1452.—W.

there to compound for the payment of his said fruits, he incurreth the danger of a great penalty, limited by a certain statute provided in that behalf against such as do intrude into the ecclesiastical function and refuse to pay the accustomed duties belonging to the same.

They pay likewise subsidies with the temporalty, but in such sort that if these pay after four shillings for land, the clergy contribute commonly after six shillings of the pound, so that of a benefice of twenty pounds by the year the incumbent thinketh himself well acquitted if, all ordinary payments being discharged, he may reserve thirteen pounds six shillings eightpence towards his own sustentation or maintenance of his family. Seldom also are they without the compass of a subsidy; for if they be one year clear from this payment (a thing not often seen of late years), they are like in the next to hear of another grant: so that I say again they are seldom without the limit of a subsidy. Herein also they somewhat find themselves grieved that the laity may at every taxation help themselves, and so they do, through consideration had of their decay and hindrance, and yet their impoverishment cannot but touch also the parson or vicar, unto whom such liberty is denied, as is daily to be seen in their accounts and tithings.

Some of them also, after the marriages of their children, will have their proportions qualified, or by friendship get themselves quite out of the book. But what stand I upon these things, who have rather to complain of the injury offered by some of our neighbours of the laity, which daily endeavour to bring us also within the compass of their fifteens or taxes for their own ease, whereas the tax of the whole realm, which is commonly greater in the champagne than woodland soil, amounteth only to 37,930 pounds ninepence halfpenny, is a burden easy enough to be borne upon so many shoulders, without the help of the clergy, whose tenths and subsidies make up commonly a double, if not treble sum unto their aforesaid payments? Sometimes also we are threatened with a *Melius inquirendum,* as if our livings were not racked high enough already. But if a man should seek out where all those church lands which in time past did contribute unto the old sum required or to be made up, no doubt no small number of the laity of all states should be contributors also with us, the prince not defrauded of her expectation and right. We are also charged with armour and munitions from thirty pounds upwards, a thing more needful than divers other charges imposed upon us are convenient, by which and other burdens our ease groweth to be more heavy by a great deal (notwithstanding our immunity from temporal services) than that of the laity, and, for aught that I see, not likely to be diminished, as if the church were now become the ass whereon every market man is to ride and cast his wallet.

The other payments due unto the archbishop and bishop at their several visitations (of which the first is double to the latter), and such also as the archdeacon receive that his synods, etc., remain still as they did without any alteration. Only this I think he added within memory of man, that at the coming of every prince his appointed officers do commonly visit the whole realm under the form of an ecclesiastical inquisition, in which the clergy do usually pay double fees, as unto the archbishop.

Hereby then, and by those already remembered, it is found that the Church of England is no less commodious to the prince's coffers than the state of the laity, if it do not far exceed the same, since their payments are certain, continual, and seldom abated, howsoever they gather up their own duties with grudging, murmuring, suit, and slanderous speeches of the payers, or have their livings otherwise hardly valued unto the uttermost farthing, or shrewdly cancelled by the covetousness of the patrons, of whom some do bestow advowsons of benefices upon their bakers, butlers, cooks, good archers, falconers, and horse-keepers, instead of other recompense, for their long and faithful service, which they employ afterward unto the most advantage.

Certes here they resemble the pope very much; for, as he sendeth out his idols, so do they their parasites, pages, chamberlains, stewards, grooms, and lackeys; and yet these be the men that first exclaim of the insufficiency of the ministers, as hoping thereby in due time to get also their glebes and grounds into their hands. In times past bishoprics went almost after the same manner under the lay princes, and then under the pope, so that he which helped a clerk unto a see was sure to have a present or purse fine, if not an annual pension, besides that which went to the pope's coffers, and was thought to be very good merchandise.

To proceed therefore with the rest, I think it good also to remember that the names usually given unto such as feed the flock remain in like sort as in times past, so that these words, *parson, vicar, curate,* and such, are not yet abolished more than the canon law itself, which is daily pleaded, as I have said elsewhere, although the statutes of the realm have greatly infringed the large scope and brought the exercise of the same into some narrower limits. There is nothing read in our churches but the canonical Scriptures, whereby it cometh to pass that the Psalter is said over once in thirty days, the New Testament four times, and the Old Testament once in the year. And hereunto, if the curate be adjudged by the bishop or his deputies sufficiently instructed in the holy Scriptures, and therewithal able to teach, he permitteth him to make some exposition or exhortation in his parish unto amendment of life. And for so much as our churches and universities have been so spoiled in time of error, as there cannot yet be had such number of able pastors as may suffice for every parish to have one, there are (beside four sermons appointed by public order in the year) certain sermons or homilies (devised by sundry learned men, confirmed for sound doctrine by consent of the divines, and public authority of the prince), and those appointed to be read by the curates of mean understanding (which homilies do comprehend the principal parts of Christian doctrine, as of original sin, of justification by faith, of charity, and such like) upon the Sabbath days unto the congregation. And, after a certain number of psalms read, which are limited according to the dates of the month, for morning and evening prayer we have two lessons, whereof the first is taken out of the Old Testament, the second out of the New; and of these latter, that in the morning is out of the Gospels, the other in the afternoon out of some one of the Epistles. After morning prayer also, we have the Litany and suffrages, an invocation in mine opinion not devised without the great assistance of the Spirit of God, although many curious mind-sick persons utterly condemn it as superstitious, and savouring of conjuration and sorcery.

This being done, we proceed unto the communion, if any communicants be to receive the Eucharist; if not, we read the Decalogue, Epistle, and Gospel, with the Nicene Creed (of some in derision called the "dry communion"), and then proceed unto an homily or sermon, which hath a psalm before and after it, and finally unto the baptism of such infants as on every Sabbath day (if occasion so require) are brought unto the churches; and thus is the forenoon bestowed. In the afternoon likewise we meet again, and, after the psalms and lessons ended, we have commonly a sermon, or at the leastwise our youth catechised by the space of an hour. And thus do we spend the Sabbath day in good and godly exercises, all done in our vulgar tongue, that each one present may hear and understand the same, which also in cathedral and collegiate churches is so ordered that the psalms only are sung by note, the rest being read (as in common parish churches) by the minister with a loud voice, saving that in the administration of the communion the choir singeth the answers, the creed, and sundry other things appointed, but in so plain, I say, and distinct manner that each one present may understand what they sing, every word having but one note, though the whole harmony consist of many parts, and those very cunningly set by the skilful in that science.

Certes this translation of the service of the church into the vulgar tongue hath not a little offended the pope almost in every age, as a thing very often attempted by divers princes, but never generally obtained, for fear lest the consenting thereunto might breed the overthrow (as it would indeed) of all his religion and hierarchy; nevertheless, in some places where the kings and princes dwelled not under his nose, it was performed maugre his resistance. Wratislaus, Duke of Bohemia, would long since have done the like also in his kingdom; but, not daring to venture so far without the consent of the pope, he wrote unto him thereof, and received his answer inhibitory unto all his proceeding in the same. . . .

I would set down two or three more of the like instruments passed from that see unto the like end, but this shall suffice, being less common than the other, which are to be had more plentifully.

As for our churches themselves, bells and times of morning and evening prayer remain as in times past, saving that all images, shrines, tabernacles, rood-lofts, and monuments of idolatry are removed, taken down, and defaced, only the stories in glass windows excepted, which, for want of sufficient store of new stuff, and by reason of extreme charge that should grow by the alteration of the same into white panes throughout the realm, are not altogether abolished in most places at once, but by little and little suffered to decay, that white glass may be provided and set up in their rooms. Finally, whereas there was wont to be a great partition between the choir and the body of the church, now it is either very small or none at all, and (to say the truth) altogether needless, sith the minister saith his service commonly in the body of the church, with his face toward the people, in a little tabernacle of wainscot provided for the purpose, by which means the ignorant do not only learn divers of the psalms and usual prayers by heart, but also such as can read do pray together with him, so that the whole congregation at one instant pour out their petitions unto the living God for the whole estate of His church in most earnest and fervent manner. Our holy and festival days are very well reduced also unto a less number; for whereas (not long since) we had under the pope four score and fifteen, called festival, and thirty *profesti,* beside the Sundays, they are all brought unto seven and twenty, and, with them, the superfluous numbers of idle wakes, guilds, fraternities, church-ales, help-ales, and soul-ales, called also dirge-ales, with the heathenish rioting at bride-ales, are well diminished and laid aside. And no great matter were it if the feasts of all our apostles, evangelists, and martyrs, with that of all saints, were brought to the holy days that follow upon Christmas, Easter, and Whitsuntide, and those of the Virgin Mary, with the rest, utterly removed from the calendars, as neither necessary nor commendable in a reformed church.

The apparel in like sort of our clergymen is comely, and, in truth, more decent than ever it was in the popish church, before the universities bound their graduates unto a stable attire, afterward usurped also even by the blind Sir Johns. For, if you peruse well my Chronology ensuing, you shall find that they went either in divers colours like players, or in garments of light hue, as yellow, red, green, etc., with their shoes piked, their hair crisped, their girdles armed with silver, their shoes, spurs, bridles, etc., buckled with like metal, their apparel (for the most part) of silk, and richly furred, their caps laced and buttoned with gold, so that to meet a priest in those days was to behold a peacock that spreadeth his tail when he danceth before the hen, which now (I say) is well reformed. Touching hospitality, there was never any greater used in England, sith by reason that marriage is permitted to him that will choose that kind of life, their meat and drink is more orderly and frugally dressed, their furniture of household more convenient and better looked unto, and the poor oftener fed generally than heretofore they have been, when only a few bishops and double or treble beneficed men did make good cheer at Christmas only, or otherwise kept great houses for the entertainment of the rich, which did often see and visit them. It is thought much peradventure that some bishops, etc., in our time do come short of the ancient gluttony and prodigality of their predecessors; but to such as do consider of the curtailing of their livings, or excessive prices whereunto things are grown, and how their course is limited by law, and estate looked into on every side, the cause of their so doing is well enough perceived. This also offended many, that they should, after their deaths, leave their substances to their wives and children, whereas they consider not that in old time such as had no lemans nor bastards (very few were there, God wot, of this sort) did leave their goods and possessions to their brethren and kinsfolks, whereby (as I can shew by good record) many houses of gentility have grown and been erected. If in any age some one of them did found a college, almshouse, or school, if you look unto these our times, you shall see no fewer deeds of charity done, nor better grounded upon the right stub of piety than before. If you say that their wives be fond, after the decease of their husbands, and bestow themselves not so advisedly as their calling requireth (which, God knoweth, these curious surveyors make small account of truth, further than thereby to gather matter of reprehension), I beseech you then to look into all states of the laity, and tell me whether some duchesses, countesses, barons' or knights' wives, do not fully so often offend in the like as they? For Eve will be Eve, though Adam would say nay. Not a few also find fault with our threadbare gowns, as if not our patrons but our wives were causes of our woe. But if it were known to all that I know to have been performed of late in Essex, where a minister taking a benefice (of less than twenty pounds in the Queen's books, so far as I remember) was enforced to pay to his patron twenty quarters of oats, ten quarters of wheat, and sixteen yearly of barley (which he called *hawks' meat*), and another let the like in farm to his patron for ten pounds by the year which is well worth forty at the least, the cause of our threadbare gowns would easily appear: for such patrons do scrape the wool from our cloaks. Wherefore I may well say that such a threadbare minister is either an ill man or hath an ill patron, or both; and when such cooks and cobbling shifters shall be removed and weeded out of the ministry, I doubt not but our patrons will prove better men, and be reformed whether they will or not, or else the single-minded bishops shall see the living bestowed upon such as do deserve it. When the Pragmatic Sanction took place first in France, it was supposed that these enormities should utterly have ceased; but when the elections of bishops came once into the hands of the canons and spiritual men, it grew to be far worse. For they also, within a while waxing covetous, by their own experience learned aforehand, raised the markets, and sought after new gains by the gifts of the greatest livings in that country, wherein (as Machiavelli writeth) are eighteen archbishoprics, one hundred forty and five bishoprics, 740 abbeys, eleven universities, 1,000,700 steeples (if his report be sound). Some are of the opinion that, if sufficient men in every town might be sent for from the universities, this mischief would soon be remedied; but

I am clean of another mind. For, when I consider whereunto the gifts of fellowships in some places are grown, the
profit that ariseth at sundry elections of scholars out of
grammar schools to the posers, schoolmasters, and preferers
of them to our universities, the gifts of a great number of
almshouses builded for the maimed and impotent soldiers
by princes and good men heretofore moved with a pitiful
consideration of the poor distressed, how rewards, pensions,
and annuities also do reign in other cases whereby the giver
is brought sometimes into extreme misery, and that not so
much as the room of a common soldier is not obtained oftentimes without a *" What will you give me?"* I am brought
into such a mistrust of the sequel of this device that I dare
pronounce (almost for certain) that, if Homer were now
alive, it should be said to him:

> " Tuque licet venias musis comitatus Homere,
> Si nihil attuleris, ibis Homere foras ! "

More I could say, and more I would say, of these and
other things, were it not that in mine own judgment I have
said enough already for the advertisement of such as be
wise. Nevertheless, before I finish this chapter, I will add
a word or two (so briefly as I can) of the old estate of
cathedral churches, which I have collected together here
and there among the writers, and whereby it shall easily
be seen what they were, and how near the government of
ours do in these days approach unto them; for that there is
an irreconcilable odds between them and those of the
Papists, I hope there is no learned man indeed but will
acknowledge and yield unto it.

We find therefore in the time of the primitive church
that there was in every see or jurisdiction one school at the
least, whereunto such as were catechists in Christian religion did resort. And hereof, as we may find great testimony for Alexandria, Antioch, Rome, and Jerusalem, so no
small notice is left of the like in the inferior sort, if the
names of such as taught in them be called to mind, and the
histories well read which make report of the same. These
schools were under the jurisdiction of the bishops, and from
thence did they and the rest of the elders choose out such

as were the ripest scholars, and willing to serve in the
ministry, whom they placed also in their cathedral churches,
there not only to be further instructed in the knowledge
of the world, but also to inure them to the delivery of the
same unto the people in sound manner, to minister the sacraments, to visit the sick and brethren imprisoned, and to perform such other duties as then belonged to their charges.
The bishop himself and elders of the church were also
hearers and examiners of their doctrine; and, being in
process of time found meet workmen for the Lord's harvest,
they were forthwith sent abroad (after imposition of hands
and prayer generally made for their good proceeding) to
some place or other then destitute of her pastor, and other
taken from the school also placed in their rooms. What
number of such clerks belonged now and then to some one
see, the Chronology following shall easily declare; and, in
like sort, what officers, widows, and other persons were daily
maintained in those seasons by the offerings and oblations
of the faithful it is incredible to be reported, if we compare
the same with the decays and oblations seen and practised
at this present. But what is that in all the world which
avarice and negligence will not corrupt and impair? And,
as this is a pattern of the estate of the cathedral churches
in those times, so I wish that the like order of government
might once again be restored unto the same, which may be
done with ease, sith the schools are already builded in every
diocese, the universities, places of their preferment unto
further knowledge, and the cathedral churches great enough
to receive so many as shall come from thence to be instructed unto doctrine. But one hindrance of this is already
and more and more to be looked for (beside the plucking
and snatching commonly seen from such houses and the
church), and that is, the general contempt of the ministry,
and small consideration of their former pains taken,
whereby less and less hope of competent maintenance by
preaching the word is likely to ensue. Wherefore the
greatest part of the more excellent wits choose rather to
employ their studies unto physic and the laws, utterly giving
over the study of the Scriptures, for fear lest they should
in time not get their bread by the same. By this means

also the stalls in their choirs would be better filled, which
now (for the most part) are empty, and prebends should be
prebends indeed, there to live till they were preferred to
some ecclesiastical function, and then other men chosen
to succeed them in their rooms, whereas now prebends are
but superfluous additiments unto former excesses, and perpetual commodities unto the owners, which before time
were but temporal (as I have said before). But as I have
good leisure to wish for these things, so it shall be a longer
time before it will be brought to pass. Nevertheless, as I
will pray for a reformation in this behold, so will I here
conclude my discourse on the estate of our churches.

CHAPTER VI

OF THE FOOD AND DIET OF THE ENGLISH

[1577, Book III., Chapter 1; 1587, Book II., Chapter 6.]

THE situation of our region, lying near unto the north, doth cause the heat of our stomachs to be of somewhat greater force: therefore our bodies do crave a little more ample nourishment than the inhabitants of the hotter regions are accustomed withal, whose digestive force is not altogether so vehement, because their internal heat is not so strong as ours, which is kept in by the coldness of the air that from time to time (especially in winter) doth environ our bodies.

It is no marvel therefore that our tables are oftentimes more plentifully garnished than those of other nations, and this trade hath continued with us even since the very beginning. For, before the Romans found out and knew the way unto our country, our predecessors fed largely upon flesh and milk, whereof there was great abundance in this isle, because they applied their chief studies unto pasturage and feeding. After this manner also did our Welsh Britons order themselves in their diet so long as they lived of themselves, but after they became to be united and made equal with the English they framed their appetites to live after our manner, so that at this day there is very little difference between us in our diets.

In Scotland likewise they have given themselves (of late years to speak of) unto very ample and large diet, wherein as for some respect nature doth make them equal with us, so otherwise they far exceed us in over much and distemperate gormandise, and so ingross their bodies that divers of them do oft become unapt to any other purpose than to spend their times in large tabling and belly cheer. Against

285

this pampering of their carcasses doth Hector Boethius in
his description of the country very sharply inveigh in the
first chapter of that treatise. Henry Wardlaw also, bishop
of St. Andrews, noting their vehement alteration from
competent frugality into excessive gluttony to be brought
out of England with James the First (who had been long
time prisoner there under the fourth and fifth Henries, and
at his return carried divers English gentlemen into his
country with him, whom he very honourably preferred
there), doth vehemently exclaim against the same in open
Parliament holden at Perth, 1433, before the three estates,
and so bringeth his purpose to pass in the end, by force of
his learned persuasions, that a law was presently made
there for the restraint of superfluous diet; amongst other
things, baked meats (dishes never before this man's days
seen in Scotland) were generally so provided for by virtue
of this Act that it was not lawful for any to eat of the
same under the degree of a gentleman, and those only but
on high and festival days. But, alas, it was soon forgotten!

In old time these north Britons did give themselves universally to great abstinence, and in time of wars their
soldiers would often feed but once or twice at the most in
two or three days (especially if they held themselves in
secret, or could have no issue out of their bogs and marshes,
through the presence of the enemy), and in this distress
they used to eat a certain kind of confection, whereof so
much as a bean would qualify their hunger above common
expectation. In woods moreover they lived with herbs and
roots, or, if these shifts served not through want of such
provision at hand, then used they to creep into the water
or said moorish plots up unto the chins, and there remain
a long time, only to qualify the heats of their stomachs by
violence, which otherwise would have wrought and been
ready to oppress them for hunger and want of sustenance.
In those days likewise it was taken for a great offence over
all to eat either goose, hare, or hen, because of a certain
superstitious opinion which they had conceived of those
three creatures; howbeit after that the Romans, I say, had
once found an entrance into this island it was not long ere
open shipwreck was made of this religious observation, so

that in process of time so well the north and south Britons as the Romans gave over to make such difference in meats as they had done before.

From thenceforth also unto our days, and even in this season wherein we live, there is no restraint of any meat either for religious sake or public order in England, but it is lawful for every man to feed upon whatsoever he is able to purchase, except it be upon those days whereon eating of flesh is especially forbidden by the laws of the realm, which order is taken only to the end our numbers of cattle may be the better increased and that abundance of fish which the sea yieldeth more generally received. Besides this, there is great consideration had in making this law for the preservation of the navy and maintenance of convenient numbers of seafaring men, both which would otherwise greatly decay if some means were not found whereby they might be increased. But, howsoever this case standeth, white meats, milk, butter, and cheese (which were never so dear as in my time, and wont to be accounted of as one of the chief stays throughout the island) are now reputed as food appertinent only to the inferior sort, whilst such as are more wealthy do feed upon the flesh of all kinds of cattle accustomed to be eaten, all sorts of fish taken upon our coasts and in our fresh rivers, and such diversity of wild and tame fowls as are either bred in our island or brought over unto us from other countries of the main.

In number of dishes and change of meat the nobility of England (whose cooks are for the most part musical-headed Frenchmen and strangers) do most exceed, sith there is no day in manner that passeth over their heads wherein they have not only beef, mutton, veal, lamb, kid, pork, cony, capon, pig, or so many of these as the season yieldeth, but also some portion of the red or fallow deer, beside great variety of fish and wild fowl, and thereto sundry other delicates wherein the sweet hand of the seafaring Portugal is not wanting: so that for a man to dine with one of them, and to taste of every dish that standeth before him (which few used to do, but each one feedeth upon that meat him best liketh for the time, the beginning of every dish notwithstanding being reserved unto the greatest personage

that sitteth at the table, to whom it is drawn up still by the
waiters as order requireth, and from whom it descendeth
again even to the lower end, whereby each one may taste
thereof), is rather to yield unto a conspiracy with a great
deal of meat for the speedy suppression of natural health
than the use of a necessary mean to satisfy himself with a
competent repast to sustain his body withal. But, as this
large feeding is not seen in their guests, no more is it in
their own persons; for, sith they have daily much resort
unto their tables (and many times unlooked for), and
thereto retain great numbers of servants, it is very requisite
and expedient for them to be somewhat plentiful in this
behalf.

The chief part likewise of their daily provision is brought
in before them (commonly in silver vessels, if they be of
the degree of barons, bishops, and upwards) and placed on
their tables, whereof, when they have taken what it pleaseth
them, the rest is reserved, and afterwards sent down to their
serving men and waiters, who feed thereon in like sort with
convenient moderation, their reversion also being bestowed
upon the poor which lie ready at their gates in great numbers to receive the same. This is spoken of the principal
tables whereat the nobleman, his lady, and guests are accustomed to sit; besides which they have a certain ordinary
allowance daily appointed for their halls, where the chief
officers and household servants (for all are not permitted
by custom to wait upon their master), and with them such
inferior guests do feed as are not of calling to associate
the nobleman himself; so that, besides those afore-men-
tioned, which are called to the principal table, there are
commonly forty or three score persons fed in those halls,
to the great relief of such poor suitors and strangers also
as oft be partakers thereof and otherwise like to dine hardly.
As for drink, it is usually filled in pots, goblets, jugs, bowls
of silver, in noblemen's houses; also in fine Venice glasses
of all forms; and, for want of these elsewhere, in pots of
earth of sundry colours and moulds, whereof many are
garnished with silver, or at the leastwise in pewter, all
which notwithstanding are seldom set on the table, but
each one, as necessity urgeth, calleth for a cup of such

drink as him listeth to have, so that, when he has tasted
of it, he delivered the cup again to some one of the standers
by, who, making it clean by pouring out the drink that
remaineth, restoreth it to the cupboard from whence he
fetched the same. By this device (a thing brought up at
the first by Mnesitheus of Athens, in conservation of the
honour of Orestes, who had not yet made expiation for the
death of his adulterous parents, Ægisthus and Clytemnestra)
much idle tippling is furthermore cut off; for, if the full
pots should continually stand at the elbow or near the
trencher, divers would always be dealing with them,
whereas now they drink seldom, and only when necessity
urgeth, and so avoid the note of great drinking, or often
troubling of the servitors with filling of their bowls. Nevertheless in the noblemen's halls this order is not used, neither
is any man's house commonly under the degree of a knight
or esquire of great revenues. It is a world to see in these
our days, wherein gold and silver most aboundeth, how that
our gentility, as loathing those metals (because of the
plenty) do now generally choose rather the Venice glasses,
both for our wine and beer, than any of those metals or
stone wherein before time we have been accustomed to
drink; but such is the nature of man generally that it most
coveteth things difficult to be attained; and such is the estimation of this stuff that many become rich only with their
new trade unto Murana (a town near to Venice, situate on
the Adriatic Sea), from whence the very best are daily to
be had, and such as for beauty do well near match the crystal
or the ancient *murrhina vasa* whereof now no man hath
knowledge. And as this is seen in the gentility, so in the
wealthy communalty the like desire of glass is not neglected,
whereby the gain gotten by their purchase is yet much
more increased to the benefit of the merchant. The
poorest also will have glass if they may; but, sith the Vene-
tian is somewhat too dear for them, they content themselves
with such as are made at home of fern and burned stone;
but in fine all go one way—that is, to shards at the last,
so that our great expenses in glasses (beside that they breed
much strife toward such as have the charge of them) are
worst of all bestowed in mine opinion, because their pieces

do turn unto no profit. If the philosopher's stone were once found, and one part hereof mixed with forty of molten glass, it would induce such a metallical toughness thereunto that a fall should nothing hurt it in such manner; yet it might peradventure bunch or batter it; nevertheless that inconvenience were quickly to be redressed by the hammer. But whither am I slipped?

The gentlemen and merchants keep much about one rate, and each of them contenteth himself with four, five, or six dishes, when they have but small resort, or peradventure with one, or two, or three at the most, when they have no strangers to accompany them at their tables. And yet their servants have their ordinary diet assigned, beside such as is left at their master's boards, and not appointed to be brought thither the second time, which nevertheless is often seen, generally in venison, lamb, or some especial dish, whereon the merchantman himself liketh to feed when it is cold, or peradventure for sundry causes incident to the feeder is better so than if it were warm or hot. To be short, at such times as the merchants do make their ordinary or voluntary feasts, it is a world to see what great provision is made of all manner of delicate meats, from every quarter of the country, wherein, beside that they are often comparable herein to the nobility of the land, they will seldom regard anything that the butcher usually killeth, but reject the same as not worthy to come in place. In such cases also jellies of all colours, mixed with a variety in the representation of sundry flowers, herbs, trees, forms of beasts, fish, fowls, and fruits, and thereunto marchpane wrought with no small curiosity, tarts of divers hues, and sundry denominations, conserves of old fruits, foreign and home-bred, suckets, codinacs, marmalades, marchpane, sugar-bread, gingerbread, florentines, wild fowls, venison of all sorts, and sundry outlandish confections, altogether seasoned with sugar (which Pliny calleth *mel ex arundinibus,* a device not common nor greatly used in old time at the table, but only in medicine, although it grew in Arabia, India, and Sicilia), do generally bear the sway, besides infinite devices of our own not possible for me to remember. Of the potato, and such venerous roots as are brought out of Spain, Portugal, and the Indies to furnish up our banquets, I speak not, wherein our mures[1] of no less force, and to be had about Crosby-Ravenswath, do now begin to have place.

But among all these, the kind of meat which is obtained with most difficulty and costs, is commonly taken for the most delicate, and thereupon each guest will soonest desire to feed. And as all estates do exceed herein, I mean for strangeness and number of costly dishes, so these forget not to use the like excess in wine, insomuch as there is no kind to be had, neither anywhere more store of all sorts than in England, although we have none growing with us but yearly to the proportion of 20,000 or 30,000 tun and upwards, notwithstanding the daily restraints of the same brought over unto us, whereof at great meetings there is not some store to be had. Neither do I mean this of small wines only, as claret, white, red, French, etc., which amount to about fifty-six sorts, according to the number of regions from whence they came, but also of the thirty kinds of Italian, Grecian, Spanish, Canarian, etc., whereof vernage, catepument, raspis, muscadell, romnie, bastard lire, osy caprie, clary, and malmesey, are not least of all accompted of, because of their strength and valour. For, as I have said in meat, so, the stronger the wine is, the more it is desired, by means whereof, in old time, the best was called *theologicum,* because it was had from the clergy and religious men, unto whose houses many of the laity would often send for bottles filled with the same, being sure they would neither drink nor be served of the worst, or such as was any ways mingled or brewed by the vinterer: nay, the merchant would have thought that his soul should have gone straightway to the devil if he should have served them with other than the best. Furthermore, when these have had their course which nature yieldeth, sundry sorts of artificial stuff as ypocras and wormwood wine must in like manner succeed in their turns, beside stale ale and strong beer, which nevertheless bear the greatest brunt in drinking, and are of so many sorts and ages as it pleaseth the brewer to make them.

[1] Sweet cicely, sometimes miscalled myrrh. Mure is the Saxon word. At one time the plant was not uncommon as a salad.—W.

The beer that is used at noblemen's tables in their fixed and standing houses is commonly a year old, or peradventure of two years' tunning or more; but this is not general. It is also brewed in March, and therefore called March beer; but, for the household, it is usually not under a month's age, each one coveting to have the same stale as he may, so that it be not sour, and his bread new as is possible, so that it be not hot.

The artificer and husbandman makes greatest account of such meat as they may soonest come by, and have it quickliest ready, except it be in London when the companies of every trade do meet on their quarter days, at which time they be nothing inferior to the nobility. Their food also consisteth principally in beef, and such meat as the butcher selleth—that is to say, mutton, veal, lamb, pork, etc., whereof he findeth great store in the markets adjoining, beside sows, brawn, bacon, fruit, pies of fruit, fowls of sundry sorts, cheese, butter, eggs, etc., as the other wanteth it not at home, by his own provision which is at the best hand, and commonly least charge. In feasting also, this latter sort, I mean the husbandmen, do exceed after their manner, especially at bridals, purifications of women, and such odd meetings, where it is incredible to tell what meat is consumed and spent, each one bringing such a dish, or so many with him, as his wife and he do consult upon, but always with this consideration, that the lesser friend shall have the better provision. This also is commonly seen at these banquets, that the good man of the house is not charged with anything saving bread, drink, sauce, house-room, and fire. But the artificers in cities and good towns do deal far otherwise; for, albeit that some of them do suffer their jaws to go oft before their claws, and divers of them, by making good cheer, do hinder themselves and other men, yet the wiser sort can handle the matter well enough in these junketings, and therefore their frugality deserveth commendation. To conclude, both the artificer and the husbandman are sufficiently liberal, and very friendly at their tables; and, when they meet, they are so merry without malice, and plain without inward Italian or French craft and subtlety, that it would do a man good to be in company among them. Herein only are the inferior sort somewhat to be blamed, that, being thus assembled, their talk is now and then such as savoureth of scurrility and ribaldry, a thing naturally incident to carters and clowns, who think themselves not to be merry and welcome if their foolish veins in this behalf be never so little restrained. This is moreover to be added in these meetings, that if they happen to stumble upon a piece of venison and a cup of wine or very strong beer or ale (which latter they commonly provide against their appointed days), they think their cheer so great, and themselves to have fared so well, as the Lord Mayor of London, with whom, when their bellies be full, they will not often stick to make comparison, because that of a subject there is no public officer of any city in Europe that may compare in port and countenance with him during the time of his office.

I might here talk somewhat of the great silence that is used at the tables of the honourable and wiser sort generally over all the realm (albeit that too much deserveth no commendation, for it belongeth to guests neither to be *muti* nor *loquaces*[2]), likewise of the moderate eating and drinking that is daily seen, and finally of the regard that each one hath to keep himself from the note of surfeiting and drunkenness (for which cause salt meat, except beef, bacon, and pork, are not any whit esteemed, and yet these three may not be much powdered); but, as in rehearsal thereof I should commend the nobleman, merchant, and frugal artificer, so I could not clear the meaner sort of husbandmen and country inhabitants of very much babbling (except it be here and there some odd yeoman), with whom he is thought to be the merriest that talketh of most ribaldry or the wisest man that speaketh fastest among them, and now and then surfeiting and drunkenness which they rather fall into for want of heed taking than wilfully following or delighting in those errors of set mind and purpose. It may be that divers of them living at home, with hard and pinching diet, small drink, and some of them having scarce enough of that, are soonest overtaken when they come into such banquets; howbeit they take it generally as no small

[2] Neither " silent " nor " garrulous."

disgrace if they happen to be cupshotten, so that it is a grief unto them, though now sans remedy, sith the thing is done and past. If the friends also of the wealthier sort come to their houses from far, they are commonly so welcome till they depart as upon the first day of their coming; whereas in good towns and cities, as London, etc., men oftentimes complain of little room, and, in reward of a fat capon or plenty of beef and mutton largely bestowed upon them in the country, a cup of wine or beer with a napkin to wipe their lips and an "You are heartily welcome!" is thought to be a great entertainment; and therefore the old country clerks have framed this saying in that behalf, I mean upon the entertainment of townsmen and Londoners after the days of their abode, in this manner:

> "Primus jucundus, tollerabilis estque secundus,
> Tertius est vanus, sed fetet quatriduanus."

The bread throughout the land is made of such grain as the soil yieldeth; nevertheless the gentility commonly provide themselves sufficiently of wheat for their own tables, whilst their household and poor neighbours in some shires are forced to content themselves with rye, or barley, yea, and in time of dearth, many with bread made either of beans, peas, or oats, or of altogether and some acorns among, of which scourge the poorest do soonest taste, sith they are least able to provide themselves of better. I will not say that this extremity is oft so well to be seen in time of plenty as of dearth, but, if I should, I could easily bring my trial. For, albeit that there be much more ground eared now almost in every place than hath been of late years, yet such a price of corn continueth in each town and market without any just cause (except it be that landlords do get licences to carry corn out of the land only to keep up the prices for their own private gains and ruin of the commonwealth), that the artificer and poor labouring man is not able to reach unto it, but is driven to content himself with horse corn—I mean beans, peas, oats, tares, and lentils: and therefore it is a true proverb, and never so well verified as now, that "Hunger setteth his first foot into the horse-manger."[3] If the world last awhile after this

rate, wheat and rye will be no grain for poor men to feed
on; and some caterpillars there are that can say so much
already.

Of bread made of wheat we have sundry sorts daily
brought to the table, whereof the first and most excellent
is the manchet, which we commonly call white bread, in
Latin *primarius panis,* whereof Budeus also speaketh, in his
first book *De asse;* and our good workmen deliver commonly
such proportion that of the flour of one bushel with another
they make forty cast of manchet, of which every loaf
weigheth eight ounces into the oven, and six ounces out,
as I have been informed. The second is the cheat or
wheaten bread, so named because the colour thereof re-
sembleth the grey or yellowish wheat, being clean and well
dressed, and out of this is the coarsest of the bran (usually
called gurgeons or pollard) taken. The ravelled is a kind
of cheat bread also, but it retaineth more of the gross, and
less of the pure substance of the wheat; and this, being
more slightly wrought up, is used in the halls of the nobility
and gentry only, whereas the other either is or should be
baked in cities and good towns of an appointed size (according to such price as the corn doth bear), and by a
statute provided by King John in that behalf.[4] The ravelled
cheat therefore is generally so made that out of one bushel
of meal, after two and twenty pounds of bran be sifted and
taken from it (whereunto they add the gurgeons that rise
from the manchet), they make thirty cast, every loaf
weighing eighteen ounces into the oven, and sixteen ounces
out; and, beside this, they so handle the matter that to every
bushel of meal they add only two and twenty, or three and
twenty, pound of water, washing also (in some houses)
their corn before it go to the mill, whereby their manchet
bread is more excellent in colour, and pleasing to the eye,
than otherwise it would be. The next sort is named brown
bread, of the colour of which we have two sorts one baked
up as it cometh from the mill, so that neither the bran nor
the flour are any whit diminished; this, Celsus called *auto-*

[3] A famine at hand is first seen in the horse-manger, when the poor do
fall to horse corn.—H.
[4] The size of bread is very ill kept or not at all looked unto in the country
towns or markets.—H.

pirus panis, lib. 2, and putteth it in the second place of nourishment. The other hath little or no flour left therein at all, howbeit he calleth it *Panem Cibarium,* and it is not only the worst and weakest of all the other sorts, but also appointed in old time for servants, slaves, and the inferior kind of people to feed upon. Hereunto likewise, because it is dry and brickle in the working (for it will hardly be made up handsomely into loaves), some add a portion of rye meal in our time, whereby the rough dryness or dry roughness thereof is somewhat qualified, and then it is named *miscelin,* that is, bread made of mingled corn, albeit that divers do sow or mingle wheat and rye of set purpose at the mill, or before it come there, and sell the same at the markets under the aforesaid name.

In champaign countries much rye and barley bread is eaten, but especially where wheat is scant and geson. As for the difference that it is between the summer and winter wheat, most husbandmen know it not, sith they are neither acquainted with summer wheat nor winter barley; yet here and there I find of both sorts, specially in the north and about Kendal, where they call it March wheat, and also of summer rye, but in so small quantities as that I dare not pronounce them to be greatly common among us.

Our drink, whose force and continuance is partly touched already, is made of barley, water, and hops, sodden and mingled together, by the industry of our brewers in a certain exact proportion. But, before our barley do come into their hands, it sustaineth great alteration, and is converted into malt, the making whereof I will here set down in such order as my skill therein may extend unto (for I am scarce a good maltster), chiefly for that foreign writers have attempted to describe the same, and the making of our beer, wherein they have shot so far wide, as the quantity of ground was between themselves and their mark. In the meantime bear with me, gentle reader (I beseech thee), that lead thee from the description of the plentiful diet of our country unto the fond report of a servile trade, or rather from a table delicately furnished into a musty malthouse; but such is now thy hap, wherefore I pray thee be contented.

Our malt is made all the year long in some great towns; but in gentlemen's and yeomen's houses, who commonly make sufficient for their own expenses only, the winter half is thought most meet for that commodity: howbeit the malt that is made when the willow doth bud is commonly worst of all. Nevertheless each one endeavoureth to make it of the best barley, which is steeped in a cistern, in greater or less quantity, by the space of three days and three nights, until it be thoroughly soaked. This being done, the water is drained from it by little and little, till it be quite gone. Afterward they take it out, and, laying it upon the clean floor on a round heap, it resteth so until it be ready to shoot at the root end, which maltsters call *combing*. When it beginneth therefore to shoot in this manner, they say it is come, and then forthwith they spread it abroad, first thick, and afterwards thinner and thinner upon the said floor (as it *combeth*), and there it lieth (with turning every day four or five times) by the space of one and twenty days at the least, the workmen not suffering it in any wise to take any heat, whereby the bud end should spire, that bringeth forth the blade, and by which oversight or hurt of the stuff itself the malt would be spoiled and turn small commodity to the brewer. When it hath gone, or been turned, so long upon the floor, they carry it to a kiln covered with hair cloth, where they give it gentle heats (after they have spread it there very thin abroad) till it be dry, and in the meanwhile they turn it often, that it may be uniformly dried. For the more it be dried (yet must it be done with soft fire) the sweeter and better the malt is, and the longer it will continue, whereas, if it be not dried down (as they call it), but slackly handled, it will breed a kind of worm called a weevil, which groweth in the flour of the corn, and in process of time will so eat out itself that nothing shall remain of the grain but even the very rind or husk.

The best malt is tried by the hardness and colour; for, if it look fresh with a yellow hue, and thereto will write like a piece of chalk, after you have bitten a kernel in sunder in the midst, then you may assure yourself that it is dried down. In some places it is dried at leisure with wood alone or straw alone, in others with wood and straw together;

but, of all, the straw dried is the most excellent. For the wood-dried malt when it is brewed, beside that the drink is higher of colour, it doth hurt and annoy the head of him that is not used thereto, because of the smoke. Such also as use both indifferently do bark, cleave, and dry their wood in an oven, thereby to remove all moisture that should procure the fume; and this malt is in the second place, and, with the same likewise, that which is made with dried furze, broom, etc.: whereas, if they also be occupied green, they are in manner so prejudicial to the corn as is the moist wood. And thus much of our malts, in brewing whereof some grind the same somewhat grossly, and, in seething well the liquor that shall be put into it, they add to every nine quarters of malt one of headcorn (which consisteth of sundry grain, as wheat and oats ground). But what have I to do with this matter, or rather so great a quantity, wherewith I am not acquainted? Nevertheless, sith I have taken occasion to speak of brewing, I will exemplify in such a proportion as I am best skilled in, because it is the usual rate for mine own family, and once in a month practised by my wife and her maid-servants, who proceed withal after this manner, as she hath oft informed me.

Having therefore ground eight bushels of good malt upon our quern, where the toll is saved, she addeth unto it half a bushel of wheat meal, and so much of oats small ground, and so tempereth or mixeth them with the malt that you cannot easily discern the one from the other; otherwise these latter would clunter, fall into lumps, and thereby become unprofitable. The first liquor (which is full eighty gallons, according to the proportion of our furnace) she maketh boiling hot, and then poureth it softly into the malt, where it resteth (but without stirring) until her second liquor be almost ready to boil. This done, she letteth her mash run till the malt be left without liquor, or at the leastwise the greatest part of the moisture, which she perceiveth by the stay and soft issue thereof; and by this time her second liquor in the furnace is ready to seethe, which is put also to the malt, as the first woort also again into the furnace, whereunto she addeth two pounds of the best English hops, and so letteth them seethe together by the space of two hours in summer or an hour and a half in winter, whereby it getteth an excellent colour, and continuance without impeachment or any superfluous tartness. But, before she putteth her first woort into the furnace, or mingleth it with the hops, she taketh out a vessel full, of eight or nine gallons, which she shutteth up close, and suffereth no air to come into it till it become yellow, and this she reserveth by itself unto further use, as shall appear hereafter, calling it *brackwoort* or *charwoort,* and, as she saith, it addeth also to the colour of the drink, whereby it yieldeth not unto amber or fine gold in hue unto the eye. By this time also her second woort is let run; and, the first being taken out of the furnace, and placed to cool, she returneth the middle woort unto the furnace, where it is stricken over, or from whence it is taken again, when it beginneth to boil, and mashed the second time, whilst the third liquor is heat (for there are three liquors), and this last put into the furnace, when the second is mashed again. When she hath mashed also the last liquor (and set the second to cool by the first), she letteth it run, and then seetheth it again with a pound and a half of new hops, or peradventure two pounds, as she seeth cause by the goodness or baseness of the hops, and, when it hath sodden, in summer two hours, and in winter an hour and a half, she striketh it also, and reserveth it unto mixture with the rest when time doth serve therefore. Finally, when she setteth her drink together, she addeth to her brackwoort or charwoort half an ounce of arras, and half a quarter of an ounce of bayberries, finely powdered, and then, putting the same into her woort, with a handful of wheat flour, she proceedeth in such usual order as common brewing requireth. Some, instead of arras and bays, add so much long pepper only, but, in her opinion and my liking, it is not so good as the first, and hereof we make three hogsheads of good beer, such (I mean) as is meet for poor men as I am to live withal, whose small maintenance (for what great thing is forty pounds a year, *computatis computandis,* able to perform?) may endure no deeper cut, the charges whereof groweth in this manner. I value my malt at ten shillings, my wood at four shillings (which I buy), my hops at twenty pence, the spice at twopence, servants' wages two shillings sixpence, with meat and

drink, and the wearing of my vessel at twenty pence, so that
for my twenty shillings I have ten score gallons of beer or
more, notwithstanding the loss in seething, which some,
being loth to forego, do not observe the time, and therefore
speed thereafter in their success, and worthily. The continuance of the drink is always determined after the quantity of the hops, so that being well *hopt* it lasteth longer.
For it feedeth upon the hop, and holdeth out so long as the
force of the same continueth, which being extinguished, the
drink must be spent, or else it dieth and becometh of no
value.

In this trade also our brewers observe very diligently the
nature of the water, which they daily occupy, and soil
through which it passeth, for all waters are not of like goodness, sith the fattest standing water is always the best; for,
although the waters that run by chalk or cledgy soils be
good, and next unto the Thames water, which is the most
excellent, yet the water that standeth in either of these is
the best for us that dwell in the country, as whereon the
sun lieth longest, and fattest fish is bred. But, of all other,
the fenny and marsh is the worst, and the clearest spring
water next unto it. In this business therefore the skilful
workman doth redeem the iniquity of that element, by changing of his proportions, which trouble in ale (sometime our
only, but now taken with many for old and sick men's drink)
is never seen nor heard of. Howbeit, as the beer well sodden
in the brewing, and stale, is clear and well coloured as muscadel or malvesey, or rather yellow as the gold noble, as
our pot-knights call it, so our ale, which is not at all or
very little sodden, and without hops, is more thick, fulsome,
and of no such continuance, which are three notable things
to be considered in that liquor. But what for that? Certes
I know some ale-knights so much addicted thereunto that
they will not cease from morrow until even to visit the same,
cleansing house after house, till they defile themselves, and
either fall quite under the board, or else, not daring to stir
from their stools, sit still pinking with their narrow eyes,
as half sleeping, till the fume of their adversary be digested
that he may go to it afresh. Such slights also have the ale-
wives for the utterance of this drink that they will mix it

with rosen and salt; but if you heat a knife red-hot, and quench it in the ale so near the bottom of the pot as you can put it, you shall see the rosen come forth hanging on the knife. As for the force of salt, it is well known by the effect, for the more the drinker tippleth, the more he may, and so doth he carry off a dry drunken noll to bed with him, except his luck be the better. But to my purpose.

In some places of England there is a kind of drink made of apples which they call cider or pomage, but that of pears is called perry, and both are ground and pressed in presses made for the nonce. Certes these two are very common in Sussex, Kent, Worcester, and other steeds where these sorts of fruit do abound, howbeit they are not their only drink at all times, but referred unto the delicate sorts of drink, as metheglin is in Wales, whereof the Welshmen make no less account (and not without cause, if it be well handled) than the Greeks did of their ambrosia or nectar, which for the pleasantness thereof was supposed to be such as the gods themselves did delight in. There is a kind of swish-swash made also in Essex, and divers other places, with honeycombs and water, which the homely country wives, putting some pepper and a little other spice among, call mead, very good in mine opinion for such as love to be loose bodied at large, or a little eased of the cough. Otherwise it differeth so much from the true metheglin as chalk from cheese. Truly it is nothing else but the washing of the combs, when the honey is wrung out, and one of the best things that I know belonging thereto is that they spend but little labour, and less cost, in making of the same, and therefore no great loss if it were never occupied. Hitherto of the diet of my countrymen, and somewhat more at large peradventure than many men will like of, wherefore I think good now to finish this tractation, and so will I when I have added a few other things incident unto that which goeth before, whereby the whole process of the same shall fully be delivered, and my promise to my friend[5] in this behalf performed.

Heretofore there hath been much more time spent in eating and drinking than commonly is in these days; for

[5] Holinshed. This occurs in the last of Harrison's prefatory matter.—W.

whereas of old we had breakfast in the forenoon, beverages or nunchions[6] after dinner, and thereto rear suppers generally when it was time to go to rest (a toy brought into England by hardy Canutus, and a custom whereof Athenæus also speaketh, lib. 1, albeit Hippocrates speaks but of twice at the most, lib. 2, *De rat vict. in feb ac*). Now, these odd repasts—thanked be God!—are very well left, and each one in manner (except here and there some young, hungry stomach that cannot fast till dinner-time) contenteth himself with dinner and supper only. The Normans, misliking the gormandise of Canutus, ordained after their arrival that no table should be covered above once in the day, which Huntingdon imputeth to their avarice; but in the end, either waxing weary of their own frugality, or suffering the cockle of old custom to overgrow the good corn of their new constitution, they fell to such liberty that in often-feeding they surmounted Canutus surnamed the Hardy. For, whereas he covered his table but three or four times in the day, these spread their cloths five or six times, and in such wise as I before rehearsed. They brought in also the custom of long and stately sitting at meat, whereby their feasts resembled those ancient pontifical banquets whereof Macrobius speaketh (lib. 3, cap. 13), and Pliny (lib. 10, cap. 10), and which for sumptuousness of fare, long sitting, and curiosity shewed in the same, exceeded all other men's feasting; which fondness is not yet left with us, notwithstanding that it proveth very beneficial for the physicians, who most abound where most excess and misgovernment of our bodies do appear, although it be a great expense of time, and worthy of reprehension. For the nobility, gentlemen, and merchantmen, especially at great meetings, do sit commonly till two or three of the clock at afternoon, so that with many it is a hard matter to rise from the table to go to evening prayer, and return from thence to come time enough to supper.[7] . . .

With us the nobility, gentry, and students do ordinarily go to dinner at eleven before noon, and to supper at five, or between five and six at afternoon. The merchants dine

[6] This word is not obsolete. South-coast countrymen still eat *nuntions* and not *luncheons.*—W.
[7] Here follows a disquisition upon the table practices of the ancients.—W.

and sup seldom before twelve at noon, and six at night, especially in London. The husbandmen dine also at high noon as they call it, and sup at seven or eight; but out of the term in our universities the scholars dine at ten. As for the poorest sort they generally dine and sup when they may, so that to talk of their order of repast it were but a needless matter. I might here take occasion also to set down the variety used by antiquity in their beginnings of their diets, wherein almost every nation had a several fashion, some beginning of custom (as we do in summer time) with salads at supper, and some ending with lettuce, some making their entry with eggs, and shutting up their tables with mulberries, as we do with fruit and conceits of all sorts. Divers (as the old Romans) began with a few crops of rue, as the Venetians did with the fish called gobius; the Belgæs with butter, or (as we do yet also) with butter and eggs upon fish days. But whereas we commonly begin with the most gross food, and end with the most delicate, the Scot, thinking much to leave the best for his menial servants, maketh his entrance at the best, so that he is sure thereby to leave the worst. We use also our wines by degrees, so that the hostess cometh last to the table: but to stand upon such toys would spend much time, and turn to small profit. Wherefore I will deal with other things more necessary for this turn.

CHAPTER VII

OF OUR APPAREL AND ATTIRE

[1577, Book III., Chapter 2; 1587, Book II., Chapter 7.]

AN Englishman, endeavouring sometime to write of our attire, made sundry platforms for his purpose, supposing by some of them to find out one steadfast ground whereon to build the sum of his discourse. But in the end (like an orator long without exercise), when he saw what a difficult piece of work he had taken in hand, he gave over his travel, and only drew the picture of a naked man,[1] unto whom he gave a pair of shears in the one hand and a piece of cloth in the other, to the end he should shape his apparel after such fashion as himself liked, sith he could find no kind of garment that could please him any while together; and this he called an Englishman. Certes this writer (otherwise being a lewd popish hypocrite and ungracious priest) shewed himself herein not to be altogether void of judgment, sith the phantastical folly of our nation (even from the courtier to the carter) is such that no form of apparel liketh us longer than the first garment is in the wearing, if it continue so long, and be not laid aside to receive some other trinket newly devised by the fickle-headed tailors, who covet to have several tricks in cutting, thereby to draw fond customers to more expense of money. For my part, I can tell better how to inveigh against this enormity than describe any certainty of our attire; sithence

---

[1] [Cut.]

"I am an English man and naked I stand here,
Musying in my mynde what rayment I shall were;
For now I will were thys, and now I will were that;
Now I will were I cannot tell what.
All new fashyons be plesaunt to me;
I wyl haue them, whether I thryve or thee."

From Andrew Boorde's *Introduction* (1541), and *Dyetary* (1542), edited by F. J. F. for Early English Text Society, 1870, p. 116. (A most quaint and interesting volume, though I say so.)—Furnivall.

such is our mutability that to-day there is none to the
Spanish guise, to-morrow the French toys are most fine
and delectable, ere long no such apparel as that which is
after the high Almaine fashion, by-and-by the Turkish manner is generally best liked of, otherwise the Morisco gowns,
the Barbarian fleeces, the mandilion worn to Colley-Weston
ward, and the short French breeches make such a comely
vesture that, except it were a dog in a doublet, you shall
not see any so disguised as are my countrymen of England.
And as these fashions are diverse, so likewise it is a world
to see the costliness and the curiosity, the excess and the
vanity, the pomp and the bravery, the change and the variety,
and finally the fickleness and the folly, that is in all degrees,
insomuch that nothing is more constant in England than
inconstancy of attire. Oh, how much cost is bestowed nowadays upon our bodies, and how little upon our souls! How
many suits of apparel hath the one, and how little furniture
hath the other! How long time is asked in decking up of
the first, and how little space left wherein to feed the latter!
How curious, how nice also, are a number of men and
women, and how hardly can the tailor please them in making it fit for their bodies! How many times must it be
sent back again to him that made it! What chafing, what
fretting, what reproachful language, doth the poor workman bear away! And many times when he doth nothing
to it at all, yet when it is brought home again it is very
fit and handsome; then must we put it on, then must the
long seams of our hose be set by a plumb-line, then we puff,
then we blow, and finally sweat till we drop, that our
clothes may stand well upon us. I will say nothing of our
heads, which sometimes are polled, sometimes curled, or
suffered to grow at length like woman's locks, many times
cut off, above or under the ears, round as by a wooden
dish. Neither will I meddle with our variety of beards, of
which some are shaven from the chin like those of Turks,
not a few cut short like to the beard of Marquess Otto,
some made round like a rubbing brush, others with a *pique
de vant* (O! fine fashion!), or now and then suffered to grow
long, the barbers being grown to be so cunning in this
behalf as the tailors. And therefore if a man have a lean

and straight face, a Marquess Otton's cut will make it broad and large; if it be platter-like, a long, slender beard will make it seem the narrower; if he be weasel-becked, then much hair left on the cheeks will make the owner look big like a bowdled hen, and as grim as a goose, if Cornelis of Chelmersford say true. Many old men do wear no beards at all. Some lusty courtiers also and gentlemen of courage do wear either rings of gold, stones, or pearl, in their ears, whereby they imagine the workmanship of God not to be a little amended. But herein they rather disgrace than adorn their persons, as by their niceness in apparel, for which I say most nations do not unjustly deride us, as also for that we do seem to imitate all nations round about us, wherein we be like to the polypus or chameleon; and thereunto bestow most cost upon our arses, and much more than upon all the rest of our bodies, as women do likewise upon their heads and shoulders. In women also, it is most to be lamented, that they do now far exceed the lightness of our men (who nevertheless are transformed from the cap even to the very shoe), and such staring attire as in time past was supposed meet for none but light housewives only is now become a habit for chaste and sober matrons. What should I say of their doublets with pendant codpieces on the breast full of jags and cuts, and sleeves of sundry colours ? Their galligascons to bear out their bums and make their attire to fit plum round (as they term it) about them. Their fardingals, and diversely coloured nether stocks of silk, jerdsey, and such like, whereby their bodies are rather deformed than commended ? I have met with some of these trulls in London so disguised that it hath passed my skill to discern whether they were men or women.

Thus it is now come to pass, that women are become men, and men transformed into monsters; and those good gifts which Almighty God hath given unto us to relieve our necessities withal (as a nation turning altogether the grace of God into wantonness, for

" Luxuriant animi rebus plerunque fecundis,")

not otherwise bestowed than in all excess, as if we wist not otherwise how to consume and waste them. I pray God that in this behalf our sin be not like unto that of Sodom and Gomorrah, whose errors were pride, excess of diet; and abuse of God's benefits abundantly bestowed upon them, beside want of charity towards the poor, and certain other points which the prophet shutteth up in silence. Certes the commonwealth cannot be said to flourish where these abuses reign, but is rather oppressed by unreasonable exactions made upon rich farmers, and of poor tenants, wherewith to maintain the same. Neither was it ever merrier with England than when an Englishman was known abroad by his own cloth, and contented himself at home with his fine carsey hosen, and a mean slop; his coat, gown, and cloak of brown, blue, or puke, with some pretty furniture of velvet or fur, and a doublet of sad tawny, or black velvet, or other comely silk, without such cuts and garish colours as are worn in these days, and never brought in but by the consent of the French, who think themselves the gayest men when they have most diversities of jags and change of colours about them. Certes of all estates our merchants do least alter their attire, and therefore are most to be commended; for albeit that which they wear be very fine and costly, yet in form and colour it representeth a great piece of the ancient gravity appertaining to citizens and burgesses, albeit the younger sort of their wives, both in attire and costly housekeeping, cannot tell when and how to make an end, as being women indeed in whom all kind of curiosity is to be found and seen, and in far greater measure than in women of higher calling. I might here name a sort of hues devised for the nonce, wherewith to please fantastical heads, as goose-turd green, peas-porridge tawny, popingay blue, lusty gallant, the devil-in-the-head (I should say the hedge), and such like; but I pass them over, thinking it sufficient to have said thus much of apparel generally, when nothing can particularly be spoken of any constancy thereof.

CHAPTER VIII

[1577, Book II., Chapter 10; 1587, Book II., Chapter 12.]

THE greatest part of our building in the cities and good
towns of England consisteth only of timber, for as
yet few of the houses of the communalty (except
here and there in the West-country towns) are made of
stone, although they may (in my opinion) in divers other
places be builded so good cheap of the one as of the other.
In old time the houses of the Britons were slightly set up
with a few posts and many raddles, with stable and all
offices under one roof, the like whereof almost is to be seen
in the fenny countries and northern parts unto this day,
where for lack of wood they are enforced to continue this
ancient manner of building. It is not in vain, therefore,
in speaking of building, to make a distinction between the
plain and woody soils; for as in these, our houses are commonly strong and well-timbered (so that in many places
there are not above four, six, or nine inches between stud
and stud), so in the open champaign countries they are
forced, for want of stuff, to use no studs at all, but only
frankposts, raisins, beams, prickposts, groundsels, summers
(or dormants), transoms, and such principals, with here
and there a girding, whereunto they fasten their splints or
raddles, and then cast it all over with thick clay to keep out
the wind, which otherwise would annoy them. Certes this
rude kind of building made the Spaniards in Queen Mary's
days to wonder, but chiefly when they saw what large diet
was used in many of these so homely cottages; insomuch
that one of no small reputation amongst them said after
this manner—"These English (quoth he) have their houses

308

made of sticks and dirt, but they fare commonly so well as the king." Whereby it appeareth that he liked better of our good fare in such coarse cabins than of their own thin diet in their prince-like habitations and palaces. In like sort as every country house is thus apparelled on the outside, so is it inwardly divided into sundry rooms above and beneath; and, where plenty of wood is, they cover them with tiles, otherwise with straw, sedge, or reed, except some quarry of slate be near hand, from whence they have for their money much as may suffice them. The clay wherewith our houses are impannelled is either white, red, or blue; and of these the first doth participate very much of the nature of our chalk; the second is called loam; but the third eftsoons changeth colour as soon as it is wrought, notwithstanding that it looks blue when it is thrown out of the pit. Of chalk also we have our excellent asbestos or white lime, made in most places, wherewith being quenched, we strike over our clay works and stone walls, in cities, good towns, rich farmers' and gentlemen's houses: otherwise, instead of chalk (where it wanteth, for it is so scant that in some places it is sold by the pound), they are compelled to burn a certain kind of red stone, as in Wales, and elsewhere other stones and shells of oysters and like fish found upon the sea coast, which, being converted into lime, doth naturally (as the other) abhor and eschew water, whereby it is dissolved, and nevertheless desire oil, wherewith it is easily mixed, as I have seen by experience. Within their doors also, such as are of ability do oft make their floors and parget of fine alabaster burned, which they call plaster of Paris, whereof in some places we have great plenty, and that very profitable against the rage of fire. In plastering likewise of our fairest houses over our heads, we use to lay first a line or two of white mortar, tempered with hair, upon laths, which are nailed one by another (or sometimes upon reed of wickers more dangerous for fire, and make fast here and there saplaths for falling down), and finally cover all with the aforesaid plaster, which, beside the delectable whiteness of the stuff itself, is laid on so even and smoothly as nothing in my judgment can be done with more exactness. The walls of our houses on the inner sides in like sort be either hanged with tapestry, arras work, or painted cloths, wherein either divers histories, or herbs, beasts, knots, and such like are stained, or else they are ceiled with oak of our own, or wainscot brought hither out of the east countries, whereby the rooms are not a little commended, made warm, and much more close than otherwise they would be. As for stoves, we have not hitherto used them greatly, yet do they now begin to be made in divers houses of the gentry and wealthy citizens, who build them not to work and feed in, as in Germany and elsewhere, but now and then to sweat in, as occasion and need shall require it.

This also hath been common in England, contrary to the customs of all other nations, and yet to be seen (for example, in most streets of London), that many of our greatest houses have outwardly been very simple and plain to sight, which inwardly have been able to receive a duke with his whole train, and lodge them at their ease. Hereby, moreover, it is come to pass that the fronts of our streets have not been so uniform and orderly builded as those of foreign cities, where (to say truth) the outer side of their mansions and dwellings have oft more cost bestowed upon them than all the rest of the house, which are often very simple and uneasy within, as experience doth confirm. Of old time, our country houses, instead of glass, did use much lattice, and that made either of wicker or fine rifts of oak in checkerwise. I read also that some of the better sort, in and before the times of the Saxons (who notwithstanding used some glass also since the time of Benedict Biscop, the monk that brought the feat of glazing first into this land), did make panels of horn instead of glass, and fix them in wooden calmes. But as horn in windows is now quite laid down in every place, so our lattices are also grown into less use, because glass is come to be so plentiful, and within a very little so good cheap, if not better than the other. I find obscure mention of the specular stone also to have been found and applied to this use in England, but in such doubtful sort as I dare not affirm it for certain. Nevertheless certain it is that antiquity used it before glass was known, under the name of *selenites*. And how glass was first found I care not greatly to remember, even at this present, although it be directly beside my purposed matter. In Syria Phenices, which bordereth upon Jewry, and near to the foot of Mount Carmel, there is a moor or marsh whereout riseth a brook called sometime Belus, and falleth into the sea near to Ptolemais. This river was fondly ascribed unto Baal, and also honoured under that name by the infidels long time before there was any king in Israel. It came to pass also, as a certain merchant sailed that way, loaden with nitrum, the passengers went to land for to repose themselves, and to take in some store of fresh water into their vessel. Being also on the shore, they kindled a fire and made provision for their dinner, but (because they wanted trevets or stones whereon to set their kettles on) ran by chance into the ship, and brought great pieces of nitrum with them, which served their turn for that present. To be short, the said substance being hot, and beginning to melt, it mixed by chance with the gravel that lay under it, and so brought forth that shining substance which now is called glass, and about the time of Semiramis. When the company saw this, they made no small accompt of their success, and forthwith began to practise the like in other mixtures, whereby great variety of the said stuff did also ensue. Certes for the time this history may well be true, for I read of glass in Job; but, for the rest, I refer me to the common opinion conceived by writers. Now, to turn again to our windows. Heretofore also the houses of our princes and noblemen were often glazed with beryl (an example whereof is yet to be seen in Sudeley Castle) and in divers other places with fine crystal, but this especially in the time of the Romans, whereof also some fragments have been taken up in old ruins. But now these are not in use, so that only the clearest glass is most esteemed: for we have divers sorts, some brought out of Burgundy, some out of Normandy, much out of Flanders, beside that which is made in England, which would be so good as the best if we were diligent and careful to bestow more cost upon it, and yet as it is each one that may will have it for his building. Moreover the mansion houses of our country towns and villages (which in champaign ground stand altogether by streets, and join-

ing one to another, but in woodland soils dispersed here
and there, each one upon the several grounds of their
owners) are builded in such sort generally as that they
have neither dairy, stable, nor brew-house annexed unto
them under the same roof (as in many places beyond the
sea and some of the north parts of our country), but all
separate from the first, and one of them from another. And
yet, for all this, they are not so far distant in sunder but
that the goodman lying in his bed may lightly hear what is
done in each of them with ease, and call quickly unto his
many if any danger should attack him.

The ancient manors and houses of our gentlemen are
yet and for the most part of strong timber, in framing
whereof our carpenters have been and are worthily preferred before those of like science among all other nations.
Howbeit such as be lately builded are commonly either of
brick or hard stone, or both, their rooms large and comely,
and houses of office further distant from their lodgings.
Those of the nobility are likewise wrought with brick and
hard stone, as provision may best be made, but so magnificent and stately as the basest house of a baron doth often
match in our days with some honours of a princes in old
time. So that, if ever curious building did flourish in England, it is in these our years wherein our workmen excel
and are in manner comparable in skill with old Vitruvius,
Leo Baptista, and Serlo. Nevertheless their estimation,
more than their greedy and servile covetousness, joined with
a lingering humour, causeth them often to be rejected, and
strangers preferred to greater bargains, who are more reasonable in their takings, and less wasters of time by a great
deal than our own.

The furniture of our houses also exceedeth, and is grown
in manner even to passing delicacy: and herein I do not
speak of the nobility and gentry only, but likewise of the
lowest sort in most places of our south country that have
anything at all to take to. Certes in noblemen's houses it
is not rare to see abundance of arras, rich hangings of
tapestry, silver vessels, and so much other plate as may
furnish sundry cupboards to the sum oftentimes of a thousand or two thousand pounds at the least, whereby the

value of this and the rest of their stuff doth grow to be
almost inestimable. Likewise in the houses of knights,
gentlemen, merchantmen, and some other wealthy citizens, it
is not geson to behold generally their great provision of
tapestry, Turkey work, pewter, brass, fine linen, and thereto
costly cupboards of plate, worth five or six hundred or a
thousand pounds to be deemed by estimation. But, as herein
all these sorts do far exceed their elders and predecessors,
and in neatness and curiosity the merchant all other, so in
times past the costly furniture stayed there, whereas now
it is descended yet lower even unto the inferior artificers
and many farmers, who, by virtue of their old and not
of their new leases, have, for the most part, learned also
to garnish their cupboards with plate, their joined beds
with tapestry and silk hangings, and their tables with carpets and fine napery, whereby the wealth of our country
(God be praised therefore, and give us grace to employ it
well) doth infinitely appear. Neither do I speak this in
reproach of any man, God is my judge, but to shew that
I do rejoice rather to see how God hath blessed us with
his good gifts; and whilst, I behold how (in a time wherein
all things are grown to most excessive prices, and what
commodity so ever is to be had is daily plucked from the
communalty by such as look into every trade) we do yet
find the means to obtain and achieve such furniture as heretofore hath been unpossible.

There are old men yet dwelling in the village where I
remain which have noted three things to be marvellously
altered in England within their sound remembrance, and
other three things too too much increased.

One is the multitude of chimneys lately erected, whereas
in their young days there were not above two or three, if
so many, in most uplandish towns of the realm (the religious houses and manor places of their lords always excepted, and peradventure some great personages), but each
one made his fire against a reredos in the hall, where he
dined and dressed his meat.

The second is the great (although not general) amendment of lodging; for, said they, our fathers, yea and we
ourselves also, have lain full oft upon straw pallets, on

rough mats covered only with a sheet, under coverlets made of dagswain or hopharlots (I use their own terms), and a good round log under their heads instead of a bolster or pillow. If it were so that our fathers—or the good man of the house had within seven years after his marriage purchased a mattress or flock bed, and thereto a stack of chaff to rest his head upon, he thought himself to be as well lodged as the lord of the town, that peradventure lay seldom in a bed of down or whole feathers, so well were they content, and with such base kind of furniture: which also is not very much amended as yet in some parts of Bedfordshire, and elsewhere, further off from our southern parts. Pillows (said they) were thought meet only for women in childbed. As for servants, if they had any sheet above them, it was well, for seldom had they any under their bodies to keep them from the pricking straws that ran oft through the canvas of the pallet and rased their hardened hides.

The third thing they tell of is the exchange of vessel, as of treen platters into pewter, and wooden spoons into silver or tin. For so common were all sorts of treen stuff in old time that a man should hardly find four pieces of pewter (of which one was peradventure a salt) in a good farmer's house, and yet for all this frugality (if it may so be justly called) they were scarce able to live and pay their rents at their days without selling of a cow, or a horse or more,[1] although they paid but four pounds at the uttermost by the year. Such also was their poverty that, if some one odd farmer or husbandman had been at the ale-house, a thing greatly used in those days, amongst six or seven of his neighbours, and there in a bravery, to shew what store he had, did cast down his purse, and therein a noble or six shillings in silver, unto them (for few such men then cared for gold, because it was not so ready payment, and they were oft enforced to give a penny for the exchange of an angel), it was very likely that all the rest could not lay down so much against it; whereas in my time, although peradventure four pounds of old rent be improved to forty, fifty, or a hundred pounds, yet will the farmer, as another

[1] This was in the time of general idleness.—H.

palm or date tree, think his gains very small toward the end of his term if he have not six or seven years' rent lying by him, therewith to purchase a new lease, beside a fair garnish of pewter on his cupboard, with so much more in odd vessel going about the house, three or four feather beds, so many coverlids and carpets of tapestry, a silver salt, a bowl for wine (if not a whole neast), and a dozen of spoons to furnish up the suit. This also he takes to be his own clear, for what stock of money soever he gathereth and layeth up in all his years it is often seen that the landlord will take such order with him for the same when he reneweth his lease, which is commonly eight or six years before the old be expired (sith it is now grown almost to a custom that if he come not to his lord so long before another shall step in for a reversion, and so defeat him outright), that it shall never trouble him more than the hair of his beard when the barber hath washed and shaved it from his chin.

And as they commend these, so (beside the decay of housekeeping whereby the poor have been relieved) they speak also of three things that are grown to be very grievous unto them—to wit, the enhancing of rents, lately mentioned; the daily oppression of copyholders, whose lords seek to bring their poor tenants almost into plain servitude and misery, daily devising new means, and seeking up all the old, how to cut them shorter and shorter, doubling, trebling, and now and then seven times increasing their fines, driving them also for every trifle to lose and forfeit their tenures (by whom the greatest part of the realm doth stand and is maintained), to the end they may fleece them yet more, which is a lamentable hearing. The third thing they talk of is usury, a trade brought in by the Jews, now perfectly practised almost by every Christian, and so commonly that he is accompted but for a fool that doth lend his money for nothing. In time past it was *sors pro sorte*—that is, the principal only for the principal; but now, beside that which is above the principal properly called *Usura,* we challenge *Foenus*—that is, commodity of soil and fruits of the earth, if not the ground itself. In time past also one of the hundred was much; from thence it rose unto two, called

in Latin *Usura, Ex sextante;* three, to wit *Ex quadrante;*
then to four, to wit, *Ex triente;* then to five, which is *Ex quin-
cunce;* then to six, called *Ex semisse,* etc. As the accompt
of the *Assis* ariseth, and coming at the last unto *Usura ex
asse,* it amounteth to twelve in the hundred, and therefore
the Latins call it *Centesima,* for that in the hundred month
it doubleth the principal; but more of this elsewhere. See
Cicero against Verres, Demosthenes against Aphobus, and
Athenæus, lib. 13, in fine; and, when thou hast read them
well, help I pray thee in lawful manner to hang up such
as take *Centum pro cento,* for they are no better worthy as
I do judge in conscience. Forget not also such landlords as
used to value their leases at a secret estimation given of
the wealth and credit of the taker, whereby they seem (as
it were) to eat them up, and deal with bondmen, so that
if the lessee be thought to be worth a hundred pounds he
shall pay no less for his new term, or else another to enter
with hard and doubtful covenants. I am sorry to report it,
much more grieved to understand of the practice, but most
sorrowful of all to understand that men of great port and
countenance are so far from suffering their farmers to
have any gain at all that they themselves become graziers,
butchers, tanners, sheepmasters, woodmen, and *denique quid
non,* thereby to enrich themselves, and bring all the wealth
of the country into their own hands, leaving the communalty
weak, or as an idol with broken or feeble arms, which may
in a time of peace have a plausible shew, but when necessity
shall enforce have a heavy and bitter sequel.

CHAPTER IX

OF PROVISION MADE FOR THE POOR

[1577, Book III., Chapter 5; 1587, Book II., Chapter 10.]

THERE is no commonwealth at this day in Europe wherein there is not great store of poor people, and those necessarily to be relieved by the wealthier sort, which otherwise would starve and come to utter confusion. With us the poor is commonly divided into three sorts, so that some are poor by impotence, as the fatherless child, the aged, blind, and lame, and the diseased person that is judged to be incurable; the second are poor by casualty, as the wounded soldier, the decayed householder, and the sick person visited with grievous and painful diseases; the third consisteth of thriftless poor, as the rioter that hath consumed all, the vagabond that will abide nowhere, but runneth up and down from place to place (as it were seeking work and finding none), and finally the rogue and the strumpet, which are not possible to be divided in sunder, but run to and fro over all the realm, chiefly keeping the champaign soils in summer to avoid the scorching heat, and the woodland grounds in winter to eschew the blustering winds.

For the first two sorts (that is to say, the poor by impotence and poor by casualty, which are the true poor indeed, and for whom the Word doth bind us to make some daily provision), there is order taken throughout every parish in the realm that weekly collection shall be made for their help and sustentation—to the end they shall not scatter abroad, and, by begging here and there, annoy both town and country. Authority also is given unto the justices in every county (and great penalties appointed for such as make default) to see that the intent of the statute in this behalf be truly executed according to the purpose and meaning of the same, so that these two sorts are sufficiently provided for; and such as can live within the limits of their allowance (as each one will do that is godly and well disposed) may well forbear to roam and range about. But if they refuse to be supported by this benefit of the law, and will rather endeavour by going to and fro to maintain their idle trades, then are they adjudged to be parcel of the third sort, and so, instead of courteous refreshing at home, are often corrected with sharp execution and whip of justice abroad. Many there are which, notwithstanding the rigour of the laws provided in that behalf, yield rather with this liberty (as they call it) to be daily under the fear and terror of the whip than, by abiding where they were born or bred, to be provided for by the devotion of the parishes. I found not long since a note of these latter sort, the effect whereof ensueth. Idle beggars are such either through other men's occasion or through their own default—by other men's occasion (as one way for example) when some covetous man (such, I mean, as have the cast or right vein daily to make beggars enough whereby to pester the land, espying a further commodity in their commons, holds, and tenures) doth find such means as thereby to wipe many out of their occupyings and turn the same unto his private gains.[1] Hereupon it followeth that, although the wise and better-minded do either forsake the realm for altogether, and seek to live in other countries, as France, Germany, Barbary, India, Muscovia, and very Calcutta, complaining of no room to be left for them at home, do so behave themselves that they are worthily to be accounted among the second sort, yet the greater part, commonly having nothing to stay upon, are wilful, and thereupon do either prove idle beggars or else continue stark thieves till the gallows do eat them up, which is a lamentable case. Certes in some men's judgment these things are but trifles, and not worthy the regarding. Some also do grudge at the great increase of people in these days, thinking a necessary brood of cattle far better than a superfluous augmentation of mankind. But I can liken such men best of all unto the pope and the devil, who practise the

[1] At whose hands shall the blood of these men be required?—H.

hindrance of the furniture of the number of the elect to
their uttermost, to the end the authority of the one upon the
earth, the deferring of the locking up of the other in everlasting chains, and the great gains of the first, may continue and
endure the longer. But if it should come to pass that any
foreign invasion should be made—which the Lord God forbid for his mercies' sake!—then should these men find that
a wall of men is far better than stacks of corn and bags
of money, and complain of the want when it is too late to
seek remedy. The like occasion caused the Romans to devise
their law *Agraria:* but the rich, not liking of it, and the
covetous, utterly condemning it as rigorous and unprofitable,
never ceased to practise disturbance till it was quite abolished. But to proceed with my purpose.

Such as are idle beggars through their own default are of
two sorts, and continue their estates either by casual or
mere voluntary means: those that are such by casual means
are in the beginning justly to be referred either to the first
or second sort of poor aforementioned, but, degenerating into
the thriftless sort, they do what they can to continue their
misery, and, with such impediments as they have, to stray
and wander about, as creatures abhorring all labour and
every honest exercise. Certes I call these casual means, not
in the respect of the original of all poverty, but of the continuance of the same, from whence they will not be delivered,
such is their own ungracious lewdness and froward disposition. The voluntary means proceed from outward causes,
as by making of corrosives, and applying the same to the
more fleshy parts of their bodies, and also laying of ratsbane,
spearwort, crowfoot, and such like unto their whole members, thereby to raise pitiful and odious sores, and move
the hearts of the goers-by such places where they lie, to
yearn at their misery, and thereupon bestow large alms upon
them. How artificially they beg, what forcible speech, and
how they select and choose out words of vehemence, whereby
they do in manner conjure or adjure the goer-by to pity
their cases, I pass over to remember, as judging the name
of God and Christ to be more conversant in the mouths of
none and yet the presence of the Heavenly Majesty further
off from no men than from this ungracious company. Which

maketh me to think that punishment is far meeter for them than liberality or alms, and sith Christ willeth us chiefly to have a regard to Himself and his poor members.

Unto this nest is another sort to be referred, more sturdy than the rest, which, having sound and perfect limbs, do yet notwithstanding sometime counterfeit the possession of all sorts of diseases. Divers times in their apparel also they will be like serving men or labourers: oftentimes they can play the mariners, and seek for ships which they never lost. But in fine they are all thieves and caterpillars in the commonwealth, and by the Word of God not permitted to eat, sith they do but lick the sweat from the true labourers' brows, and bereave the godly poor of that which is due unto them, to maintain their excess, consuming the charity of well-disposed people bestowed upon them, after a most wicked and detestable manner.

It is not yet full threescore years since this trade began: but how it hath prospered since that time it is easy to judge, for they are now supposed, of one sex and another, to amount unto above 10,000 persons, as I have heard reported. Moreover, in counterfeiting the Egyptian rogues, they have devised a language among themselves, which they name " Canting," but others, " pedler's French," a speech compact thirty years since, of English and a great number of odd words of their own devising, without all order or reason, and yet such is it as none but themselves are able to understand. The first deviser thereof was hanged by the neck—a just reward, no doubt, for his deserts, and a common end to all of that profession.

A gentleman also of late hath taken great pains to search out the secret practices of this ungracious rabble. And among other things he setteth down and describeth three and twenty sorts of them, whose names it shall not be amiss to remember whereby each one may take occasion to read and know as also by his industry what wicked people they are, and what villainy remaineth in them.

The several disorders and degrees amongst our idle vagabonds.

1. Rufflers.	3. Hookers or anglers.
2. Uprightmen.	4. Rogues.

5. Wild rogues.
6. Priggers or pransers.
7. Palliards.
8. Fraters.
9. Abrams.

10. Freshwater mariners or
    whipiacks
11. Drummerers.
12. Drunken tinkers.
13. Swadders or pedlers.

14. Jarkemen or patricoes.

Of the women kind.

1. Demanders for glimmar or
2. Bawdy-baskets.   [fire.
3. Mortes.
4. Autem mortem.

5. Walking mortes.
6. Doxies.
7. Dells.
8. Kinching mortes.

9. Kinching cooes.

The punishment that is ordained for this kind of people is very sharp, and yet it cannot restrain them from their gadding: wherefore the end must needs be martial law,[2] to be exercised upon them, as upon thieves, robbers, despisers of all laws, and enemies to the commonwealth and welfare of the land. What notable robberies, pilferies, murders, rapes, and stealings of young children, burning, breaking, and disfiguring their limbs to make them pitiful in the sight of the people, I need not to rehearse; but for their idle rogueing about the country, the law ordaineth this manner of correction. The rogue being apprehended, committed to prison, and tried in the next assizes (whether they be of gaol delivery or sessions of the peace), if he happen to be convicted for a vagabond, either by inquest of office or the testimony of two honest and credible witnesses upon their oaths, he is then immediately adjudged to be grievously whipped and burned through the gristle of the right ear with a hot iron of the compass of an inch about, as a manifestation of his wicked life, and due punishment received for the same. And this judgment is to be executed upon him except some honest person worth five pounds in the queen's books in goods, or twenty shillings in land, or some rich householder to be allowed by the justices, will be bound in recognisance to retain him in his service for one whole year. If he be taken the second time, and proved to have forsaken his said service, he shall then be whipped again, bored likewise through the other ear, and set to service: from whence if he depart before a year be expired, and happen afterwards

[2] Law of the Marshal.—Furnivall.

to be attached again, he is condemned to suffer pains of death as a felon (except before excepted) without benefit of clergy or sanctuary, as by the statute doth appear. Among rogues and idle persons, finally, we find to be comprised all proctors that go up and down with counterfeit licences, cozeners, and such as gad about the country, using unlawful games, practisers of physiogonomy and palmestry, tellers of fortunes, fencers, players, minstrels, jugglers, pedlers, tinkers, pretended scholars, shipmen, prisoners gathering for fees, and others so oft as they be taken without sufficient licence. From among which company our bearwards are not excepted, and just cause: for I have read that they have, either voluntarily or for want of power to master their savage beasts, been occasion of the death and devouration of many children in sundry countries by which they have passed, whose parents never knew what was become of them. And for that cause there is and have been many sharp laws made for bearwards in Germany, whereof you may read in other. But to our rogues. Each one also that harboureth or aideth them with meat or money is taxed and compelled to fine with the queen's majesty for every time that he doth succour them as it shall please the justices of peace to assign, so that the taxation exceed not twenty, as I have been informed. And thus much of the poor and such provision as is appointed for them within the realm of England.

CHAPTER X

OF THE AIR AND SOIL AND COMMODITIES OF THIS ISLAND

[1577, Book I., Chapter 13; 1587, Book I., Chapter 18.]

THE air (for the most part) throughout the island is such as by reason in manner of continual clouds is reputed to be gross, and nothing so pleasant as that of the main. Howbeit, as they which affirm these things have only respect to the impediment or hindrance of the sunbeams by the interposition of the clouds and of ingrossed air, so experience teacheth us that it is no less pure, wholesome, and commodious than is that of other countries, and (as Cæsar himself hereto addeth) much more temperate in summer than that of the Gauls, from whom he adventured hither. Neither is there any thing found in the air of our region that is not usually seen amongst other nations lying beyond the seas. Wherefore we must needs confess that the situation of our island (for benefit of the heavens) is nothing inferior to that of any country of the main, wheresoever it lie under the open firmament. And this Plutarch knew full well, who affirmeth a part of the Elysian Fields to be found in Britain, and the isles that are situated about it in the ocean.

The soil of Britain is such as by the testimonies and reports both of the old and new writers, and experience also of such as now inhabit the same, is very fruitful, and such indeed as bringeth forth many commodities, whereof other countries have need, and yet itself (if fond niceness were abolished) needless of those that are daily brought from other places. Nevertheless it is more inclined to feeding and grazing than profitable for tillage and bearing of corn, by reason whereof the country is wonderfully replenished with neat and all kind of cattle; and such store is

there also of the same in every place that the fourth part of
the land is scarcely manured for the provision and maintenance of grain. Certes this fruitfulness was not unknown
unto the Britons long before Cæsar's time, which was the
cause wherefore our predecessors living in those days in
manner neglected tillage and lived by feeding and grazing
only. The graziers themselves also then dwelled in movable
villages by companies, whose custom was to divide the
ground amongst them, and each one not to depart from the
place where his lot lay (a thing much like the Irish Criacht)
till, by eating up of the country about him, he was enforced
to remove further and seek for better pasture. And this
was the British custom, as I learn, at first. It hath been
commonly reported that the ground of Wales is neither so
fruitful as that of England, neither the soil of Scotland so
bountiful as that of Wales, which is true for corn and for
the most part; otherwise there is so good ground in some
parts of Wales as is in England, albeit the best of Scotland
be scarcely comparable to the mean of either of both. Howbeit, as the bounty of the Scotch doth fail in some respect,
so doth it surmount in other, God and nature having not
appointed all countries to yield forth like commodities.

But where our ground is not so good as we would wish,
we have—if need be—sufficient help to cherish our ground
withal, and to make it more fruitful. For, beside the compest that is carried out of the husbandmen's yards, ditches,
ponds, dung-houses, or cities and great towns, we have
with us a kind of white marl which is of so great force
that if it be cast over a piece of land but once in threescore
years it shall not need of any further compesting. Hereof
also doth Pliny speak (lib. 17, cap. 6, 7, 8), where he affirmeth that our marl endureth upon the earth by the space
of fourscore years: insomuch that it is laid upon the same
but once in a man's life, whereby the owner shall not need
to travel twice in procuring to commend and better his soil.
He calleth it *marga,* and, making divers kinds thereof, he
finally commendeth ours, and that of France, above all
other, which lieth sometime a hundred foot deep, and far
better than the scattering of chalk upon the same, as the
Hedui and Pictones did in his time, or as some of our days

also do practise: albeit divers do like better to cast on lime, but it will not so long endure, as I have heard reported.

There are also in this island great plenty of fresh rivers and streams, as you have heard already, and these thoroughly fraught with all kinds of delicate fish accustomed to be found in rivers. The whole isle likewise is very full of hills, of which some (though not very many) are of exceeding height, and divers extending themselves very far from the beginning; as we may see by Shooter's Hill, which, rising east of London and not far from the Thames, runneth along the south side of the island westward until it come to Cornwall. Like unto these also are the Crowdon Hills, which, though under divers names (as also the other from the Peak), do run into the borders of Scotland. What should I speak of the Cheviot Hills, which reach twenty miles in length? of the Black Mountains in Wales, which go from (*) to (*) miles at the least in length? of the Clee Hills in Shropshire, which come within four miles of Ludlow, and are divided from some part of Worcester by the Leme? of the Crames in Scotland, and of our Chiltern, which are eighteen miles at the least from one end of them, which reach from Henley in Oxfordshire to Dunstable in Bedfordshire, and are very well replenished with wood and corn, notwithstanding that the most part yield a sweet short grass, profitable for sheep? Wherein albeit they of Scotland do somewhat come behind us, yet their outward defect is inwardly recompensed, not only with plenty of quarries (and those of sundry kinds of marble, hard stone, and fine alabaster), but also rich mines of metal, as shall be shewed hereafter.

In this island the winds are commonly more strong and fierce than in any other places of the main (which Cardane also espied): and that is often seen upon the naked hills not guarded with trees to bear and keep it off. That grievous inconvenience also enforceth our nobility, gentry, and communality to build their houses in the valleys, leaving the high grounds unto their corn and cattle, lest the cold and stormy blasts of winter should breed them greater

* Here lacks.—H.

annoyance; whereas in other regions each one desireth to set his house aloft on the hill, not only to be seen afar off, and cast forth his beams of stately and curious workman- ship into every quarter of the country, but also (in hot habitations) for coldness sake of the air, sith the heat is never so vehement on the hill-top as in the valley, because the reverberation of the sun's beams either reacheth not so far as the highest, or else becometh not so strong as when it is reflected upon the lower soil.

But to leave our buildings unto the purposed place (which notwithstanding have very much increased, I mean for curiosity and cost, in England, Wales, and Scotland, within these few years) and to return to the soil again. Certainly it is even now in these our days grown to be much more fruitful than it hath been in times past. The cause is for that our countrymen are grown to be more painful, skilful, and careful through recompense of gain, than heretofore they have been: insomuch that my *synchroni* or time fellows can reap at this present great commodity in a little room; whereas of late years a great compass hath yielded but small profit, and this only through the idle and negligent occupation of such as daily manured and had the same in occupying. I might set down examples of these things out of all the parts of this island—that is to say, many of England, more out of Scotland, but most of all out of Wales: in which two last rehearsed, very other little food and livelihood was wont to be looked for (beside flesh) more than the soil of itself and the cow gave, the people in the meantime living idly, dissolutely, and by picking and stealing one from another. All which vices are now (for the most part) relinquished, so that each nation manureth her own with triple commodity to that it was before time.

The pasture of this island is according to the nature and bounty of the soil, whereby in most places it is plentiful, very fine, batable, and such as either fatteth our cattle with speed or yieldeth great abundance of milk and cream whereof the yellowest butter and finest cheese are made. But where the blue clay aboundeth (which hardly drinketh up the winter's water in long season) there the grass is speary, rough, and very apt for bushes: by which occasion

it becometh nothing so profitable unto the owner as the
other. The best pasture ground of all England is in Wales,
and of all the pasture in Wales that of Cardigan is the
chief. I speak of the same which is to be found in the
mountains there, where the hundredth part of the grass
growing is not eaten, but suffered to rot on the ground,
whereby the soil becometh matted and divers bogs and
quickmoors made withal in long continuance: because all
the cattle in the country are not able to eat it down. If it
be accounted good soil on which a man may lay a wand
over night and on the morrow find it hidden and overgrown
with grass, it is not hard to find plenty thereof in many
places of this land. Nevertheless such is the fruitfulness
of the aforesaid county that it far surmounteth this proportion, whereby it may be compared for batableness with
Italy, which in my time is called the paradise of the world,
although by reason of the wickedness of such as dwell
therein it may be called the sink and drain of hell: so that
whereas they were wont to say of us that our land is good
but our people evil, they did but only speak it; whereas we
know by experience that the soil of Italy is a noble soil, but
the dwellers therein far off any virtue or goodness.

Our meadows are either bottoms (whereof we have great
store, and those very large, because our soil is hilly) or
else such as we call land meads, and borrowed from the
best and fattest pasturages. The first of them are yearly
and often overflown by the rising of such streams as pass
through the same, or violent falls of land-waters, that
descend from the hills about them. The other are seldom
or never overflown, and that is the cause wherefore their
grass is shorter than that of the bottoms, and yet is it far
more fine, wholesome, and batable, sith the hay of our low
meadows is not only full of sandy cinder, which breedeth
sundry diseases in our cattle, but also more rowty, foggy,
and full of flags, and therefore not so profitable for store
and forrage as the higher meads be. The difference furthermore in their commodities is great; for, whereas in our
land meadows we have not often above one good load of
hay, or peradventure a little more in an acre of ground (I
use the word *carrucata*, or *carruca*, which is a wain load,

and, as I remember, used by Pliny, lib. 33, cap. 2), in low meadows we have sometimes three, but commonly two or upwards, as experience hath oft confirmed.

Of such as are twice mowed I speak not, sith their later math is not so wholesome for cattle as the first; although in the mouth more pleasant for the time: for thereby they become oftentimes to be rotten, or to increase so fast in blood, that the garget and other diseases do consume many of them before the owners can seek out any remedy, by phlebotomy or otherwise. Some superstitious fools suppose that they which die of the garget are ridden with the nightmare, and therefore they hang up stones which naturally have holes in them, and must be found unlooked for; as if such a stone were an apt cockshot for the devil to run through and solace himself withal, while the cattle go scot-free and are not molested by him! But if I should set down but half the toys that superstition hath brought into our husbandmen's heads in this and other behalf, it would ask a greater volume than is convenient for such a purpose, wherefore it shall suffice to have said thus much of these things.

The yield of our corn-ground is also much after this rate following. Throughout the land (if you please to make an estimate thereof by the acre) in mean and indifferent years, wherein each acre of rye or wheat, well tilled and dressed, will yield commonly sixteen or twenty bushels, an acre of barley six-and-thirty bushels, of oats and such like four or five quarters, which proportion is notwithstanding oft abated toward the north, as it is oftentimes surmounted in the south. Of mixed corn, as peas and beans, sown together, tares and oats (which they call bulmong), rye and wheat (named miscelin), here is no place to speak, yet their yield is nevertheless much after this proportion, as I have often marked. And yet is not this our great foison comparable to that of hotter countries of the main. But, of all that I ever read, the increase which Eldred Danus writeth of in his *De imperie Judæorum in Æthiopia* surmounteth, where he saith that in the field near to the Sabbatike river, called in old time Gosan, the ground is so fertile that every grain of barley growing doth yield an hundred kernels at the least unto the owner.

Of late years also we have found and taken up a great trade in planting of hops, whereof our moory hitherto and unprofitable grounds do yield such plenty and increase that there are few farmers or occupiers in the country which have not gardens and hops growing of their own, and those far better than do come from Flanders unto us. Certes the corruptions used by the Flemings, and forgery daily practised in this kind of ware, gave us occasion to plant them here at home; so that now we may spare and send many over unto them. And this I know by experience, that some one man by conversion of his moory grounds into hopyards, whereof before he had no commodity, doth raise yearly by so little as twelve acres in compass two hundred marks—all charges borne towards the maintenance of his family. Which industry God continue! though some secret friends of Flemings let not to exclaim against this commodity, as a spoil of wood, by reason of the poles, which nevertheless after three years do also come to the fire, and spare their other fuel.

The cattle which we breed are commonly such as for greatness of bone, sweetness of flesh, and other benefits to be reaped by the same, give place unto none other; as may appear first by our oxen, whose largeness, height, weight, tallow, hides, and horns are such as none of any other nation do commonly or may easily exceed them. Our sheep likewise, for good taste of flesh, quantity of limbs, fineness of fleece, caused by their hardness of pasturage and abundance of increase (for in many places they bring forth two or three at an eaning), give no place unto any, more than do our goats, who in like sort do follow the same order, and our deer come not behind. As for our conies, I have seen them so fat in some soils, especially about Meall and Disnege, that the grease of one being weighed hath peised very near six or seven ounces. All which benefits we first refer to the grace and goodness of God, and next of all unto the bounty of our soil, which he hath endued with so notable and commodious fruitfulness.

But, as I mean to intreat of these things more largely hereafter, so will I touch in this place one benefit which our nation wanteth, and that is wine, the fault whereof is not in our soil, but the negligence of our countrymen (especially of the south parts), who do not inure the same to this commodity, and which by reason of long discontinuance is now become inapt to bear any grapes almost for pleasure and shadow, much less then the plain fields or several vineyards for advantage and commodity. Yet of late time some have essayed to deal for wine (as to your lordship also is right well known). But sith that liquor, when it cometh to the drinking, hath been found more hard than that which is brought from beyond the sea, and the cost of planting and keeping thereof so chargeable that they may buy it far better cheap from other countries, they have given over their enterprises without any consideration that, as in all other things, so neither the ground itself in the beginning, nor success of their travel, can answer their expectation at the first, until such time as the soil be brought as it were into acquaintance with this commodity, and that provision may be made for the more easiness of charge to be employed upon the same.

If it be true that where wine doth last and endure well there it will grow no worse, I muse not a little wherefore the planting of vines should be neglected in England. That this liquor might have grown in this island heretofore, first the charter that Probus the Emperor gave equally to us, the Gauls, and Spaniards, is one sufficient testimony. And that it did grow here (beside the testimony of Beda, lib. 1., cap. 1) the old notes of tithes for wine that yet remain in the accounts of some parsons and vicars in Kent, elsewhere, besides the records of sundry suits, commenced in divers ecclesiastical courts, both in Kent, Surrey, etc., also the enclosed parcels almost in every abbey yet called the vineyards, may be a notable witness, as also the plot which we now call East Smithfield in London, given by Canutus, sometime king of this land, with other soil thereabout, unto certain of his knights, with the liberty of a Guild which thereof was called Knighton Guild. The truth is (saith John Stow, our countryman and diligent traveller in the old estate of this my native city) that it is now named Portsoken Ward, and given in time past to the religious house within Aldgate. Howbeit first Otwell, the archovel, Otto,

and finally Geffrey Earl of Essex, constables of the Tower
of London, withheld that portion from the said house until
the reign of King Stephen, and thereof made a vineyard to
their great commodity and lucre. The Isle of Ely also was
in the first times of the Normans called Le Ile des Vignes.
And good record appeareth that the bishop there had yearly
three or four tun at the least given him *nomine decimæ,*
beside whatsoever over-sum of the liquor did accrue to
him by leases and other excheats whereof also I have seen
mention. Wherefore our soil is not to be blamed, as though
our nights were so exceeding short that in August and
September the moon, which is lady of moisture and chief
ripener of this liquor, cannot in any wise shine long enough
upon the same: a very mere toy and fable, right worthy to
be suppressed, because experience convinceth the upholders
thereof even in the Rhenish wines.

The time hath been also that woad, wherewith our
countrymen dyed their faces (as Cæsar saith), that they
might seem terrible to their enemies in the field (and also
women and their daughters-in-law did stain their bodies
and go naked, in that pickle, to the sacrifices of their gods,
coveting to resemble therein the Ethiopians, as Pliny saith,
(lib. 22, cap. 1), and also madder have been (next unto our
tin and wools) the chief commodities and merchandise of
this realm. I find also that rape oil hath been made within
this land. But now our soil either will not, or at the leastwise may not, bear either woad or madder. I say not that
the ground is not able so to do, but that we are negligent,
afraid of the pilling of our grounds, and careless of our
own profits, as men rather willing to buy the same of others
than take any pain to plant them here at home. The like
I may say of flax, which by law ought to be sown in every
country town in England, more or less; but I see no success
of that good and wholesome law, sith it is rather con-
temptuously rejected than otherwise dutifully kept in any
place in England.

Some say that our great number of laws do breed a general negligence and contempt of all good order, because we
have so many that no subject can live without the trans-
gression of some of them, and that the often alteration of

our ordinances doth much harm in this respect, which (after Aristotle) doth seem to carry some reason withal, for (as Cornelius Gallus hath)—

"Eventus varios res. nova semper habet."[1]

But very many let not to affirm that the greedy corruption of the promoters on the one side, facility in dispensing with good laws and first breach of the same in the lawmakers and superiors and private respects of their establishment on the other, are the greatest causes why the inferiors regard no good order, being always so ready to offend without any faculty one way as they are otherwise to presume upon the examples of their betters when any hold is to be taken. But as in these things I have no skill, so I wish that fewer licences for the private commodity but of a few were granted (not that thereby I deny the maintenance of the prerogative royal, but rather would with all my heart that it might be yet more honourably increased), and that every one which by fee'd friendship (or otherwise) doth attempt to procure ought from the prince that may profit but few and prove hurtful to many might be at open assizes and sessions denounced enemy to his country and commonwealth of the land.

Glass also hath been made here in great plenty before, and in the time of the Romans; and the said stuff also, beside fine scissors, shears, collars of gold and silver for women's necks, cruises and cups of amber, were a parcel of the tribute which Augustus in his days laid upon this island. In like sort he charged the Britons with certain implements and vessels of ivory (as Strabo saith); whereby it appeareth that in old time our countrymen were far more industrious and painful in the use and application of the benefits of their country than either after the coming of the Saxons or Normans, in which they gave themselves more to idleness and following of the wars.

If it were requisite that I should speak of the sundry kinds of mould, as the cledgy, or clay, whereof are divers sorts (red, blue, black, and white), also the red or white

---

[1] " An innovation has always mixed effects."

sandy, the loamy, roselly, gravelly, chalky, or black, I could say that there are so many divers veins in Britain as elsewhere in any quarter of like quantity in the world. Howbeit this I must need confess, that the sand and clay do bear great sway: but clay most of all, as hath been and yet is always seen and felt through plenty and dearth of corn. For if this latter (I mean the clay) do yield her full increase (which it doth commonly in dry years for wheat), then is there general plenty: whereas if it fail, then have we scarcity, according to the old rude verse set down of England, but to be understood of the whole island, as experience doth confirm—

> " When the sand doth serve the clay,
>   Then may we sing well-away;
>   But when the clay doth serve the sand,
>   Then is it merry with England."

I might here intreat of the famous valleys in England, of which one is called the Vale of White Horse, another of Evesham (commonly taken for the granary of Worcestershire), the third of Aylesbury, that goeth by Thame, the roots of Chiltern Hills to Dunstable, Newport Pagnel, Stony Stratford, Buckingham, Birstane Park, etc. Likewise of the fourth, of Whitehart or Blackmoor in Dorsetshire. The fifth, of Ringdale or Renidale, corruptly called Kingtaile, that lieth (as mine author saith) upon the edge of Essex and Cambridgeshire, and also the Marshwood Vale: but, forsomuch as I know not well their several limits, I give over to go any further in their description. In like sort it should not be amiss to speak of our fens, although our country be not so full of this kind of soil as the parts beyond the seas (to wit, Narbonne, etc.), and thereto of other pleasant bottoms, the which are not only endued with excellent rivers and great store of corn and fine fodder for neat and horses in time of the year (whereby they are exceeding beneficial unto their owners), but also of no small compass and quantity in ground. For some of our fens are well known to be either of ten, twelve, sixteen, twenty, or thirty miles in length, that of the Girwies yet passing all the rest, which is full sixty (as I have often read). Wherein also Ely, the famous isle, standeth, which is seven miles every way, and whereunto there is no access but by three causies, whose inhabitants in like sort by an old privilege may take wood, sedge turf, etc., to burn, likewise hay for their cattle and thatch for their houses of custom, and each occupier in his appointed quantity throughout the isle; albeit that covetousness hath now begun somewhat to abridge this large benevolence and commodity, as well in the said isle as most other places of this land.

Finally, I might discourse in like order of the large commons, laid out heretofore by the lords of the soil for the benefit of such poor as inhabit within the compass of their manors. But, as the true intent of the givers is now in most places defrauded, insomuch that not the poor tenants inhabitating upon the same, but their landlords, have all the commodity and gain. Wherefore I mean not at this present to deal withal, but reserve the same wholly unto the due place, whilst I go forward with the rest, setting down nevertheless by the way a general commendation of the whole island, which I find in an ancient monument, much unto this effect—

> " Illa quidem longè celebris splendore, beata,
> Glebis, lacte, favis, supereminet insula cunctis,
> Quas regit ille Deus, spumanti cujus ab ore
> Profluit oceanus," etc.

And a little after—

> " Testis Lundoniaratibus, Wintonia Baccho,
> Herefordia grege, Worcestria frugeredundans,
> Batha lacu, Salabyra feris, Cantuaria pisce,
> Eboraca sylvis, Excestria clara metallis,
> Norwicum Dacis hybernis, Cestria Gallis,
> Cicestrum Norwagenis, Dunelmia præpinguis,
> Testis Lincolnia gens infinita decore,
> Testis Eli formosa situ, Doncastria visu," etc.

CHAPTER XI

OF SUNDRY MINERALS AND METALS

[1577, Book III., Chapters 16 and 18; 1587, Book III., Chapters 10 and 11.]

WITH how great benefits this island of ours hath been endued from the beginning I hope there is no godly man but will readily confess, and yield unto the Lord God his due honour for the same. For we are blessed every way, and there is no temporal commodity necessary to be had or craved by any nation at God's hand that he hath not in most abundant manner bestowed upon us Englishmen, if we could see to use it, and be thankful for the same. But alas! (as I said in the chapter precedent) we love to enrich them that care not for us, but for our great commodities: and one trifling toy not worth the carriage, coming (as the proverb saith) in three ships from beyond the sea, is more worth with us than a right good jewel easy to be had at home. They have also the cast to teach us to neglect our own things; for, if they see that we begin to make any account of our commodities (if it be so that they have also the like in their own countries) they will suddenly abase the same to so low a price that our gain not being worthy our travel, and the same commodity with less cost ready to be had at home from other countries (though but for a while), it causeth us to give over our endeavours and as it were by-and-by to forget the matter whereabout we went before, to obtain them at their hands. And this is the only cause wherefore our commodities are oft so little esteemed of. Some of them can say, without any teacher, that they will buy the case of a fox of an Englishman for a groat, and make him afterwards give twelve pence for the tail. Would to God we might once

335

wax wiser, and each one endeavour that the commonwealth of England may flourish again in her old rate, and that our commodities may be fully wrought at home (as cloth if you will for an example) and not carried out to be shorn and dressed abroad, while our clothworkers here do starve and beg their bread, and for lack of daily practice utterly neglect to be skilful in this science! But to my purpose.

We have in England great plenty of quicksilver, antimony, sulphur, black lead, and orpiment red and yellow. We have also the finest alum (wherein the diligence of one of the greatest favourers of the commonwealth of England of a subject[1] hath been of late egregriously abused, and even almost with barbarous incivility) and of no less force against fire, if it were used in our parietings, than that of Lipari, which only was in use sometime amongst the Asians and Romans and whereof Sylla had such trial that when he meant to have burned a tower of wood erected by Archelaus, the lieutenant of Mithridates, he could by no means set it on fire in a long time, because it was washed over with alum, as were also the gates of the temple of Jerusalem with like effect, and perceived when Titus commanded fire to be put unto the same. Besides this, we have also the natural cinnabarum or vermillion, the sulphurous glebe called bitumen in old time, for mortar, and yet burned in lamps where oil is scant and geson; the chrysocolla, copperas, and mineral stone, whereof petriolum is made, and that which is most strange, the mineral pearl, which as they are for greatness and colour most excellent of all other, so are they digged out of the main land and in sundry places far distant from the shore. Certes the western part of the land hath in times past greatly abounded with these and many other rare and excellent commodities, but now they are washed away by the violence of the sea, which hath devoured the greatest part of Cornwall and Devonshire on either side; and it doth appear yet by good record that, whereas now there is a great distance between the Scilly Isles and the point of the Land's End, there was of late years to speak of scarcely a brook or drain of one fathom water between them, if so much, as by those evi-

[1] The Lord Mountjoy.—H.

dences appeareth, and are yet to be seen in the hands of the lord and chief owner of those isles. But to proceed.

Of coal-mines we have such plenty in the north and western parts of our island as may suffice for all the realm of England; and so must they do hereafter indeed, if wood be not better cherished than it is at this present. And so say the truth, notwithstanding that very many of them are carried into other countries of the main, yet their greatest trade beginneth now to grow from the forge into the kitchen and hall, as may appear already in most cities and towns that lie about the coast, where they have but little other fuel except it be turf and hassock. I marvel not a little that there is no trade of these into Sussex and Southamptonshire, for want thereof the smiths do work their iron with charcoal. I think that far carriage be the only cause, which is but a slender excuse to enforce us to carry them into the main from hence.

Besides our coal-mines, we have pits in like sort of white plaster, and of fat and white and other coloured marble, wherewith in many places the inhabitors do compest their soil, and which doth benefit their land in ample manner for many years to come. We have saltpetre for our ordinance and salt soda for our glass, and thereto in one place a kind of earth (in Southery; as I ween, hard by Codington, and sometime in the tenure of one Croxton of London) which is so fine to make moulds for goldsmiths and casters of metal, that a load of it was worth five shillings thirty years ago; none such again they say in England. But whether there be or not, let us not be unthankful to God, for these and other his benefits bestowed upon us, whereby he sheweth himself a loving and merciful father unto us, which contrariwise return unto him in lieu of humility and obedience nothing but wickedness, avarice, mere contempt of his will, pride, excess, atheism, and no less than Jewish ingratitude.[2]

All metals receive their beginning of quicksilver and sulphur, which are as mother and father to them. And such is the purpose of nature in their generations that she

[2] Here ends the chapter entitled "Minerals," and the one on "Metals" begins.—W.

tendeth always to the procreation of gold; nevertheless she
seldom reacheth unto that her end, because of the unequal
mixture and proportion of these two in the substance engendered, whereby impediment and corruption is induced,
which as it is more or less doth shew itself in the metal that
is produced. . . .

And albeit that we have no such abundance of these (as
some other countries do yield), yet have my rich countrymen store enough of both in their purses, where in time
past they were wont to have least, because the garnishing
of our churches, tabernacles, images, shrines, and apparel
of the priests consumed the greatest part, as experience
hath confirmed.

Of late my countrymen have found out I wot not what
voyage into the West Indies, from whence they have
brought some gold, whereby our country is enriched; but
of all that ever adventured into those parts, none have sped
better than Sir Francis Drake, whose success (1582) hath
far passed even his own expectation. One John Frobisher
in like manner, attempting to seek out a shorter cut by the
northerly regions into the peaceable sea and kingdom of
Cathay, happened (1577) upon certain islands by the way,
wherein great plenty of much gold appeared, and so much
that some letted not to give out for certainty that Solomon
had his gold from thence, wherewith he builded the temple.
This golden shew made him so desirous also of like success
that he left off his former voyage and returned home to
bring news of such things as he had seen. But, when after
another voyage it was found to be but dross, he gave over
both the enterprises, and now keepeth home without any
desire at all to seek into far countries. In truth, such
was the plenty of ore there seen and to be had that, if it
had holden perfect, might have furnished all the world
with abundance of that metal; the journey also was short
and performed in four or five months, which was a notable
encouragement. But to proceed.

Tin and lead, metals which Strabo noteth in his time to
be carried unto Marsilis from hence, as Diodorus also confirmeth, are very plentiful with us, the one in Cornwall,
Devonshire, and elsewhere in the north, the other in Derby-

shire, Weredale, and sundry places of this island; whereby
my countrymen do reap no small commodity, but especially
our pewterers, who in times past employed the use of pewter
only upon dishes, pots, and a few other trifles for service
here at home, whereas now they are grown unto such
exquisite cunning that they can in manner imitate by in-
fusion any form or fashion of cup, dish, salt bowl, or
goblet, which is made by goldsmiths' craft, though they be
never so curious, exquisite, and artificially forged.   Such
furniture of household of this metal as we commonly call
by the name of *vessel* is sold usually by the garnish, which
doth contain twelve platters, twelve dishes, twelve saucers,
and those are either of silver fashion or else with broad or
narrow brims, and bought by the pound, which is now
valued at six or seven pence, or peradventure at eight pence.
Of porringers, pots, and other like, I speak not, albeit that
in the making of all these things there is such exquisite
diligence used, I mean for the mixture of the metal and
true making of this commodity (by reason of sharp laws
provided in that behalf), as the like is not to be found in
any other trade.   I have been also informed that it consisteth of a composition which hath thirty pounds of kettle
brass to a thousand pounds of tin, whereunto they add
three or four pounds of tin-glass; but as too much of this
doth make the stuff brickle, so the more the brass be, the
better is the pewter, and more profitable unto him that doth
buy and purchase the same.   But to proceed.

In some places beyond the sea a garnish of good flat
English pewter of an ordinary making (I say flat, because
dishes and platters in my time begin to be made deep like
basins, and are indeed more convenient both for sauce,
broth, and keeping the meat warm) is esteemed almost so
precious as the like number of vessels that are made of fine
silver, and in manner no less desired amongst the great
estates, whose workmen are nothing so skilful in that trade
as ours, neither their metal so good, nor plenty so great, as
we have here in England.   The Romans made excellent
looking-glasses of our English tin, howbeit our workmen
were not then so exquisite in that feat as the Brundusians,
wherefore the wrought metal was carried over unto them

by way of merchandise, and very highly were those glasses esteemed of till silver came generally in place, which in the end brought the tin into such contempt that in manner every dishwasher refused to look in other than silver glasses for the attiring of her head. Howbeit the making of silver glasses had been in use before Britain was known unto the Romans, for I read that one Praxiteles devised them in the young time of Pompey, which was before the coming of Cæsar into this island.

There were mines of lead sometimes also in Wales, which endured so long till the people had consumed all their wood by melting of the same (as they did also at Comeriswith, six miles from Stradfleur), and I suppose that in Pliny's time the abundance of lead (whereof he speaketh) was to be found in those parts, in the seventeenth of his thirty-fourth book; also he affirmeth that it lay in the very sward of the earth, and daily gotten in such plenty that the Romans made a restraint of the carriage thereof to Rome, limiting how much should yearly be wrought and transported over the sea.[3]

Iron is found in many places, as in Sussex, Kent, Weredale, Mendip, Walshall, as also in Shropshire, but chiefly in the woods betwixt Belvos and Willock (or Wicberry) near Manchester, and elsewhere in Wales. Of which mines divers do bring forth so fine and good stuff as any that cometh from beyond the sea, beside the infinite gains to the owners, if we would so accept it, or bestow a little more cost in the refining of it. It is also of such toughness, that it yieldeth to the making of claricord wire in some places of the realm. Nevertheless, it was better cheap with us when strangers only brought it hither; for it is our quality when we get any commodity to use it with extremity towards our own nation, after we have once found the means to shut out foreigners from the bringing in of the like. It breedeth in like manner great expense and waste of wood, as doth the making of our pots and table vessels of glass, wherein is much loss, sith it is so quickly broken; and yet (as I think) easy to be made tougher, if our alchemists could once find the true birth or production of the red man,

[3] Here follow two stories about crows and miners.—W.

whose mixture would induce a metallic toughness unto it, whereby it should abide the hammer.

Copper is lately not found, but rather restored again to light. For I have read of copper to have been heretofore gotten in our island; howbeit as strangers have most commonly the governance of our mines, so they hitherto make small gains of this in hand in the north parts; for (as I am informed) the profit doth very hardly countervail the charges, whereat wise men do not a little marvel, considering the abundance which that mine doth seem to offer, and, as it were, at hand. Leland, our countryman, noteth sundry great likelihoods of natural copper mines to be eastwards, as between Dudman and Trewardth, in the sea cliffs, beside other places, whereof divers are noted here and there in sundry places of this book already, and therefore it shall be but in vain to repeat them here again. As for that which is gotten out of the marchasite, I speak not of it, sith it is not incident to my purpose. In Dorsetshire also a copper mine lately found is brought to good perfection.

As for our steel, it is not so good for edge-tools as that of Cologne, and yet the one is often sold for the other, and like tale used in both, that is to say, thirty gads to the sheaf, and twelve sheaves to the burden.

Our alchemy is artificial, and thereof our spoons and some salts are commonly made and preferred before our pewter with some,[4] albeit in truth it be much subject to corruption, putrefaction, more heavy and foul to handle than our pewter; yet some ignorant persons affirm it to be a metal more natural, and the very same which Encelius calleth *plumbum cinereum,* the Germans *wisemute, mithan,* and *counterfeie,* adding that where it groweth silver cannot be far off. Nevertheless it is known to be a mixture of brass, lead, and tin (of which this latter occupieth the one-half), but after another proportion than is used in pewter. But alas, I am persuaded that neither the old Arabians nor new alchemists of our time did ever hear of it, albeit that the name thereof do seem to come out of their forge. For the common sort indeed do call it alchemy, an unwholesome metal (God wot) and worthy to be banished and driven

[4] Some tell me that it is a mixture of brass, lead, and tin.—H.

out of the land. And thus I conclude with this discourse, as having no more to say of the metals of my country, except I should talk of brass, bell metal, and such as are brought over for merchandise from other countries; and yet I cannot but say that there is some brass found also in England, but so small is the quantity that it is not greatly to be esteemed or accounted for.

CHAPTER XII

OF CATTLE KEPT FOR PROFIT

[1577, Book III., Chapter 8; 1587, Book III., Chapter 1.]

THERE is no kind of tame cattle usually to be seen in these parts of the world whereof we have not some, and that great store, in England, as horses, oxen, sheep, goats, swine, and far surmounting the like in other countries, as may be proved with ease. For where are oxen commonly made more large of bone, horses more decent and pleasant in pace, kine more commodious for the pail, sheep more profitable for wool, swine more wholesome of flesh, and goats more gainful to their keepers than here with us in England ? But, to speak of them peculiarly, I suppose that our kine are so abundant in yield of milk, whereof we make our butter and cheese, as the like any where else, and so apt for the plough in divers places as either our horses or oxen. And, albeit they now and then twin, yet herein they seem to come short of that commodity which is looked for in other countries, to wit, in that they bring forth most commonly but one calf at once. The gains also gotten by a cow (all charges borne) hath been valued at twenty shillings yearly; but now, as land is enhanced, this proportion of gain is much abated, and likely to decay more and more, if ground arise to be yet dearer—which God forbid, if it be His will and pleasure. I heard of late of a cow in Warwickshire, belonging to Thomas Breuer of Studley, which in six years had sixteen calves, that is four at once in three calvings and twice twins, which unto many may seem a thing incredible. In like manner our oxen are such as the like are not to be found in any country of Europe, both for greatness of body and sweetness of flesh or else would not the Roman writers have preferred them before those of Liguria.

In most places our graziers are now grown to be so cunning that if they do but see an ox or bullock, and come to the feeling of him, they will give a guess at his weight, and how many score or stone of flesh and tallow he beareth, how the butcher may live by the sale, and what he may have for the skin and tallow, which is a point of skill not commonly practised heretofore. Some such graziers also are reported to ride with velvet coats and chains of gold about them and in their absence their wives will not let to supply those turns with no less skill than their husbands: which is a hard work for the poor butcher, sith he through this means can seldom be rich or wealthy by his trade. In like sort the flesh of our oxen and kine is sold both by hand and by weight as the buyer will; but in young ware rather by weight especially for the steer and heifer, sith the finer beef is the lightest, whereas the flesh of bulls and old kine, etc., is of sadder substance, and therefore much heavier as it lieth in the scale. Their horns also are known to be more fair and large in England than in any other places, except those which are to be seen among the Pæones, which quality, albeit that it be given to our breed generally by nature, yet it is now and then helped also by art. For, when they be very young, many graziers will oftentimes anoint their budding horns or tender tips with honey, which mollifieth the natural hardness of that substance, and thereby maketh them to grow unto a notable greatness. Certes it is not strange in England to see oxen whose horns have the length of a yard or three feet between the tips, and they themselves thereto so tall as the height of a man of mean and indifferent stature is scarce equal unto them. Nevertheless it is much to be lamented that our general breed of cattle is not better looked unto; for the greatest occupiers wean least store, because they can buy them (as they say) far better cheap than to raise and bring them up. In my time a cow hath risen from four nobles to four marks by this means, which notwithstanding were no great price if they did yearly bring forth more than one calf a piece, as I hear they do in other countries.

Our horses, moreover, are high, and, although not commonly of such huge greatness as in other places of the main, yet, if you respect the easiness of their pace, it is hard to say where their like are to be had. Our land doth yield no asses, and therefore we want the generation also of mules and somers, and therefore the most part of our carriages is made by these, which, remaining stoned, are either reserved for the cart or appointed to bear such burdens as are convenient for them. Our cart or plough horses (for we use them indifferently) are commonly so strong that five or six of them (at the most) will draw three thousand weight of the greatest tale with ease for a long journey, although it be not a load of common usage, which consisteth only of two thousand, or fifty foot of timber, forty bushels of white salt, or six-and-thirty of bay, of five quarters of wheat, experience daily teacheth, and I have elsewhere remembered. Such as are kept also for burden will carry four hundred-weight commonly without any hurt or hindrance. This furthermore is to be noted, that our princes and the nobility have their carriage commonly made by carts, whereby it cometh to pass that when the queen's majesty doth remove from any one place to another, there are usually 400 care-wares, which amount to the sum of 2400 horses, appointed out of the countries adjoining, whereby her carriage is conveyed safely unto the appointed place. Hereby also the ancient use of somers and sumpter horses is in manner utterly relinquished, which causeth the trains of our princes in their progresses to shew far less than those of the kings of other nations.

Such as serve for the saddle are commonly gelded, and now grew to be very dear among us, especially if they be well coloured, justly limbed, and have thereto an easy ambling pace. For our countrymen, seeking their ease in every corner where it is to be had, delight very much in those qualities, but chiefly in their excellent paces, which, besides that it is in manner peculiar unto horses of our soil, and not hurtful to the rider or owner sitting on their backs, it is moreover very pleasant and delectable in his ears, in that the noise of their well-proportioned pace doth yield comfortable sound as he travelleth by the way. Yet is there no greater deceit used anywhere than among our horsekeepers, horsecoursers, and hostlers; for such is the subtle knavery of a great sort of them (without exception of any of them be it spoken which deal for private gain) that an honest-meaning man shall have very good luck among them if he be not deceived by some false trick or other.

There are certain notable markets wherein great plenty of horses and colts is bought and sold, and whereunto such as have need resort yearly to buy and make their necessary provision of them, as Ripon, Newport Pond, Wolfpit, Harboro', and divers others. But, as most drovers are very diligent to bring great store of these unto those places, so many of them are too too lewd in abusing such as buy them. For they have a custom, to make them look fair to the eye, when they come within two days' journey of the market to drive them till they sweat, and for the space of eight or twelve hours, which, being done, they turn them all over the backs into some water, where they stand for a season, and then go forward with them to the place appointed, where they make sale of their infected ware, and such as by this means do fall into many diseases and maladies. Of such outlandish horses as are daily brought over unto us I speak not, as the jennet of Spain, the courser of Naples, the hobby of Ireland, the Flemish roile and the Scottish nag, because that further speech of them cometh not within the compass of this treatise, and for whose breed and maintenance (especially of the greatest sort) King Henry the Eighth erected a noble studdery, and for a time had very good success with them, till the officers, waxing weary, procured a mixed brood of bastard races, whereby his good purpose came to little effect. Sir Nicholas Arnold of late hath bred the best horses in England, and written of the manner of their production: would to God his compass of ground were like to that of Pella in Syria, wherein the king of that nation had usually a studdery of 30,000 mares and 300 stallions, as Strabo doth remember, lib. 16. But to leave this, let us see what may be said of sheep.

Our sheep are very excellent, sith for sweetness of flesh they pass all other. And so much are our wools to be preferred before those of Milesia and other places that if Jason had known the value of them that are bred and to be had in Britain he would never have gone to Colchis to look for any there. For, as Dionysius Alexandrinus saith in his *De situ Orbis,* it may by spinning be made comparable to the spider's web. What fools then are our countrymen, in that they seek to bereave themselves of this commodity by practising daily how to transfer the same to other nations, in carrying over their rams and ewes to breed and increase among them! The first example hereof was given under Edward the Fourth, who, not understanding the bottom of the suit of sundry traitorous merchants that sought a present gain with the perpetual hindrance of their country licensed them to carry over certain numbers of them into Spain, who, having licence but for a few, shipped very many: a thing practised in other commodities also, whereby the prince and his land are not seldom times defrauded. But such is our nature, and so blind are we indeed, that we see no inconvenience before we feel it; and for a present gain we regard not what damage may ensue to our posterity. Hereto some other man would add also the desire that we have to benefit other countries and to impeach our own. And it is, so sure as God liveth, that every trifle which cometh from beyond the sea, though it be not worth threepence, is more esteemed than a continual commodity at home with us, which far exceedeth that value. In time past the use of this commodity consisteth (for the most part) in cloth and woolsteds; but now, by means of strangers succoured here from domestic persecution, the same hath been employed unto sundry other uses, as mockados, bays, vellures, grograines, etc., whereby the makers have reaped no small commodity. It is furthermore to be noted, for the low countries of Belgie know it, and daily experience (notwithstanding the sharpness of our laws to the contrary) doth yet confirm it, that, although our rams and wethers do go thither from us never so well headed according to their kind, yet after they have remained there a while they cast there their heads, and from thenceforth they remain polled without any horns at all. Certes this kind of cattle is more cherished in England than standeth well with the commodity of the commons or prosperity of divers towns, whereof some are wholly converted to their feeding; yet such a profitable sweetness is their fleece, such necessity in their flesh, and so great a benefit in the manuring of barren soil with their dung and piss, that their superfluous members are the better born withal. And there is never a husbandman (for now I speak not of our great sheepmasters, of whom some one man hath 20,000) but hath more or less of this cattle feeding on his fallows and short grounds, which yield the finer fleece.

Nevertheless the sheep of our country are often troubled with the rot (as are our swine with the measles, though never so generally), and many men are now and then great losers by the same; but, after the calamity is over, if they can recover and keep their new stock sound for seven years together, the former loss will easily be recompensed with double commodity. Cardan writeth that our waters are hurtful to our sheep; howbeit this is but his conjecture, for we know that our sheep are infected by going to the water, and take the same as a sure and certain token that a rot hath gotten hold of them, their livers and lights being already distempered through excessive heat, which enforceth them the rather to seek unto the water. Certes there is no parcel of the main wherein a man shall generally find more fine and wholesome water than in England; and therefore it is impossible that our sheep should decay by tasting of the same. Wherefore the hindrance by rot is rather to be ascribed to the unseasonableness and moisture of the weather in summer, also their licking in of mildews, gossamire, rowtie fogs, and rank grass, full of superfluous juice, but especially (I say) to over moist weather, whereby the continual rain piercing into their hollow fells soaketh forthwith into their flesh, which bringeth them to their baines. Being also infected, their first shew of sickness is their desire to drink, so that our waters are not unto them *causa ægritudinis,* but *signum morbi,* whatsoever Cardan do maintain to the contrary. There are (and peradventure no small babes) which are grown to be such good husbands that they can make account of every ten kine to be clearly worth twenty pounds in common and indifferent years, if the milk of five sheep be daily added to the same. But, as I wot not how true this surmise is, because it is no part of my trade, so I am sure hereof that some housewives can and do add daily a less portion of ewe's milk unto the cheese of so many kine, whereby their cheese doth the longer abide moist and eateth more brickle and mellow than otherwise it would.

Goats we have plenty, and of sundry colours, in the west parts of England, especially in and towards Wales and amongst the rocky hills, by whom the owners do reap so small advantage: some also are cherished elsewhere in divers steeds, for the benefit of such as are diseased with sundry maladies, unto whom (as I hear) their milk, cheese, and bodies of their young kids are judged very profitable, and therefore inquired for of many far and near. Certes I find among the writers that the milk of a goat is next in estimation to that of the woman, for that it helpeth the stomach, removeth oppilations and stoppings of the liver, and looseth the belly. Some place also next unto it the milk of the ewe, and thirdly that of the cow. But hereof I can shew no reason; only this I know, that ewe's milk is fulsome, sweet, and such in taste as (except such as are used unto it) no man will gladly yield to live and feed withal.

As for swine, there is no place that hath greater store, nor more wholesome in eating, than are these here in England, which nevertheless do never any good till they come to the table. Of these some we eat green for pork, and other dried up into bacon to have it in more continuance. Lard we make some, though very little, because it is chargeable: neither have we such use thereof as is to be seen in France and other countries, sith we do either bake our meat with sweet suet of beef or mutton and baste all our meat with sweet or salt butter or suffer the fattest to baste itself by leisure. In champaign countries they are kept by herds, and a hogherd appointed to attend and wait upon them, who commonly gathereth them together by his noise and cry, and leadeth them forth to feed abroad in the fields. In some places also women do scour and wet their clothes with their dung, as other do with hemlocks and nettles; but such is the savour of the clothes touched withal that I cannot abide to wear them on my body, more than such as are scoured with the refuse soap, than the which (in mine opinion) there is none more unkindly savour.

Of our tame boars we make brawn, which is a kind of

meat not usually known to strangers (as I take it), otherwise
would not the swart Rutters and French cooks, at the loss of
Calais (where they found great store of this provision almost
in every house), have attempted with ridiculous success to
roast, bake, broil, and fry the same for their masters, till they
were better informed. I have heard moreover how a nobleman of England not long since did send over a hogshead of
brawn ready soused to a Catholic gentleman of France, who,
supposing it to be fish, reserved it till Lent, at which time he
did eat thereof with great frugality. Thereto he so well liked
the provision itself that he wrote over very earnestly, and
with offer of great recompense, for more of the same fish
against the year ensuing; whereas if he had known it to
have been flesh he would not have touched it (I dare say)
for a thousand crowns without the pope's dispensation. A
friend of mine also dwelling some time in Spain, having
certain Jews at his table, did set brawn before them, whereof
they did eat very earnestly, supposing it to be a kind of
fish not common in those parts; but when the goodman of
the house brought in the head in pastime among them, to
shew what they had eaten, they rose from the table, hied
them home in haste, each of them procuring himself to
vomit, some by oil and some by other means, till (as they
supposed) they had cleansed their stomachs of that pro-
hibited food. With us it is accounted a great piece of service
at the table from November until February be ended, but
chiefly in the Christmas time. With the same also we begin
our dinners each day after other; and, because it is somewhat hard of digestion, a draught of malvesey, bastard, or
muscadel, is usually drank after it, where either of them are
conveniently to be had; otherwise the meaner sort content
themselves with their own drink, which at that season
is generally very strong, and stronger indeed than it is all
the year beside. It is made commonly of the fore part of a
tame boar, set up for the purpose by the space of a whole
year or two, especially in gentlemen's houses (for the husbandmen and farmers never frank them for their own use
above three or four months, or half a year at the most),
in which time he is dieted with oats and peason, and lodged
on the bare planks of an uneasy coat, till his fat be hardened

sufficiently for their purpose: afterward he is killed, scalded, and cut out, and then of his former parts is our brawn made. The rest is nothing so fat, and therefore it beareth the name of sowse only, and is commonly reserved for the serving-man and hind, except it please the owner to have any part thereof baked, which are then handled of custom after this manner: the hinder parts being cut off, they are first drawn with lard, and then sodden; being sodden, they are soused in claret wine and vinegar a certain space, and afterward baked in pasties, and eaten of many instead of the wild boar, and truly it is very good meat: the pestles may be hanged up a while to dry before they be drawn with lard, if you will, and thereby prove the better. But hereof enough, and therefore to come again unto our brawn. The neck pieces, being cut off round, are called collars of brawn, the shoulders are named shilds, only the ribs retain the former denomination, so that these aforesaid pieces deserve the name of brawn: the bowels of the beast are commonly cast away because of their rankness, and so were likewise his stones, till a foolish fantasy got hold of late amongst some delicate dames, who have now found the means to dress them also with great cost for a dainty dish, and bring them to the board as a service among other of like sort, though not without note of their desire to the provocation of fleshly lust which by this their fond curiosity is not a little revealed. When the boar is thus cut out each piece is wrapped up, either with bulrushes, ozier, peels, tape inkle,[1] or such like, and then sodden in a lead or caldron together, till they be so tender that a man may thrust a bruised rush or straw clean through the fat: which being done, they take it up and lay it abroad to cool. Afterward, putting it into close vessels, they pour either good small ale or beer mingled with verjuice and salt thereto till it be covered, and so let it lie (now and then altering and changing the sousing drink lest it should wax sour) till occasion serve to spend it out of the way. Some use to make brawn of great barrow hogs, and seethe them, and souse the whole as they do that of the boar; and in my judgment it is the better of both, and more easy of digestion. But of brawn thus much, and so much may seem sufficient.

[1] Tape.

CHAPTER XIII

OF WILD AND TAME FOWLS

[1577, Book III., Chapters 9 and 11; 1587, Book III., Chapters 2 and 5.]

ORDER requireth that I speak somewhat of the fowls also of England, which I may easily divide into the wild and tame; but, alas! such is my small skill in fowls that, to say the truth, I can neither recite their numbers nor well distinguish one kind of them from another. Yet this I have by general knowledge, that there is no nation under the sun which hath already in the time of the year more plenty of wild fowl than we, for so many kinds as our island doth bring forth, and much more would have if those of the higher soil might be spared but one year or two from the greedy engines of covetous fowlers which set only for the pot and purse. Certes this enormity bred great troubles in King John's days, insomuch that, going in progress about the tenth of his reign, he found little or no game wherewith to solace himself or exercise his falcons. Wherefore, being at Bristow in the Christmas ensuing, he restrained all manner of hawking or taking of wild fowl throughout England for a season, whereby the land within few years was thoroughly replenished again. But what stand I upon this impertinent discourse? Of such therefore as are bred in our land, we have the crane, the bitter,[1] the wild and tame swan, the bustard, the heron, curlew, snite, wildgoose, wind or doterell, brant, lark, plover (of both sorts), lapwing, teal, widgeon, mallard, sheldrake, shoveller, peewitt, seamew, barnacle, quail (who, only with man, are subject to the falling sickness), the knot, the oliet or olive, the dunbird, woodcock, partridge, and pheasant, besides divers others, whose names to me are utterly un-

[1] The proper English name of the bird which vulgar acceptance forces us to now call *bittern*.—W.

352

known, and much more the taste of their flesh, wherewith
I was never acquainted. But as these serve not at all seasons, so in their several turns there is no plenty of them
wanting whereby the tables of the nobility and gentry
should seem at any time furnished. But of all these the
production of none is more marvellous, in my mind, than that
of the barnacle, whose place of generation we have sought
ofttimes as far as the Orchades, whereas peradventure we
might have found the same nearer home, and not only upon
the coasts of Ireland, but even in our own rivers. If I
should say how either these or some such other fowl not
much unlike unto them have bred of late times (for their
place of generation is not perpetual, but as opportunity
serveth and the circumstances do minister occasion) in the
Thames mouth, I do not think that many will believe me;
yet such a thing hath there been seen where a kind of fowl
had his beginning upon a short tender shrub standing near
unto the shore, from whence, when their time came, they
fell down, either into the salt water and lived, or upon the
dry land and perished, as Pena the French herbarian hath
also noted in the very end of his herbal. What I, for mine
own part, have seen here by experience, I have already so
touched upon in the chapter of islands, that it should be
but time spent in vain to repeat it here again. Look therefore in the description of Man (or Manaw) for more of
these barnacles, as also in the eleventh chapter of the description of Scotland, and I do not doubt but you shall in
some respect be satisfied in the generation of these fowls.
As for egrets, pawpers, and such like, they are daily brought
unto us from beyond the sea, as if all the fowl of our country could not suffice to satisfy our delicate appetites.

Our tame fowl are such (for the most part) as are
common both to us and to other countries, as cocks, hens,
geese, ducks, peacocks of Ind, pigeons, now a hurtful fowl
by reason of their multitudes, and number of houses daily
erected for their increase (which the boors of the country
call in scorn almshouses, and dens of thieves, and such like),
whereof there is great plenty in every farmer's yard. They
are kept there also to be sold either for ready money in the
open markets, or else to be spent at home in good company

amongst their neighbours without reprehension or fines. Neither are we so miserable in England (a thing only granted unto us by the especial grace of God and liberty of our princes) as to dine or sup with a quarter of a hen, or to make as great a repast with a cock's comb as they do in some other countries; but, if occasion serve, the whole carcases of many capons, hens, pigeons, and such like do oft go to wrack, beside beef, mutton, veal, and lamb, all of which at every feast are taken for necessary dishes amongst the communalty of England.

The gelding of cocks, whereby capons are made, is an ancient practice brought in of old time by the Romans when they dwelt here in this land; but the gelding of turkeys or Indish peacocks is a newer device, and certainly not used amiss, sith the rankness of that bird is very much abated thereby and the strong taste of the flesh in sundry wise amended. If I should say that ganders grow also to be gelded, I suppose that some will laugh me to scorn, neither have I tasted at any time of such a fowl so served, yet have I heard it more than once to be used in the country, where their geese are driven to the field like herds of cattle by a gooseherd, a toy also no less to be marvelled at than the other. For, as it is rare to hear of a gelded gander, so is it strange to me to see or hear of geese to be led to the field like sheep; yet so it is, and their gooseherd carrieth a rattle of paper or parchment with him when he goeth about in the morning to gather his goslings together, the noise whereof cometh no sooner to their ears than they fall to gaggling, and hasten to go with him. If it happen that the gates be not yet open, or that none of the house be stirring, it is ridiculous to see how they will peep under the doors, and never leave creaking and gaggling till they be let out unto him to overtake their fellows. With us, where I dwell, they are not kept in this sort, nor in many other places, neither are they kept so much for their bodies as their feathers. Some hold furthermore an opinion that in over rank soils their dung doth so qualify the batableness of the soil that their cattle is thereby kept from the garget, and sundry other diseases, although some of them come to their ends now and then by licking up of their feathers. I might here make

mention of other fowls produced by the industry of man,
as between the pheasant cock and dunghill hen, or between
the pheasant and the ringdove, the peacock and the turkey
hen, the partridge and the pigeon; but, sith I have no more
knowledge of these than what I have gotten by mine ear, I
will not meddle with them. Yet Cardan, speaking of the
second sort, doth affirm it to be a fowl of excellent beauty.
I would likewise intreat of other fowls which we repute
unclean, as ravens, crows, pies, choughs, rooks, kites, jays,
ringtails, starlings, woodspikes, woodnaws, etc.; but, sith
they abound in all countries, though peradventure most of
all in England (by reason of our negligence), I shall not
need to spend any time in the rehearsal of them. Neither
are our crows and choughs cherished of purpose to catch
up the worms that breed in our soils (as Polydor supposeth),
sith there are no uplandish towns but have (or should have)
nets of their own in store to catch them withal. Sundry
acts of Parliament are likewise made for their utter destruction, as also the spoil of other ravenous fowls hurtful
to poultry, conies, lambs, and kids, whose valuation of reward to him that killeth them is after the head: a device
brought from the Goths, who had the like ordinance for the
destruction of their white crows, and tale made by the beck,
which killed both lambs and pigs. The like order is taken
with us for our vermin as with them also for the rootage out
of their wild beasts, saving that they spared their greatest bears, especially the white, whose skins are by custom
and privilege reserved to cover those planchers whereupon
their priests do stand at mass, lest he should take some un-
kind cold in such a long piece of work: and happy is the
man that may provide them for him, for he shall have
pardon enough for that so religious an act, to last if he
will till doomsday do approach, and many thousands after.
Nothing therefore can be more unlikely to be true than that
these noisome creatures are nourished amongst us to devour
our worms, which do not abound much more in England than
elsewhere in other countries of the main. It may be that
some look for a discourse also of our other fowls in this
place at my hand, as nightingales, thrushes, blackbirds, ma-
vises, ruddocks, redstarts or dunocks, larks, tivits, king-

fishers, buntings, turtles (white or grey), linnets, bullfinches, goldfinches, washtails, cherrycrackers, yellowhammers, field-fares, etc.; but I should then spend more time upon them than is convenient. Neither will I speak of our costly and curious aviaries daily made for the better hearing of their melody, and observation of their natures; but I cease also to go any further in these things, having (as I think) said enough already of these that I have named.[2] . . .

I cannot make as yet any just report how many sorts of hawks are bred within this realm. Howbeit which of those that are usually had among us are disclosed within this land, I think it more easy and less difficult to set down. First of all, therefore, that we have the eagle common experience doth evidently confirm, and divers of our rocks whereon they breed, if speech did serve, could well declare the same. But the most excellent eyrie of all is not much from Chester, at a castle called Dinas Bren, sometime builded by Brennus, as our writers do remember. Certes this castle is no great thing, but yet a pile sometime very strong and inaccessible for enemies, though now all ruinous as many others are. It standeth upon a hard rock, in the side whereof an eagle breedeth every year. This also is notable in the overthrow of her nest (a thing oft attempted), that he which goeth thither must be sure of two large baskets, and so provide to be let down thereto, that he may sit in the one and be covered with the other: for otherwise the eagle would kill him and tear the flesh from his bones with her sharp talons, though his apparel were never so good. The common people call this fowl an erne; but, as I am ignorant whether the word eagle and erne do shew any difference of sex, I mean between the male and the female, so we have great store of them. And, near to the places where they breed, the commons complain of great harm to be done by them in their fields; for they are able to bear a young lamb or kid unto their nests, therewith to feed their young and come again for more. I was once of the opinion that there was a diversity of kind between the eagle and the erne, till I perceived that our nation used the word erne in most places for

[2] Here ends the first chapter of "fowls," that which follows being restricted to "hawks and ravenous fowls."—W.

the eagle. We have also the lanner and the lanneret, the
tersel and the goshawk, the musket and the sparhawk, the
jack and the hobby, and finally some (though very few)
marleons. And these are all the hawks that I do hear as yet
to be bred within this island. Howbeit, as these are not
wanting with us, so are they not very plentiful: wherefore
such as delight in hawking do make their chief purveyance
and provision for the same out of Danske, Germany, and
the eastern countries, from whence we have them in great
abundance and at excellent prices, whereas at home and
where they be bred they are sold for almost right nought,
and usually brought to the markets as chickens, pullets, and
pigeons are with us, and there bought up to be eaten (as we
do the aforesaid fowl) almost of every man. It is said
that the sparhawk pryeth not upon the fowl in the morning, that she taketh over even, but as loath to have double
benefit by one seelie fowl doth let it go to make some shift for
itself. But hereof as I stand in some doubt. So this I
find among the writers worthy the noting: that the sparhawk is enemy to young children, as is also the ape, but of
the peacock she is marvellously afraid, and so appalled that
all courage and stomach for a time is taken from her upon
the sight thereof. But to proceed with the rest. Of other
ravenous birds we have also very great plenty, as the buz-
zard, the kite, the ringtail, dunkite, and such as often annoy
our country dames by spoiling of their young breeds of
chickens, ducks, and goslings, whereunto our very ravens
and crows have learned also the way: and so much are
ravens given to this kind of spoil that some idle and curious
heads of set purpose have manned, reclaimed, and used them
instead of hawks, when other could not be had. Some do
imagine that the raven should be the vulture, and I was
almost persuaded in times past to believe the same; but,
finding of late, a description of the vulture, which better
agreeth with the form of a second kind of eagle, I freely
surcease to be longer of that opinion: for, as it hath, after
a sort, the shape, colour, and quantity of an eagle, so are the
legs and feet more hairy and rough, their sides under their
wings better covered with thick down (wherewith also their
gorge or a part of their breast under their throats is armed,

and not with feathers) than are the like parts of the eagle,
and unto which portraiture there is no member of the raven
(who is almost black of colour) that can have any resem-
blance: we have none of them in England to my knowledge;
if we have, they go generally under the name of eagle or
erne. Neither have we the pygargus or grip, wherefore
I have no occasion to treat further. I have seen the car-
rion crows so cunning also by their own industry of late that
they have used to soar over great rivers (as the Thames for
example) and, suddenly coming down, have caught a small
fish in their feet and gone away withal without wetting of
their wings. And even at this present the aforesaid river
is not without some of them, a thing (in my opinion) not
a little to be wondered at. We have also osprays, which
breed with us in parks and woods, whereby the keepers of
the same do reap in breeding time no small commodity; for,
so soon almost as the young are hatched, they tie them to
the butt ends or ground ends of sundry trees, where the old
ones, finding them, do never cease to bring fish unto them,
which the keepers take and eat from them, and commonly
is such as is well fed or not of the worst sort. It hath not
been my hap hitherto to see any of these fowl, and partly
through mine own negligence; but I hear that it hath one
foot like a hawk, to catch hold withal, and another resem-
bling a goose, wherewith to swim; but, whether it be so or
not so, I refer the further search and trial thereof unto
some other. This nevertheless is certain, that both alive
and dead, yea even her very oil, is a deadly terror to such
fish as come within the wind of it. There is no cause
whereof I should describe the cormorant amongst hawks, of
which some be black and many pied, chiefly about the Isle
of Ely, where they are taken for the night raven, except I
should call him a water hawk. But, sith such dealing is not
convenient, let us now see what may be said of our venomous worms, and how many kinds we have of them within
our realm and country.[3]

[3] This on "venomous beasts" will be found included in the "savage
beasts" of the following.

CHAPTER XIV

OF SAVAGE BEASTS AND VERMIN

[**1577**, Book III., Chapters 7 and 12; 1587, Book III., Chapters 4 and 6.]

IT IS none of the least blessings wherewith God hath endued this island that it is void of noisome beasts, as lions, bears, tigers, pardes, wolves, and such like, by means whereof our countrymen may travel in safety, and our herds and flocks remain for the most part abroad in the field without any herdman or keeper.

This is chiefly spoken of the south and south-west parts of the island. For, whereas we that dwell on this side of the Tweed may safely boast of our security in this behalf, yet cannot the Scots do the like in every point wherein their kingdom, sith they have grievous wolves and cruel foxes, beside some others of like disposition continually conversant among them, to the general hindrance of their husbandmen, and no small damage unto the inhabitants of those quarters. The happy and fortunate want of these beasts in England is universally ascribed to the politic government of King Edgar.[1] . . .

Of foxes we have some, but no great store, and also badgers in our sandy and light grounds, where woods, furze, broom, and plenty of shrubs are to shroud them in when they be from their burrows, and thereunto warrens of conies at hand to feed upon at will. Otherwise in clay, which we call the cledgy mould, we seldom hear of any, because the moisture and the toughness of the soil is such as will not suffer them to draw and make their burrows deep. Certes, if I may freely say what I think, I suppose

---

[1] Here follows an account of the extermination of wolves, and a reference to lions and wild bulls rampant in Scotland of old.—W.

that these two kinds (I mean foxes and badgers) are rather preserved by gentlemen to hunt and have pastime withal at their own pleasures than otherwise suffered to live as not able to be destroyed because of their great numbers. For such is the scantity of them here in England, in comparison of the plenty that is to be seen in other countries, and so earnestly are the inhabitants bent to root them out, that, except it had been to bear thus with the recreations of their superiors in this behalf, it could not otherwise have been chosen but that they should have been utterly destroyed by many years agone.

I might here intreat largely of other vermin, as the polecat, the miniver, the weasel, stote, fulmart, squirrel, fitchew, and such like, which Cardan includeth under the word *Mustela*: also of the otter, and likewise of the beaver, whose hinder feet and tail only are supposed to be fish. Certes the tail of this beast is like unto a thin whetstone, as the body unto a monstrous rat: as the beast also itself is of such force in the teeth that it will gnaw a hole through a thick plank, or shere through a double billet in a night; it loveth also the stillest rivers, and it is given to them by nature to go by flocks unto the woods at hand, where they gather sticks wherewith to build their nests, wherein their bodies lie dry above the water, although they so provide most commonly that their tails may hang within the same. It is also reported that their said tails are a delicate dish, and their stones of such medicinal force that (as Vertomannus saith) four men smelling unto them each after other did bleed at the nose through their attractive force, proceeding from a vehement savour wherewith they are endued. There is greatest plenty of them in Persia, chiefly about Balascham, from whence they and their dried cods are brought into all quarters of the world, though not without some forgery by such as provide them. And of all these here remembered, as the first sorts are plentiful in every wood and hedgerow, so these latter, especially the otter (for, to say the truth, we have not many beavers, but only in the Teisie in Wales) is not wanting or to seek in many, but most, streams and rivers of this isle; but it shall suffice in this sort to have named them, as I do finally the martern, a beast of the chase, although for number I worthily doubt whether that of our beavers or marterns may be thought to be the less.

Other pernicious beasts we have not, except you repute the great plenty of red and fallow deer whose colours are oft garled white and black, all white or all black, and store of conies amongst the hurtful sort. Which although that of themselves they are not offensive at all, yet their great numbers are thought to be very prejudicial, and therefore justly reproved of many, as are in like sort our huge flocks of sheep, whereon the greatest part of our soil is employed almost in every place, and yet our mutton, wool, and felles never the better cheap. The young males which our fallow deer do bring forth are commonly named according to their several ages: for the first year it is a fawn, the second a pricket, the third a sorel, the fourth a soare, the fifth a buck of the first head, not bearing the name of a buck till he be five years old: and from henceforth his age is commonly known by his head or horns. Howbeit this notice of his years is not so certain but that the best woodman may now and then be deceived in that account: for in some grounds a buck of the first head will be as well headed as another in a high rowtie soil will be in the fourth. It is also much to be marvelled at that, whereas they do yearly mew and cast their horns, yet in fighting they never break off where they do grife or mew. Furthermore, in examining the condition of our red deer, I find that the young male is called in the first year a calf, in the second a broket, the third a spay, the fourth a staggon or stag, the fifth a great stag, the sixth a hart, and so forth unto his death. And with him in degree of venerie are accounted the hare, boar, and wolf. The fallow deer, as bucks and does, are nourished in parks, and conies in warrens and burrows. As for hares, they run at their own adventure, except some gentleman or other (for his pleasure) do make an enclosure for them. Of these also the stag is accounted for the most noble game, the fallow deer is the next, then the roe, whereof we have indifferent store, and last of all the hare, not the least in estimation, because the hunting of that seely beast is mother to all the terms, blasts, and artificial devices that hunters

do use. All which (notwithstanding our custom) are pas-
times more meet for ladies and gentlewomen to exercise
(whatsoever Franciscus Patritius saith to the contrary in
his *Institution of a Prince*) than for men of courage to
follow, whose hunting should practise their arms in tasting
of their manhood, and dealing with such beasts as eftsoons
will turn again and offer them the hardest, rather than their
horses' feet which many times may carry them with dishonour from the field.[2] . . .

If I should go about to make any long discourse of
venomous beasts or worms bred in England, I should attempt more than occasion itself would readily offer, sith we
have very few worms, but no beasts at all, that are thought
by their natural qualities to be either venomous or hurtful.
First of all, therefore, we have the adder (in our old Saxon
tongue called an atter), which some men do not rashly take
to be the viper. Certes, if it be so, then is not the viper
author of the death of her [3] parents, as some histories affirm,
and thereto Encelius, a late writer, in his *De re Metallica*, lib.
3, cap. 38, where he maketh mention of a she adder which
he saw in Sala, whose womb (as he saith) was eaten out
after a like fashion, her young ones lying by her in the
sunshine, as if they had been earthworms. Nevertheless,
as he nameth them *viperas*, so he calleth the male *echis*,
and the female *echidna*, concluding in the end that *echis* is
the same serpent which his countrymen to this day call
ein atter, as I have also noted before out of a Saxon dic-
tionary. For my part I am persuaded that the slaughter
of their parents is either not true at all, or not always (although I doubt not but that nature hath right well provided
to inhibit their superfluous increase by some means or other),
and so much the rather am I led hereunto for that I gather
by Nicander that of all venomous worms the viper only
bringeth out her young alive, and therefore is called in
Latin *vipera quasivivipara*, but of her own death he doth
not (to my remembrance) say anything. It is testified also
by other in other words, and to the like sense, that "*Echis*

[2] Here follows a discourse on ancient boar-hunting, exalting it above
the degenerate sports of the day. This ends the chapter on "savage
beasts."—W.
[3] Galenus, *De Theriaca ad Pisonem;* Pliny, lib. 10, cap. 62.—H.

id est vipera sola ex serpentibus non ova sed animalia parit." [4]
And it may well be, for I remember that I have read in
Philostratus, *De vita Appollonii,* how he saw a viper licking
her young. I did see an adder once myself that lay (as I
thought) sleeping on a molehill, out of whose mouth came
eleven young adders of twelve or thirteen inches in length
apiece, which played to and fro in the grass one with another, till some of them espied me. So soon therefore as
they saw my face they ran again into the mouth of their
dam, whom I killed, and then found each of them shrouded
in a distinct cell or pannicle in her belly, much like unto
a soft white jelly, which maketh me to be of the opinion
that our adder is the viper indeed. The colour of their
skin is for the most part like rusty iron or iron grey, but
such as be very old resemble a ruddy blue; and as once in
the year (to wit, in April or about the begininng of May)
they cast their old skins (whereby as it is thought their
age reneweth), so their stinging bringeth death without
present remedy be at hand, the wounded never ceasing to
swell, neither the venom to work till the skin of the one
break, and the other ascend upward to the heart, where it
finisheth the natural effect, except the juice of dragons (in
Latin called *dracunculus minor*) be speedily ministered and
drunk in strong ale, or else some other medicine taken of
like force that may countervail and overcome the venom
of the same. The length of them is most commonly two
feet, and somewhat more, but seldom doth it extend into two
feet six inches, except it be in some rare and monstrous
one, whereas our snakes are much longer, and seen sometimes to surmount a yard, or three feet, although their
poison be nothing so grievous and deadly as the others.
Our adders lie in winter under stones, as Aristotle also saith
of the viper (lib. 8, cap. 15), and in holes of the earth,
rotten stubs of trees, and amongst the dead leaves; but in
the heat of the summer they come abroad, and lie either
round in heaps or at length upon some hillock, or elsewhere
in the grass. They are found only in our woodland countries and highest grounds, where sometimes (though seldom)

[4] " The adder or viper alone among serpents brings forth not eggs but
living creatures."

a speckled stone called *echites,* in Dutch *ein atter stein,* is gotten out of their dried carcases, which divers report to be good against their poison.[5] As for our snakes, which in Latin are properly named *angues,* they commonly are seen in moors, fens, loam, walls, and low bottoms.

As we have great store of toads where adders commonly are found, so do frogs abound where snakes do keep their residence. We have also the slow-worm, which is black and greyish of colour, and somewhat shorter than an adder. I was at the killing once of one of them, and thereby perceived that she was not so called of any want of nimble motion, but rather of the contrary. Nevertheless we have a blind-worm, to be found under logs, in woods and timber that hath lain long in a place, which some also do call (and upon better ground) by the name of slow-worms, and they are known easily by their more or less variety of striped colours, drawn long-ways from their heads, their whole bodies little exceeding a foot in length, and yet is their venom deadly. This also is not to be omitted; and now and then in our fenny countries other kinds of serpents are found of greater quantity than either our adder or our snake, but, as these are not ordinary and oft to be seen, so I mean not to intreat of them among our common annoyances. Neither have we the scorpion, a plague of God sent not long since into Italy, and whose poison (as Apollodorus saith) is white, neither the tarantula or Neapolitan spider, whose poison bringeth death, except music be at hand. Wherefore I suppose our country to be the more happy (I mean in part) for that it is void of these two grievous annoyances wherewith other nations are plagued.

We have also efts both of the land and water, and likewise the noisome swifts, whereof to say any more it would be but loss of time, sith they are all well known, and no region to my knowledge found to be void of many of them. As for flies (sith it shall not be amiss a little to touch them also), we have none that can do hurt or hindrance naturally unto any: for whether they be cut-waisted or whole-bodied, they are void of poison and all venomous inclination. The

[5] Sallust, cap. 40; Pliny, lib. 37, cap. 2.—H.

cut or girt waisted (for so I English the word *insecta*) are
the hornets, wasps, bees, and such like, whereof we have
great store, and of which an opinion is conceived that the
first do breed of the corruption of dead horses, the second
of pears and apples corrupted, and the last of kine and oxen:
which may be true, especially the first and latter in some
parts of the beast, and not their whole substances, as also
in the second, sith we have never wasps but when our fruit
beginneth to wax ripe. Indeed Virgil and others speak of
a generation of bees by killing or smothering a bruised
bullock or calf and laying his bowels or his flesh wrapped
up in his hide in a close house for a certain season; but
how true it is, hitherto I have not tried. Yet sure I am
of this, that no one living creature corrupteth without the
production of another, as we may see by ourselves, whose
flesh doth alter into lice, and also in sheep for excessive
numbers of flesh flies, if they be suffered to lie unburied or
uneaten by the dogs and swine, who often and happily
present such needless generations.

As concerning bees, I think it good to remember that,
whereas some ancient writers affirm it to be a commodity
wanting in our island, it is now found to be nothing so.
In old times peradventure we had none indeed; but in my
days there is such plenty of them in manner everywhere
that in some uplandish towns there are one hundred or two
hundred hives of them, although the said hives are not so
huge as those of the east country, but far less, and not able
to contain above one bushel of corn or five pecks at the
most. Pliny (a man that of set purpose delighteth to write
of wonders), speaking of honey, noteth that in the north
regions the hives in his time were of such quantity that
some one comb contained eight foot in length, and yet (as
it should seem) he speaketh not of the greatest. For in
Podolia, which is now subject to the King of Poland,
their hives are so great, and combs so abundant, that huge
boars, overturning and falling into them, are drowned in
the honey before they can recover and find the means to
come out.

Our honey also is taken and reputed to be the best, because it is harder, better wrought, and cleanlier vesselled

up, than that which cometh from beyond the sea, where
they stamp and strain their combs, bees, and young blow-
ings altogether into the stuff, as I have been informed. In
use also of medicine our physicians and apothecaries eschew
the foreign, especially that of Spain and Pontus, by reason
of a venomous quality naturally planted in the same, as some
write, and choose the home-made: not only by reason of
our soil (which hath no less plenty of wild thyme growing
therein than in Sicilia and about Athens, and maketh the
best stuff) as also for that it breedeth (being gotten in
harvest time) less choler, and which is oftentimes (as I have
seen by experience) so white as sugar, and corned as if it
were salt. Our hives are made commonly of rye straw and
wattled about with bramble quarters; but some make the
same of wicker, and cast them over with clay. We cherish
none in trees, but set our hives somewhere on the warmest
side of the house, providing that they may stand dry and
without danger both of the mouse and the moth. This
furthermore is to be noted, that whereas in vessels of oil
that which is nearest the top is counted the finest and of
wine that in the middest, so of honey the best which is
heaviest and moistest is always next the bottom, and ever-
more casteth and driveth his dregs upward toward the very
top, contrary to the nature of other liquid substances, whose
grounds and leeze do generally settle downwards. And
thus much as by the way of our bees and English honey.

As for the whole-bodied, as the *cantharides,* and such
venomous creatures of the same kind, to be abundantly
found in other countries, we hear not of them: yet have we
beetles, horseflies, turdbugs or dors (called in Latin *scar-
abei*), the locust or the grasshopper (which to me do seem
to be one thing, as I will anon declare), and such like,
whereof let other intreat that make an exercise in catching
of flies, but a far greater sport in offering them to spiders,
as did Domitian sometime, and another prince yet living
who delighted so much to see the jolly combats betwixt a
stout fly and an old spider that divers men have had great rewards given them for their painful provision of flies made
only for this purpose. Some parasites also, in the time of the
aforesaid emperor (when they were disposed to laugh at

his folly, and yet would seem in appearance to gratify his fantastical head with some shew of dutiful demeanour), could devise to set their lord on work by letting a flesh fly privily into his chamber, which he forthwith would eagerly have hunted (all other business set apart) and never ceased till he had caught her into his fingers, wherewith arose the proverb, "*Ne musca quidem*," uttered first by Vibius Priscus, who being asked whether anybody was with Domitian, answered "*Ne musca quidem*," whereby he noted his folly. There are some cockscombs here and there in England, learning it abroad as men transregionate, which make account also of this pastime, as of a notable matter, telling what a sight is seen between them, if either of them be lusty and courageous in his kind. One also hath made a book of the spider and the fly, wherein he dealeth so profoundly, and beyond all measure of skill that neither he himself that made it nor any one that readeth it can reach unto the meaning thereof. But if those jolly fellows, instead of the straw that they must thrust into the fly's tail (a great injury no doubt to such a noble champion), would bestow the cost to set a fool's cap upon their own heads, then might they with more security and less reprehension behold these notable battles.

Now, as concerning the locust, I am led by divers of my country, who (as they say) were either in Germany, Italy, or Pannonia, 1542, when those nations were greatly annoyed with that kind of fly, and affirm very constantly that they saw none other creature than the grasshopper during the time of that annoyance, which was said to come to them from the Meotides. In most of our translations also of the Bible the word *locusta* is Englished a grasshopper, and thereunto (Leviticus xi.) it is reputed among the clean food, otherwise John the Baptist would never have lived with them in the wilderness. In Barbary, Numidia, and sundry other places of Africa, as they have been,[6] so are they eaten to this day powdered in barrels, and therefore the people of those parts are called *Acedophagi*: nevertheless they shorten the life of the eaters, by the production at the last of an irksome and filthy disease. In India they are three foot

[6] See Diodorus Siculus.—H.

long, in Ethiopia much shorter, but in England seldom above an inch. As for the cricket, called in Latin *cicada*, he hath some likelihood, but not very great, with the grasshopper, and therefore he is not to be brought in as an umpire in this case. Finally, Matthiolus and so many as describe the locust do set down none other form than that of our grasshopper, which maketh me so much the more to rest upon my former imagination, which is that the locust and the grasshopper are one.

CHAPTER XV

OF OUR ENGLISH DOGS AND THEIR QUALITIES

[1577, Book III., Chapter 13; 1587, Book III., Chapter 7.]

THERE is no country that may (as I take it) compare with ours in number, excellency, and diversity of dogs.

The first sort therefore he divideth either into such as rouse the beast, and continue the chase, or springeth the bird, and bewrayeth her flight by pursuit. And as these are commonly called spaniels, so the other are named hounds, whereof he maketh eight sorts, of which the foremost excelleth in perfect smelling, the second in quick espying, the third in swiftness and quickness, the fourth in smelling and nimbleness, etc., and the last in subtlety and deceitfulness. These (saith Strabo) are most apt for game, and called Sagaces by a general name, not only because of their skill in hunting, but also for that they know their own and the names of their fellows most exactly. For if the hunter see any one to follow skilfully, and with likelihood of good success, he biddeth the rest to hark and follow such a dog, and they eftsoones obey so soon as they hear his name. The first kind of these are often called harriers, whose game is the fox, the hare, the wolf (if we had any), hart, buck, badger, otter, polecat, lopstart, weasel, conie, etc.: the second height a terrier and it hunteth the badger and grey only: the third a bloodhound, whose office is to follow the fierce, and now and then to pursue a thief or beast by his dry foot: the fourth height a gazehound, who hunteth by the eye: the fifth a greyhound, cherished for his strength and swiftness and stature, commended by Bratius in his *De Venatione,* and not unremembered by Hercules Stroza in a like treatise, and above all other those of Britain, where he saith: "Magna

369

spectandi mole Britanni;" also by Nemesianus, libro Cyne-
geticôn, where he saith: "Divisa Britannia mittit Veloces
nostrique orbis venatibus aptos," of which sort also some
be smooth, of sundry colours, and some shake-haired: the
sixth a liemer, that excelleth in smelling and swift-running:
the seventh a tumbler: and the eighth a thief whose offices
(I mean of the latter two) incline only to deceit, wherein
they are oft so skilful that few men would think so mischievous a wit to remain in such silly creatures. Having
made this enumeration of dogs which are apt for the chase
and hunting, he cometh next to such as serve the falcons in
their time, whereof he maketh also two sorts. One that
findeth his game on the land, another that putteth up such
fowl as keepeth in the water: and of these this is commonly
most usual for the net or train, the other for the hawk, as
he doth shew at large. Of the first he saith that they have
no peculiar names assigned to them severally but each of
them is called after the bird which by natural appointment
he is alloted to hunt or serve, for which consideration some
be named dogs for the pheasant, some for the falcon, and
some for the partridge. Howbeit the common name for
all is spaniel (saith he), and thereupon alluded as if these
kinds of dogs had been brought hither out of Spain. In
like sort we have of water spaniels in their kind. The third
sort of dogs of the gentle kind is the spaniel gentle, or com-
forter, or (as the common term is) the fistinghound, and
t'ose are called Melitei, of the Island Malta, from whence
they were brought hither. These are little and pretty,
proper and fine, and sought out far and near to falsify the
nice delicacy of dainty dames, and wanton women's wills,
instruments of folly to play and dally withal, in trifling away
the treasure of time, to withdraw their minds from more
commendable exercises, and to content their corrupt con-
cupiscences with vain disport—a silly poor shift to shun
their irksome idleness. The Sybaritical puppies the smaller
they be (and thereto if they have a hole in the fore parts
of their heads) the better they are accepted, the more pleasure also they provoke, as meet playfellows for mincing
mistresses to bear in their bosoms, to keep company withal
in their chambers, to succour with sleep in bed, and nourish

with meat at board, to lie in their laps, and lick their lips as they lie (like young Dianas) in their waggons and coaches. And good reason it should be so, for coarseness with fineness hath no fellowship, but featness with neatness hath neighbourhood enough. That plausible proverb therefore versified sometime upon a tyrant—namely, that he loved his sow better than his son—may well be applied to some of this kind of people, who delight more in their dogs, that are deprived of all possibility of reason, than they do in children that are capable of wisdom and judgment. Yea, they oft feed them of the best where the poor man's child at their doors can hardly come by the worst. But the former abuse peradventure reigneth where there hath been long want of issue, else where barrenness is the best blossom of beauty: or, finally, where poor men's children for want of their own issue are not ready to be had. It is thought of some that it is very wholesome for a weak stomach to bear such a dog in the bosom, as it is for him that hath the palsy to feel the daily smell and savour of a fox. But how truly this is affirmed let the learned judge: only it shall suffice for Doctor Caius to have said thus much of spaniels and dogs of the gentle kind.

Dogs of the homely kind are either shepherd's curs or mastiffs. The first are so common that it needeth me not to speak of them. Their use also is so well known in keeping the herd together (either when they grass or go before the shepherd) that it should be but in vain to spend any time about them. Wherefore I will leave this cur unto his own kind, and go in hand with the mastiff, tie dog, or band dog, so called because many of them are tied up in chains and strong bonds in the daytime, for doing hurt abroad, which is a huge dog, stubborn, ugly, eager, burthenous of body (and therefore of but little swiftness), terrible and fearful to behold, and oftentimes more fierce and fell than any Archadian or Corsican cur. Our Englishmen, to the extent that these dogs may be more cruel and fierce, assist nature with some art, use, and custom. For although this kind of dog be capable of courage, violent, valiant, stout, and bold: yet will they increase these their stomachs by teaching them to bait the bear, the bull, the lion, and other such like cruel and bloody beasts (either brought over or kept up at home for the same purpose), without any collar to defend their throats, and oftentimes there too they train them up in fighting and wrestling with a man (having for the safeguard of his life either a pikestaff, club, sword, privy coat), whereby they become the more fierce and cruel unto strangers. The Caspians make so much account sometimes of such great dogs that every able man would nourish sundry of them in his house of set purpose, to the end they should devour their carcases after their deaths thinking the dog's bellies to be the most honourable sepulchres. The common people also followed the same rate, and therefore there were tie dogs kept up by public ordinance, to devour them after their deaths: by means whereof these beasts became the more eager, and with great difficulty after a while restrained from falling upon the living. But whither am I digressed? In returning therefore to our own, I say that of mastiffs, some bark only with fierce and open mouth but will not bite; but the cruelest do either not bark at all or bite before they bark, and therefore are more to be feared than any of the other. They take also their name of the word "mase" and "thief" (or "master-thief" if you will), because they often stound and put such persons to their shifts in towns and villages, and are the principal causes of their apprehension and taking. The force which is in them surmounteth all belief, and the fast hold which they take with their teeth exceedeth all credit: for three of them against a bear, four against a lion, are sufficient to try mastries with them. King Henry the Seventh, as the report goeth, commanded all such curs to be hanged, because they durst presume to fight against the lion, who is their king and sovereign. The like he did with an excellent falcon, as some say, because he feared not hand-to-hand match with an eagle, willing his falconers in his own presence to pluck off his head after he was taken down, saying that it was not meet for any subject to offer such wrong unto his lord and superior, wherein he had a further meaning. But if King Henry the Seventh had lived in our time what would he have done to our English mastiff, which alone and without any help at all pulled down first a huge bear, then a pard, and last of all a lion, each after other before the French king in one day, when the Lord Buckhurst was ambassador unto him, and whereof if I should write the circumstances, that is, how he took his advantage being let loose unto them, and finally drave them into such exceeding fear, that they were all glad to run away when he was taken from them, I should take much pains, and yet reap but small credit: wherefore it shall suffice to have said thus much thereof. Some of our mastiffs will rage only in the night, some are to be tied up both day and night. Such also as are suffered to go loose about the house and yard are so gentle in the daytime that children may ride on their backs and play with them at their pleasures. Divers of them likewise are of such jealousy over their master and whosoever of his household, that if a stranger do embrace or touch any of them, they will fall fiercely upon them, unto their extreme mischief if their fury be not prevented. Such a one was the dog of Nichomedes, king sometime of Bithynia, who seeing Consigne the queen to embrace and kiss her husband as they walked together in a garden, did tear her all to pieces, maugre his resistance and the present aid of such as attended on them. Some of them moreover will suffer a stranger to come in and walk about the house or yard where he listeth, without giving over to follow him: but if he put forth his hand to touch anything, then will they fly upon them and kill them if they may. I had one myself once, which would not suffer any man to bring in his weapon further than my gate: neither those that were of my house to be touched in his presence. Or if I had beaten any of my children, he would gently have essayed to catch the rod in his teeth and take it out of my hand or else pluck down their clothes to save them from the stripes: which in my opinion is not unworthy to be noted.

The last sort of dogs consisteth of the currish kind meet for many toys, of which the whappet or prick-eared cur is one. Some men call them warners, because they are good for nothing else but to bark and give warning when anybody doth stir or lie in wait about the house in the night season. Certes it is impossible to describe these curs in any order, because they have no one kind proper unto them-

selves, but are a confused company mixed of all the rest.
The second sort of them are called turnspits, whose office
is not unknown to any. And as these are only reserved for
this purpose, so in many places our mastiffs (beside the use
which tinkers have of them in carrying their heavy budgets)
are made to draw water in great wheels out of deep wells,
going much like unto those which are framed for our turnspits, as is to be seen at Roiston, where this feat is often
practised. Besides these also we have sholts or curs daily
brought out of Ireland, and made much of among us, because of their sauciness and quarrelling. Moreover they
bite very sore, and love candles exceedingly, as do the men
and women of their country; but I may say no more of them,
because they are not bred with us. Yet this will I make
report of by the way, for pastime's sake, that when a great
man of those parts came of late into one of our ships which
went thither for fish, to see the form and fashion of the
same, his wife apparelled in fine sables, abiding on the deck
whilst her husband was under the hatches with the mariners,
espied a pound or two of candles hanging on the mast, and
being loath to stand there idle alone, she fell to and eat
them up every one, supposing herself to have been at a
jolly banquet, and shewing very pleasant gesture when her
husband came up again unto her.

The last kind of toyish curs are named dancers, and those
being of a mongrel sort also, are taught and exercised to
dance in measure at the musical sound of an instrument, as
at the just stroke of a drum, sweet accent of the citharne,
and pleasant harmony of the harp, shewing many tricks by
the gesture of their bodies: as to stand bolt upright, to lie
flat on the ground, to turn round as a ring holding their
tails in their teeth, to saw and beg for meat, to take a man's
cap from his head, and sundry such properties, which they
learn of their idle roguish masters, whose instruments they
are to gather gain, as old apes clothed in motley and coloured
short-waisted jackets are for the like vagabonds, who seek
no better living than that which they may get by fond
pastime and idleness. I might here intreat of other dogs,
as of those which are bred between a bitch and a wolf, also
between a bitch and a fox, or a bear and a mastiff. But as

we utterly want the first sort, except they be brought unto us: so it happeneth sometimes that the other two are engendered and seen at home amongst us. But all the rest heretofore remembered in this chapter there is none more ugly and odious in sight, cruel and fierce in deed, nor untractable in hand, than that which is begotten between the bear and the bandog. For whatsoever he catcheth hold of he taketh it so fast that a man may sooner tear and rend his body in sunder than get open his mouth to separate his chaps. Certes he regardeth neither wolf, bear, nor lion, and therefore may well be compared with those two dogs which were sent to Alexander out of India (and procreated as it is thought between a mastiff and a male tiger, as be those also of Hircania), or to them that are bred in Archadia, where copulation is oft seen between lions and bitches, as the lion is in France (as I said) between she wolves and dogs, whereof let this suffice, sith the further tractation of them doth not concern my purpose, more than the confutation of Cardan's talk, *De subt.*, lib. 10, who saith that after many generations dogs do become wolves, and contrariwise, which if it were true, then could not England be without many wolves: but nature hath set a difference between them, not only in outward form, but also inward disposition of their bones, whereof it is impossible that his assertion can be sound.

CHAPTER XVI

OF THE NAVY OF ENGLAND

[1577, Book II., Chapter 13; 1587, Book II., Chapter 17.]

THERE is nothing that hath brought me into more admiration of the power and force of antiquity than their diligence and care had of their navies: wherein, whether I consider their speedy building, or great number of ships which some one kingdom or region possessed at one instant, it giveth me still occasion either to suspect the history, or to think that in our times we come very far behind them.[1] . . .

I must needs confess therefore that the ancient vessels far exceeded ours for capacity, nevertheless if you regard the form, and the assurance from peril of the sea, and therewithal the strength and nimbleness of such as are made in our time, you shall easily find that ours are of more value than theirs: for as the greatest vessel is not always the fastest, so that of most huge capacity is not always the aptest to shift and brook the seas: as might be seen by the *Great Henry,* the hugest vessel that ever England framed in our times. Neither were the ships of old like unto ours in mould and manner of building above the water (for of low galleys in our seas we make small account) nor so full of ease within, since time hath engendered more skill in the wrights, and brought all things to more perfection than they had in the beginning. And now to come unto our purpose at the first intended.

The navy of England may be divided into three sorts, of which the one serveth for the wars, the other for burden, and the third for fishermen which get their living by fishing on the sea. How many of the first order are maintained within

---

[1] Here follows an account of Roman and Carthaginian galleys which "did not only match, but far exceed" in capacity our ships and galleys of 1587.—W.

the realm it passeth my cunning to express; yet, since it may be parted into the navy royal and common fleet, I think good to speak of those that belong unto the prince, and so much the rather, for that their number is certain and well known to very many. Certainly there is no prince in Europe that hath a more beautiful or gallant sort of ships than the queen's majesty of England at this present, and those generally are of such exceeding force that two of them, being well appointed and furnished as they ought, will not let to encounter with three or four of those of other countries, and either bowge them or put them to flight, if they may not bring them home.

Neither are the moulds of any foreign barks so conveniently made, to brook so well one sea as another lying upon the shore of any part of the continent, as those of England. And therefore the common report that strangers make of our ships amongst themselves is daily confirmed to be true, which is, that for strength, assurance, nimbleness, and swiftness of sailing, there are no vessels in the world to be compared with ours. And all these are committed to the regiment and safe custody of the admiral, who is so called (as some imagine) of the Greek word *almiras,* a captain on the sea; for so saith Zonaras in *Basilio Macedone* and *Basilio Porphyriogenito,* though others fetch it from *ad mare,* the Latin words, another sort from *Amyras,* the Saracen magistrate, or from some French derivation: but these things are not for this place, and therefore I pass them over. The queen's highness hath at this present (which is the four-and-twentieth of her reign) already made and furnished, to the number of four or five-and-twenty great ships, which lie for the most part in Gillingham Road, beside three galleys, of whose particular names and furniture (so far forth as I can come by them) it shall not be amiss to make report at this time.

The names of so many ships belonging to her majesty as I could come by at this present.

| The Bonadventure. | White Bear. |
| Elizabeth Jonas.[2] | Philip and Mary. |

[2] A name devised by her grace in remembrance of her own deliverance from the fury of her enemies, from which in one respect she was no less

Triumph.	Aid.
Bull.	Handmaid.
Tiger.[3]	Dreadnought.
Antelope.	Swallow.
Hope.	Genet.
Lion.	Bark of Bullen.
Victory.	Achates.
Mary Rose.	Falcon.
Foresight.	George.
Swift sute.	Revenge.

It is said that as kings and princes have in the young days of the world, and long since, framed themselves to erect every year a city in some one place or other of their kingdom (and no small wonder that Sardanapalus should begin and finish two, to wit, Anchialus and Tarsus, in one day), so her grace doth yearly build one ship or other to the better defence of her frontiers from the enemy. But, as of this report I have no assured certainty, so it shall suffice to have said so much of these things; yet this I think worthy further to be added, that if they should all be driven to service at one instance (which God forbid) she should have a power by sea of about nine or ten thousand men, which were a notable company, beside the supply of other vessels appertaining to her subjects to furnish up her voyage.

Beside these, her grace hath other in hand also, of whom hereafter, as their turns do come about, I will not let to leave some further remembrance. She hath likewise three notable galleys: the Speedwell, the Try Right, and the Black Galley, with the sight whereof, and the rest of the navy royal, it is incredible to say how greatly her grace is delighted: and not without great cause (I say) since by their means her coasts are kept in quiet, and sundry foreign enemies put back, which otherwise would invade us. The number of those that serve for burden with the other, whereof I have made mention already and whose use is daily seen, as occasion serveth in time of the wars, is to me utterly unknown. Yet if the report of one record be anything at all to be credited, there are one hundred and thirty-five ships that exceed five hundred ton; topmen, under one hundred

miraculously preserved than was the prophet Jonas from the belly of the whale.—H.

[3] So called of her exceeding nimbleness in sailing and swiftness of course.—H.

and above forty, six hundred and fifty-six; hoys, one hundred; but of hulks, catches, fisherboats, and crayers, it lieth not in me to deliver the just account, since they are hard to come by. Of these also there are some of the queen's majesty's subjects that have two or three; some, four or six; and (as I heard of late) one man, whose name I suppress for modesty's sake, hath been known not long since to have had sixteen or seventeen, and employed them wholly to the wafting in and out of our merchants, whereby he hath reaped no small commodity and gain. I might take occasion to tell of the notable and difficult voyages made into strange countries by Englishmen, and of their daily success there; but as these things are nothing incident to my purpose, so I surcease to speak of them. Only this will I add, to the end all men shall understand somewhat of the great masses of treasure daily employed upon our navy, how there are few of those ships, of the first and second sort, that, being apparelled and made ready to sail, are not worth one thousand pounds, or three thousand ducats at the least, if they should presently be sold. What shall we think then of the greater, but especially of the navy royal, of which some one vessel is worth two of the other, as the shipwrights have often told me? It is possible that some covetous person, hearing this report, will either not credit it at all, or suppose money so employed to be nothing profitable to the queen's coffers: as a good husband said once when he heard there should be a provision made for armour, wishing the queen's money to be rather laid out to some speedier return of gain unto her grace, "because the realm (saith he) is in case good enough," and so peradventure he thought. But if, as by store of armour for the defence of the country, he had likewise understanded that the good keeping of the sea is the safeguard of our land, he would have altered his censure, and soon given over his judgment. For in times past, when our nation made small account of navigation, how soon did the Romans, then the Saxons, and last of all the Danes, invade this island? whose cruelty in the end enforced our countrymen, as it were even against their wills, to provide for ships from other places, and build at home of their own, whereby their enemies were oftentimes distressed. But most of all were the Normans therein to be commended. For, in a short process of time after the conquest of this island, and good consideration had for the well-keeping of the same, they supposed nothing more commodious for the defence of the country than the maintenance of a strong navy, which they speedily provided, maintained, and thereby reaped in the end their wished security, wherewith before their times this island was never acquainted. Before the coming of the Romans I do not read that we had any ships at all, except a few made of wicker and covered with buffalo hides, like unto which there are some to be seen at this present in Scotland (as I hear), although there be a little (I wot not well what) difference between them. Of the same also Solinus speaketh, so far as I remember: nevertheless it may be gathered from his words how the upper parts of them above the water only were framed of the said wickers, and that the Britons did use to fast all the whiles they went to the sea in them; but whether it were done for policy or superstition, as yet I do not read.

In the beginning of the Saxons' regiment we had some ships also; but as their number and mould was little, and nothing to the purpose, so Egbert was the first prince that ever thoroughly began to know this necessity of a navy and use the service thereof in the defence of his country. After him also other princes, as Alfred, Edgar, Ethelred, etc., endeavoured more and more to store themselves at the full with ships of all quantities, but chiefly Edgar, for he provided a navy of 1600 *aliàs* 3600 sail, which he divided into four parts, and sent them to abide upon four sundry coasts of the land, to keep the same from pirates. Next unto him (and worthy to be remembered) is Ethelred, who made a law that every man that hold 310 hidelands should find a ship furnished to serve him in the wars. Howbeit, as I said before, when all their navy was at the greatest, it was not comparable for force and sure building to that which afterward the Normans provided, neither that of the Normans anything like to the same that is to be seen now in these our days. For the journeys also of our ships, you shall understand that a well-builded vessel will run or sail commonly three hundred leagues or nine hundred miles in a week, or peradventure some will go 2200 leagues in six weeks and a half. And surely, if their lading be ready against they come thither, there be of them that will be here, at the West Indies, and home again in twelve or thirteen weeks from Colchester, although the said Indies be eight hundred leagues from the cape or point of Cornwall, as I have been informed. This also I understand by report of some travellers, that, if any of our vessels happen to make a voyage to Hispaniola or New Spain (called in time past Quinquegia and Haiti), which lieth between the north tropic and the Equator, after they have once touched at the Canaries (which are eight days' sailing or two hundred and fifty leagues from St. Lucas de Barameda, in Spain) they will be there in thirty or forty days, and home again in Cornwall in other eight weeks, which is a goodly matter, beside the safety and quietness in the passage, but more of this elsewhere.

CHAPTER XVII

OF SUNDRY KINDS OF PUNISHMENT APPOINTED FOR
OFFENDERS

[1577, Book III., Chapter 6; 1587, Book II., Chapter 11.]

IN cases of felony, manslaughter, robbery, murder, rape, piracy, and such capital crimes as are not reputed for treason or hurt of the estate, our sentence pronounced upon the offender is, to hang till he be dead. For of other punishments used in other countries we have no knowledge or use; and yet so few grievous crimes committed with us as elsewhere in the world. To use torment also or question by pain and torture in these common cases with us is greatly abhorred, since we are found always to be such as despise death, and yet abhor to be tormented, choosing rather frankly to open our minds than to yield our bodies unto such servile haulings and tearings as are used in other countries. And this is one cause wherefore our condemned persons do go so cheerfully to their deaths; for our nation is free, stout, haughty, prodigal of life and blood, as Sir Thomas Smith saith, lib. 2, cap. 25, *De Republica,* and therefore cannot in any wise digest to be used as villains and slaves, in suffering continually beating, servitude, and servile torments. No, our gaolers are guilty of felony, by an old law of the land, if they torment any prisoner committed to their custody for the revealing of his accomplices.

The greatest and most grievous punishment used in England for such as offend against the State is drawing from the prison to the place of execution upon an hurdle or sled, where they are hanged till they be half dead, and then taken down, and quartered alive; after that, their members and bowels are cut from their bodies, and thrown into a

382

fire, provided near hand and within their own sight, even for the same purpose.

Sometimes, if the trespass be not the more heinous, they are suffered to hang till they be quite dead. And whensoever any of the nobility are convicted of high treason by their peers, that is to say, equals (for an inquest of yeomen passeth not upon them, but only of the lords of parliament), this manner of their death is converted into the loss of their heads only, notwithstanding that the sentence do run after the former order. In trial of cases concerning treason, felony, or any other grievous crime not confessed, the party accused doth yield, if he be a noble man, to be tried by an inquest (as I have said) and his peers; if a gentleman, by gentlemen; and an inferior, by God and by the country, to wit, the yeomanry (for combat or battle is not greatly in use), and, being condemned of felony, manslaughter, etc., he is eftsoons hanged by the neck till he be dead, and then cut down and buried. But if he be convicted of wilful murder, done either upon pretended malice or in any notable robbery, he is either hanged alive in chains near the place where the fact was committed (or else upon compassion taken, first strangled with a rope), and so continueth till his bones consume to nothing. We have use neither of the wheel nor of the bar, as in other countries; but, when wilful manslaughter is perpetrated, beside hanging, the offender hath his right hand commonly stricken off before or near unto the place where the act was done, after which he is led forth to the place of execution, and there put to death according to the law.

The word felon is derived of the Saxon words *fell* and *one,* that is to say, an evil and wicked one, a one of untameable nature and lewdness not to be suffered for fear of evil example and the corruption of others. In like sort in the word *felony* are many grievous crimes contained, as breach of prison (Ann. 1 of Edward the Second), disfigurers of the prince's liege people (Ann. 5 of Henry the Fourth), hunting by night with painted faces and visors (Ann. 1 of Henry the Seventh), rape, or stealing of women and maidens (Ann. 3 of Henry Eight), conspiracies against the person of the prince (Ann. 3 of Henry the Seventh), embezzling of goods committed by the master to the servant above the value of forty shillings (Ann. 17 of Henry the Eighth), carrying of horses or mares into Scotland (Ann. 23 of Henry Eight), sodomy and buggery (Ann. 25 of Henry the Eighth), conjuring, forgery, witchcraft, and digging up of crosses (Ann. 33 of Henry Eight), prophesying upon arms, cognisances, names, and badges (Ann. 33 of Henry Eight), casting of slanderous bills (Ann. 37, Henry Eight), wilful killing by poison (Ann. 1 of Edward the Sixth), departure of a soldier from the field (Ann. 2 of Edward the Sixth), diminution of coin, all offences within case of premunire, embezzling of records, goods taken from dead men by their servants, stealing of whatsoever cattle, robbing by the high way, upon the sea, or of dwelling houses, letting out of ponds, cutting of purses, stealing of deer by night, counterfeits of coin, evidences charters, and writings, and divers other needless to be remembered. If a woman poison her husband, she is burned alive; if the servant kill his master, he is to be executed for petty treason; he that poisoneth a man is to be boiled to death in water or lead, although the party die not of the practice; in cases of murder, all the accessories are to suffer pains of death accordingly. Perjury is punished by the pillory, burning in the forehead with the letter P, the rewalting of the trees growing upon the grounds of the offenders, and loss of all his movables. Many trespasses also are punished by the cutting off of one or both ears from the head of the offender, as the utterance of seditious words against the magistrates, fraymakers, petty robbers, etc. Rogues are burned through the ears; carriers of sheep out of the land, by the loss of their hands; such as kill by poison are either boiled or scalded to death in lead or seething water. Heretics are burned quick; harlots and their mates, by carting, ducking, and doing of open penance in sheets in churches and market steeds, are often put to rebuke. Howbeit, as this is counted with some either as no punishment at all to speak of, or but little regarded of the offenders, so I would with adultery and fornication to have some sharper law. For what great smart is it to be turned out of hot sheet into a cold, or after a little washing in the water to be let loose again unto their former trades? Howbeit the dragging of some of them over the Thames between Lambeth and Westminster at the tail of a boat is a punishment that most terrifieth them which are condemned thereto; but this is inflicted upon them by none other than the knight marshall, and that within the compass of his jurisdiction and limits only. Canutus was the first that gave authority to the clergy to punish whoredom, who at that time found fault with the former laws as being too severe in this behalf. For, before the time of the said Canutus, the adulterer forfeited all his goods to the king and his body to be at his pleasure; and the adulteress was to lose her eyes or nose, or both if the case were more than common: whereby it appears of what estimation marriage was amongst them, since the breakers of that holy estate were so grievously rewarded. But afterward the clergy dealt more favourably with them, shooting rather at the punishments of such priests and clerks as were married than the reformation of adultery and fornication, wherein you shall find no example that any severity was shewed except upon such lay men as had defiled their nuns. As in theft therefore, so in adultery and whoredom, I would wish the parties trespassing to be made bond or slaves unto those that received the injury, to sell and give where they listed, or to be condemned to the galleys: for that punishment would prove more bitter to them than half-an-hour's hanging, or than standing in a sheet, though the weather be never so cold.

Manslaughter in time past was punished by the purse, wherein the quantity or quality of the punishment was rated after the state and calling of the party killed: so that one was valued sometime at 1200, another at 600, or 200 shillings. And by a statute made under Henry the First, a citizen of London at 100, whereof elsewhere I have spoken more at large. Such as kill themselves are buried in the field with a stake driven through their bodies.

Witches are hanged, or sometimes burned; but thieves are hanged (as I said before) generally on the gibbet or gallows, saving in Halifax, where they are beheaded after a strange manner, and whereof I find this report. There is and

has been of ancient time a law, or rather a custom, at
Halifax, that whosoever does commit any felony, and is
taken with the same, or confesses the fact upon examination,
if it be valued by four constables to amount to the sum of
thirteenpence-halfpenny, he is forthwith beheaded upon one
of the next market days (which fall usually upon the
Tuesdays, Thursdays, and Saturdays), or else upon the same
day that he is so convicted, if market be then holden. The
engine wherewith the execution is done is a square block
of wood of the length of four feet and a half, which does
ride up and down in a slot, rabbet, or regall, between two
pieces of timber, that are framed and set upright, of five
yards in height. In the nether end of the sliding block
is an axe, keyed or fastened with an iron into the wood,
which being drawn up to the top of the frame is there
fastened by a wooden pin (with a notch made into the same,
after the manner of a Samson's post), unto the midst of
which pin also there is a long rope fastened that cometh
down among the people, so that, when the offender hath
made his confession and hath laid his neck over the nether-
most block, every man there present doth either take hold
of the rope (or putteth forth his arm so near to the same
as he can get, in token that he is willing to see true justice
executed), and, pulling out the pin in this manner, the
head-block wherein the axe is fastened doth fall down with
such a violence that, if the neck of the transgressor were
as big as that of a bull, it should be cut in sunder at a stroke
and roll from the body by a huge distance. If it be so that
the offender be apprehended for an ox, oxen, sheep, kine,
horse, or any such cattle, the self beast or other of the
same kind shall have the end of the rope tied somewhere
unto them, so that they, being driven, do draw out the pin,
whereby the offender is executed. Thus much of Halifax
law, which I set down only to shew the custom of that
country in this behalf.

Rogues and vagabonds are often stocked and whipped;
scolds are ducked upon cucking-stools in the water. Such
felons as stand mute, and speak not at their arraignment,
are pressed to death by huge weights laid upon a board,
that lieth over their breast, and a sharp stone under their

backs; and these commonly held their peace, thereby to save
their goods unto their wives and children, which, if they
were condemned, should be confiscated to the prince. Thieves
that are saved by their books and clergy, for the first offence, if they have stolen nothing else but oxen, sheep,
money, or such like, which be no open robberies, as by
the highway side, or assailing of any man's house in the
night, without putting him in fear of his life, or breaking
up his walls or doors, are burned in the left hand, upon
the brawn of the thumb, with a hot iron, so that, if they
be apprehended again, that mark betrayeth them to have
been arraigned of felony before, whereby they are sure
at that time to have no mercy. I do not read that this
custom of saving by the book is used anywhere else than
in England; neither do I find (after much diligent enquiry)
what Saxon prince ordained that law. Howbeit this I
generally gather thereof, that it was devised to train the
inhabitants of this land to the love of learning, which
before contemned letters and all good knowledge, as men
only giving themselves to husbandry and the wars: the like
whereof I read to have been amongst the Goths and Vandals,
who for a time would not suffer even their princes to be
learned, for weakening of their courage, nor any learned
men to remain in the council house, but by open procla-
mation would command them to avoid whensoever anything
touching the state of the land was to be consulted upon.
Pirates and robbers by sea are condemned in the Court of
the Admiralty, and hanged on the shore at low-water mark,
where they are left till three tides have overwashed them.
Finally, such as having walls and banks near unto the sea,
and do suffer the same to decay (after convenient admoni-
tion), whereby the water entereth and drowneth up the
country, are by a certain ancient custom apprehended, condemned, and staked in the breach, where they remain for
ever as parcel of the foundation of the new wall that is
to be made upon them, as I have heard reported.

And thus much in part of the administration of justice
used in our country, wherein, notwithstanding that we do not
often hear of horrible, merciless, and wilful murders (such I
mean as are not seldom seen in the countries of the main),

yet now and then some manslaughter and bloody robberies are perpetrated and committed, contrary to the laws, which be severely punished, and in such wise as I have before reported. Certes there is no greater mischief done in England than by robberies, the first by young shifting gentlemen, which oftentimes do bear more port than they are able to maintain. Secondly by serving-men, whose wages cannot suffice so much as to find them breeches; wherefore they are now and then constrained either to keep highways, and break into the wealthy men's houses with the first sort, or else to walk up and down in gentlemen's and rich farmers' pastures, there to see and view which horses feed best, whereby they many times get something, although with hard adventure: it hath been known by their confession at the gallows that some one such chapman hath had forty, fifty, or sixty stolen horses at pasture here and there abroad in the country at a time, which they have sold at fairs and markets far off, they themselves in the mean season being taken about home for honest yeomen, and very wealthy drovers, till their dealings have been betrayed. It is not long since one of this company was apprehended, who was before time reputed for a very honest and wealthy townsman; he uttered also more horses than any of his trade, because he sold a reasonable pennyworth and was a fairspoken man. It was his custom likewise to say, if any man hucked hard with him about the price of a gelding, " So God help me, gentlemen (or sir), either he did cost me so much, or else, by Jesus, I stole him ! " Which talk was plain enough; and yet such was his estimation that each believed the first part of his tale, and made no account of the latter, which was truer indeed.

Our third annoyers of the commonwealth are rogues, which do very great mischief in all places where they become. For, whereas the rich only suffer injury by the first two, these spare neither rich nor poor; but, whether it be great gain or small, all is fish that cometh to net with them. And yet, I say, both they and the rest are trussed up apace. For there is not one year commonly wherein three hundred or four hundred of them are not devoured and eaten up by the gallows in one place and other. It appeareth by Cardan (who writeth it upon the report of the bishop of Lexovia), in the geniture of King Edward the Sixth, how Henry the Eighth, executing his laws very severely against such idle persons, I mean great thieves, petty thieves, and rogues, did hang up threescore and twelve thousand of them in his time. He seemed for a while greatly to have terrified the rest; but since his death the number of them is so increased, yea, although we have had no wars, which are a great occasion of their breed (for it is the custom of the more idle sort, having once served, or but seen the other side of the sea under colour of service, to shake hand with labour for ever, thinking it a disgrace for himself to return unto his former trade), that, except some better order be taken, or the laws already made be better executed, such as dwell in uplandish towns and little villages shall live but in small safety and rest. For the better apprehension also of thieves and mankillers, there is an old law in England very well provided whereby it is ordered that, if he that is robbed (or any man) complain and give warning of slaughter or murder committed, the constable of the village whereunto he cometh and crieth for succour is to raise the parish about him, and to search woods, groves, and all suspected houses and places, where the trespasser may be, or is supposed to lurk; and not finding him there, he is to give warning unto the next constable, and so one constable, after search made, to advertise another from parish to parish, till they come to the same where the offender is harboured and found. It is also provided that, if any parish in this business do not her duty, but suffereth the thief (for the avoiding of trouble sake) in carrying him to the gaol, if he should be apprehended, or other letting of their work to escape, the same parish is not only to make fine to the king, but also the same, with the whole hundred wherein it standeth, to repay the party robbed his damages, and leave his estate harmless. Certainly this is a good law; howbeit I have known by my own experience felons being taken to have escaped out of the stocks, being rescued by other for want of watch and guard, that thieves have been let pass, because the covetous and greedy parishioners would neither take the pains nor be at the charge, to carry them to prison, if it were far off; that when hue and cry have been made even to the faces of some constables, they have said: "God restore your loss! I have other business at this time." And by such means the meaning of many a good law is left unexecuted, malefactors emboldened, and many a poor man turned out of that which he hath sweat and taken great pains toward the maintenance of himself and his poor children and family.

CHAPTER XVIII

OF UNIVERSITIES

[1577, Book II., Chapter 6; 1587, Book II., Chapter 3.]

THERE have been heretofore, and at sundry times, divers famous universities in this island, and those even in my days not altogether forgotten, as one at Bangor, erected by Lucius, and afterward converted into a monastery, not by Congellus (as some write), but by Pelagius the monk. The second at Caerleon-upon-Usk, near to the place where the river doth fall into the Severn, founded by King Arthur. The third at Thetford, wherein were six hundred students, in the time of one Rond, sometime king of that region. The fourth at Stamford, suppressed by Augustine the monk. And likewise other in other places, as Salisbury, Eridon or Cricklade, Lachlade, Reading, and Northampton; albeit that the two last rehearsed were not authorised, but only arose to that name by the departure of the students from Oxford in time of civil dissension unto the said towns, where also they continued but for a little season. When that of Salisbury began I cannot tell; but that it flourished most under Henry the Third and Edward the First I find good testimony by the writers, as also by the discord which fell, 1278, between the chancellor for the scholars there on the one part and William the archdeacon on the other, whereof you shall see more in the chronology here following. In my time there are three noble universities in England—to wit, one at Oxford, the second at Cambridge, and the third in London; of which the first two are the most famous, I mean Cambridge and Oxford, for that in them the use of the tongues, philosophy, and the liberal sciences, besides the profound studies of the civil law, physic, and theology, are daily taught and had: whereas in the latter the laws of the realm are only read and learned by such as give their minds unto the knowledge of the same. In the first there are not only divers goodly houses builded four square for the most part of hard freestone or brick, with great numbers of lodgings and chambers in the same for students, after a sumptuous sort, through the exceeding liberality of kings, queens, bishops, noblemen and ladies of the land; but also large livings and great revenues bestowed upon them (the like whereof is not to be seen in any other region, as Peter Martyr did oft affirm) to the maintenance only of such convenient numbers of poor men's sons as the several stipends bestowed upon the said houses are able to support.[1] . . .

Of these two, that of Oxford (which lieth west and by north from London) standeth most pleasantly, being environed in manner round about with woods on the hills aloft, and goodly rivers in the bottoms and valleys beneath, whose courses would breed no small commodity to that city and country about if such impediments were removed as greatly annoy the same and hinder the carriage which might be made thither also from London. That of Cambridge is distant from London about forty and six miles north and by east, and standeth very well, saving that it is somewhat near unto the fens, whereby the wholesomeness of the air is not a little corrupted. It is excellently well served with all kinds of provisions, but especially of fresh water fish and wild fowl, by reason of the river that passeth thereby; and thereto the Isle of Ely, which is so near at hand. Only wood is the chief want to such as study there, wherefore this kind of provision is brought them either from Essex and other places thereabouts, as is also their coal, or otherwise the necessity thereof is supplied with gall (a bastard kind of mirtus as I take it) and seacoal, whereof they have great plenty led thither by the Grant. Moreover it hath not such store of meadow ground as may suffice for the ordinary expenses of the town and university, wherefore the inhabitants are enforced in like sort to provide their hay from other villages about, which minister the same unto them in very great abundance.

[1] Here follows a paragraph about the legendary foundation of the universities.—W.

Oxford is supposed to contain in longitude eighteen degrees and eight and twenty minutes, and in latitude one and fifty degrees and fifty minutes: whereas that of Cambridge standing more northerly, hath twenty degrees and twenty minutes in longitude, and thereunto fifty and two degrees and fifteen minutes in latitude, as by exact supputation is easy to be found.

The colleges of Oxford, for curious workmanship and private commodities, are much more stately, magnificent, and commodious than those of Cambridge: and thereunto the streets of the town for the most part are more large and comely. But for uniformity of building, orderly compaction, and politic regiment, the town of Cambridge, as the newer workmanship,[2] exceeds that of Oxford (which otherwise is, and hath been, the greater of the two) by many a fold (as I guess), although I know divers that are of the contrary opinion. This also is certain, that whatsoever the difference be in building of the town streets, the townsmen of both are glad when they may match and annoy the students, by encroaching upon their liberties, and keep them bare by extreme sale of their wares, whereby many of them become rich for a time, but afterward fall again into poverty, because that goods evil gotten do seldom long endure.[3] . . .

In each of these universities also is likewise a church dedicated to the Virgin Mary, wherein once in the year—to wit, in July—the scholars are holden, and in which such as have been called to any degree in the year precedent do there receive the accomplishment of the same, in solemn and sumptuous manner. In Oxford this solemnity is called an Act, but in Cambridge they use the French word *Commencement;* and such resort is made yearly unto the same from all parts of the land by the friends of those who do proceed that all the town is hardly able to receive and lodge those guests. When and by whom the churches aforesaid were built I have elsewhere made relation. That of Oxford also was repaired in the time of Edward the Fourth and Henry the Seventh, when Doctor Fitz James, a great helper in that work, was warden of Merton College; but ere long, after it

[2] Cambridge burned not long since.—H.
[3] Here follows an account of Oxford and Cambridge castles, and the legend of the building of Osney Abbey by Robert and Edith D'Oyley.—W.

was finished, one tempest in a night so defaced the same that
it left few pinnacles standing about the church and steeple,
which since that time have never been repaired. There
were sometime four and twenty parish churches in the town
and suburbs; but now there are scarcely sixteen. There
have been also 1200 burgesses, of which 400 dwelt in the
suburbs; and so many students were there in the time of
Henry the Third that he allowed them twenty miles compass about the town for their provision of victuals.

The common schools of Cambridge also are far more beautiful than those of Oxford, only the Divinity School of
Oxford excepted, which for fine and excellent workmanship cometh next the mould of the King's Chapel in Cambridge, than the which two, with the Chapel that King
Henry the Seventh did build at Westminster, there are not
(in my opinion) made of lime and stone three more notable
piles within the compass of Europe.

In all the other things there is so great equality between
these two universities as no man can imagine how to set
down any greater, so that they seem to be the body of one
well-ordered commonwealth, only divided by distance of place
and not in friendly consent and orders. In speaking therefore of the one I cannot but describe the other; and in commendation of the first I cannot but extol the latter; and, so
much the rather, for that they are both so dear unto me as
that I cannot readily tell unto whether of them I owe the
most good-will. Would to God my knowledge were such as
that neither of them might have cause to be ashamed of their
pupil, or my power so great that I might worthily requite
them both for those manifold kindnesses that I have received
of them! But to leave these things, and proceed with other
more convenient to my purpose.

The manner to live in these universities is not as in some
other of foreign countries we see daily to happen, where
the students are enforced for want of such houses to dwell
in common inns, and taverns, without all order or discipline.
But in these our colleges we live in such exact order, and
under so precise rules of government, as that the famous
learned man Erasmus of Rotterdam, being here among us
fifty years passed, did not let to compare the trades in

living of students in these two places, even with the very
rules and orders of the ancient monks, affirming moreover,
in flat words, our orders to be such as not only came near
unto, but rather far exceeded, all the monastical institutions
that ever were devised.

In most of our colleges there are also great numbers of
students, of which many are found by the revenues of the
houses and other by the purveyances and help of their rich
friends, whereby in some one college you shall have two
hundred scholars, in others an hundred and fifty, in divers
a hundred and forty, and in the rest less numbers, as the
capacity of the said houses is able to receive: so that at this
present, of one sort and other, there are about three thousand students nourished in them both (as by a late survey
it manifestly appeared). They were erected by their founders at the first only for poor men's sons, whose parents were
not able to bring them up unto learning; but now they have
the least benefit of them, by reason the rich do so encroach
upon them. And so far has this inconvenience spread
itself that it is in my time a hard matter for a poor man's
child to come by a fellowship (though he be never so good
a scholar and worthy of that room). Such packing also is
used at elections that not he which best deserveth, but he
that has most friends, though he be the worst scholar, is
always surest to speed, which will turn in the end to the
overthrow of learning. That some gentlemen also whose
friends have been in times past benefactors to certain of
those houses do intrude into the disposition of their estates
without all respect of order or statutes devised by the
founders, only thereby to place whom they think good (and
not without some hope of gain), the case is too too evident:
and their attempt would soon take place if their superiors
did not provide to bridle their endeavours. In some grammar schools likewise which send scholars to these universities, it is lamentable to see what bribery is used; for, ere
the scholar can be preferred, such bribage is made that poor
men's children are commonly shut out, and the richer sort
received (who in time past thought it dishonour to live as it
were upon alms), and yet, being placed, most of them
study little other than histories, tables, dice, and trifles, as

men that make not the living by their study the end of
their purposes, which is a lamentable hearing. Beside this,
being for the most part either gentlemen or rich men's sons,
they often bring the universities into much slander. For,
standing upon their reputation and liberty, they ruffle and
roíst it out, exceeding in apparel, and banting riotous company (which draweth them from their books unto another
trade), and for excuse, when they are charged with breach
of all good order, think it sufficient to say that they be gentlemen, which grieveth many not a little. But to proceed
with the rest.

Every one of these colleges have in like manner their
professors or readers of the tongues and several sciences, as
they call them, which daily trade up the youth there abiding privately in their halls, to the end they may be able afterward (when their turn cometh about, which is after twelve
terms) to shew themselves abroad, by going from thence
into the common schools and public disputations (as it were
"In aream") there to try their skill, and declare how they
have profited since their coming thither.

Moreover, in the public schools of both the universities,
there are found at the prince's charge (and that very
largely) fine professors and readers, that is to say, of divinity, of the civil law, physic, the Hebrew and the Greek
tongues. And for the other lectures, as of philosophy,
logic, rhetoric, and the quadrivials (although the latter, I
mean arithmetic, music, geometry, and astronomy, and with
them all skill in the perspectives, are now smally regarded
in either of them), the universities themselves do allow
competent stipends to such as read the same, whereby they
are sufficiently provided for, touching the maintenance of
their estates, and no less encouraged to be diligent in their
functions.

These professors in like sort have all the rule of disputations and other school exercises which are daily used in
common schools severally assigned to each of them, and
such of their hearers as by their skill shewed in the said
disputations are thought to have attained to any convenient
ripeness of knowledge according to the custom of other
universities (although not in like order) are permitted

solemnly to take their deserved degrees of school in the same science and faculty wherein they have spent their travel. From that time forward also they use such difference in apparel as becometh their callings, tendeth unto gravity, and maketh them known to be called to some countenance.

The first degree is that of the general sophisters, from whence, when they have learned more sufficiently the rules of logic, rhetoric, and obtained thereto competent skill in philosophy, and in the mathematicals, they ascend higher unto the estate of bachelors of art, after four years of their entrance into their sophistry. From thence also, giving their minds to more perfect knowledge in some or all the other liberal sciences and the tongues, they rise at the last (to wit, after other three or four years) to be called masters of art, each of them being at that time reputed for a doctor in his faculty, if he profess but one of the said sciences (besides philosophy), or for his general skill, if he be exercised in them all. After this they are permitted to choose what other of the higher studies them liketh to follow, whether it be divinity, law, or physic, so that, being once masters of art, the next degree, if they follow physic, is the doctorship belonging to that profession; and likewise in the study of the law, if they bend their minds to the knowledge of the same. But, if they mean to go forward with divinity, this is the order used in that profession. First, after they have necessarily proceeded masters of art, they preach one sermon to the people in English, and another to the university in Latin. They answer all comers also in their own persons unto two several questions of divinity in the open schools at one time for the space of two hours, and afterward reply twice against some other man upon a like number and on two several dates in the same place, which being done with commendation, he receiveth the fourth degree, that is, bachelor of divinity, but not before he has been master of arts by the space of seven years, according to their statutes.

The next, and last degree of all, is the doctorship, after other three years. for the which he must once again perform all such exercises and acts as are before remembered;

and then is he reputed able to govern and teach others, and likewise taken for a doctor. I have read that John of Beverley was the first doctor that ever was in Oxford, as Beda was in Cambridge. But I suppose herein that the word "doctor" is not so strictly to be taken in this report as it is now used, since every teacher is in Latin called by that name, as also such in the primitive church as kept schools of catechists, wherein they were trained up in the rudiments and principles of religion, either before they were admitted unto baptism or any office in the Church.

Thus we see that from our entrance into the university unto the last degree received is commonly eighteen or twenty years, in which time, if a student has not obtained sufficient learning thereby to serve his own turn and benefit his commonwealth, let him never look by tarrying longer to come by any more. For after this time, and forty years of age, the most part of students do commonly give over their wonted diligence, and live like drone bees on the fat of colleges, withholding better wits from the possession of their places, and yet doing little good in their own vocation and calling. I could rehearse a number (if I listed) of this sort, as well in one university as the other. But this shall suffice instead of a large report, that long continuance in those places is either a sign of lack of friends, or of learning, or of good and upright life, as Bishop Fox[4] sometime noted, who thought it sacrilege for a man to tarry any longer at Oxford than he had a desire to profit.

A man may (if he will) begin his study with the law, or physic (of which this giveth wealth, the other honour), so soon as he cometh to the university, if his knowledge in the tongues and ripeness of judgment serve therefor: which if he do, then his first degree is bachelor of law, or physic; and for the same he must perform such acts in his own science as the bachelors or doctors of divinity do for their parts, the only sermons except, which belong not to his calling. Finally, this will I say, that the professors of either of those faculties come to such perfection in both universities as the best students beyond the sea do in their own or elsewhere. One thing only I mislike in them, and that

[4] This Fox builded Corpus Christi College, in Oxford.—H.

is their usual going into Italy, from whence very few without special grace do return good men whatsoever they pretend of conference or practice, chiefly the physicians[5] who under pretence of seeking of foreign simples do oftentimes learn the framing of such compositions as were better unknown than practised, as I have heard often alleged, and therefore it is most true that Doctor Turner said: "Italy is not to be seen without a guide, that is, without special grace given from God, because of the licentious and corrupt behaviour of the people."

There is moreover in every house a master or provost, who has under him a president and certain censors or deans, appointed to look to the behaviour and manners of the students there, whom they punish very severely if they make any default, according to the quantity and quality of their trespass. And these are the usual names of governors in Cambridge. Howbeit in Oxford the heads of houses are now and then called presidents in respect of such bishops as are their visitors and founders. In each of these also they have one or more treasurers, whom they call *bursarios* or bursars, beside other officers whose charge is to see unto the welfare and maintenance of these houses. Over each university also there is a several chancellor, whose offices are perpetual, howbeit their substitutes, whom we call vice-chancellors, are changed every year, as are also the proctors, taskers, masters of the streets, and other officers, for the better maintenance of their policy and estate.

And thus much at this time of our two universities, in each of which I have received such degree as they have vouchsafed—rather of their favour than my desert—to yield and bestow upon me, and unto whose students I wish one thing, the execution whereof cannot be prejudicial to any that meaneth well, as I am resolutely persuaded, and the case now standeth in these our days. When any benefice therefor becometh void it were good that the patron did signify the vacation thereof to the bishop, and the bishop the act of the patron to one of the universities, with request that the vice-chancellor with his assistants might provide some such able man to succeed in the place as should by their judg-

[5] So much also may be inferred of lawyers.—H.

ment be meet to take the charge upon him. Certainly if
this order were taken, then should the church be provided
of good pastors, by whom God should be glorified, the universities better stored, the simoniacal practices of a number
of patrons utterly abolished, and the people better trained
to live in obedience toward God and their prince, which
were a happier estate.

To these two also we may in like sort add the third, which
is at London (serving only for such as study the laws of the
realm) where there are sundry famous houses, of which
three are called by the name of Inns of the Court, the rest
of the Chancery, and all built before time for the furtherance
and commodity of such as apply their minds to our common
laws. Out of these also come many scholars of great fame,
whereof the most part have heretofore been brought up in
one of the aforesaid universities, and prove such commonly
as in process of time rise up (only through their profound
skill) to great honour in the commonwealth of England.
They have also degrees of learning among themselves, and
rules of discipline, under which they live most civilly in their
houses, albeit that the younger of them abroad in the streets
are scarcely able to be bridled by any good order at all.
Certainly this error was wont also greatly to reign in Cambridge and Oxford, between the students and the burgesses;
but, as it is well left in these two places, so in foreign countries it cannot yet be suppressed.

Besides these universities, also there are great number
of grammar schools throughout the realm, and those very
liberally endowed, for the better relief of poor scholars, so
that there are not many corporate towns now under the
Queen's dominion that have not one grammar school at the
least, with a sufficient living for a master and usher appointed to the same.

There are in like manner divers collegiate churches, as
Windsor, Winchester, Eton, Westminster (in which I was
some time an unprofitable grammarian under the reverend
father Master Nowell, now dean of Paul's), and in those a
great number of poor scholars, daily maintained by the
liberality of the founders, with meat, books, and apparel,
from whence, after they have been well entered in the

knowledge of the Latin and Greek tongues, and rules of versifying (the trial whereof is made by certain apposers yearly appointed to examine them), they are sent to certain special houses in each university, where they are received and trained up in the points of higher knowledge in their private halls, till they be adjudged meet to shew their faces in the schools as I have said already.

And thus much have I thought good to note of our universities, and likewise of colleges in the same, whose names I will also set down here, with those of their founders, to the end the zeal which they bare unto learning may appear, and their remembrance never perish from among the wise and learned.

OF THE COLLEGES OF CAMBRIDGE WITH THEIR FOUNDERS

Years of the Foundation	Colleges	Founders
1546..	1 Trinity College	King Henry 8.
1441..	2 The King's College	King Henry 6, Edward 4, Henry 7, and Henry 8.
1511..	3 St. John's	Lady Margaret, grandmother to Henry 8.
1505..	4 Christ's College	King Henry 6 and the Lady Margaret aforesaid.
1446..	5 The Queen's College	Lady Margaret, wife to King Henry 6.
1496..	6 Jesus College	John Alcock, bishop of Ely.
1342..	7 Bennet College	The brethren of a Popish guild called *Corporis Christi*.
1343..	8 Pembroke Hall	Maria de Valentia, Countess of Pembroke.
1256..	9 Peter College	Hugh Balsham, bishop of Ely.
1348..10	Gundewill and Caius	
1557..	College	Edmund Gundevill, parson of Terrington, and John Caius, doctor of physic.
1354..11	Trinity Hall	William Bateman, bishop of Norwich.
1326..12	Clare Hall	Richard Badow, chancellor of Cambridge.
1459..13	Catherine Hall	Robert Woodlark, doctor of divinity.
1519..14	Magdalen College	Edward, Duke of Buckingham, and Thomas, lord Audley.
1585..15	Emanuel College	Sir Walter Mildmay, etc.

Years of the Foundation	Colleges	Founders
1539.. 1	Christ's Church.......	King Henry 8.
1459.. 2	Magdalen College.....	William Wainfleet, first fellow of Merton College, then scholar at Winchester, and afterwards bishop there.[6]
1375.. 3	New College..........	William Wickham, bishop of Winchester.
1276.. 4	Merton College.......	Walter Merton, bishop of Rochester.
1437.. 5	All Souls' College.....	Henry Chicheley, archbishop of Canterbury.
1516.. 6	Corpus Christi College.	Richard Fox, bishop of Winchester.
1430.. 7	Lincoln College.......	Richard Fleming, bishop of Lincoln.
1323.. 8	Auriel College........	Adam Broune, almoner to Edward 2.
1340.. 9	The Queen's College..	R. Eglesfeld, chaplain to Philip, queen of England, wife to Edward 3.
1263..10	Balliol College........	John Balliol, king of Scotland.
1557..11	St. John's............	Sir Thomas White, knight.
1556..12	Trinity College.......	Sir Thomas Pope, knight.
1316..13	Excester College......	Walter Stapleten, bishop of Excester.
1513..14	Brasen Nose..........	William Smith, bishop of Lincoln.
1249..15	University College....	William, archdeacon of Duresine.
16	Gloucester College....	John Crifford, who made it a cell for thirteen monks.
17	St. Mary's College....	
18	Jesus College, now in hand	Hugh ap Rice, doctor of the civil law.

There are also in Oxford certain hotels or halls which may right well be called by the names of colleges, if it were not that there is more liberty in them than is to be seen in the other. In my opinion the livers in these are very like to those that are of the inns in the chancery, their names also are these so far as I now remember:

Brodegates.	St. Mary Hall.
Hart Hall.	White Hall.
Magdalen Hall.	New Inn.
Alburne Hall.	Edmond Hall.
Postminster Hall.	

The students also that remain in them are called hostlers or halliers. Hereof it came of late to pass that the right

[6] He founded also a good part of Eton College, and a free school at Wainfleet, where he was born.

Reverend Father in God, Thomas, late archbishop of Canterbury, being brought up in such an house at Cambridge, was of the ignorant sort of Londoners called an "Hostler," supposing that he had served with some inn-holder in the stable, and therefore, in despite, divers hung up bottles of hay at his gate when he began to preach the gospel, whereas indeed he was a gentleman born of an ancient house, and in the end a faithful witness of Jesus Christ, in whose quarrel he refused not to shed his blood, and yield up his life, unto the fury of his adversaries.

Besides these there is mention and record of divers other halls or hostels that have been there in times past, as Beef Hall, Mutton Hall, etc., whose ruins yet appear: so that if antiquity be to be judged by the shew of ancient buildings which is very plentiful in Oxford to be seen, it should be an easy matter to conclude that Oxford is the elder university. Therein are also many dwelling-houses of stone yet standing that have been halls for students, of very antique workmanship, besides the old walls of sundry others, whose plots have been converted into gardens since colleges were erected.

In London also the houses of students at the Common Law are these:

Sergeant's Inn.	Furnival's Inn.
Gray's Inn.	Clifford's Inn.
The Temple.	Clement's Inn.
Lincoln's Inn.	Lion's Inn.
David's Inn.	Barnard's Inn.
Staple Inn.	Newmann.

And thus much in general of our noble universities, whose lands some greedy gripers do gape wide for, and of late have (as I hear) propounded sundry reasons whereby they supposed to have prevailed in their purposes. But who are those that have attempted this suit, other than such as either hate learning, piety, and wisdom, or else have spent all their own, and know not otherwise than by encroaching upon other men how to maintain themselves? When such a motion was made by some unto King Henry the Eighth, he could answer them in this manner: "Ah, sirra! I perceive the Abbey lands have fleshed you, and set your teeth

on edge, to ask also those colleges. And, whereas we had
a regard only to pull down sin by defacing the monasteries,
you have a desire also to overthrow all goodness, by sub-
version of colleges. I tell you, sirs, that I judge no land in
England better bestowed than that which is given to our
universities; for by their maintenance our realm shall be
well governed when we be dead and rotten. As you love
your welfares therefore, follow no more this vein, but
content yourselves with that you have already, or else seek
honest means whereby to increase your livelihoods; for I
love not learning so ill that I will impair the revenues of
any one house by a penny, whereby it may be upholden."
In King Edward's days likewise the same suit was once
again attempted (as I have heard), but in vain; for, saith
the Duke of Somerset, among other speeches tending to that
end—who also made answer thereunto in the king's presence by his assignation: " If learning decay, which of wild
men maketh civil; of blockish and rash persons, wise and
goodly counsellors; of obstinate rebels, obedient subjects;
and of evil men, good and godly Christians; what shall we
look for else but barbarism and tumult? For when the
lands of colleges be gone, it shall be hard to say whose staff
shall stand next the door; for then I doubt not but the
state of bishops, rich farmers, merchants, and the nobility,
shall be assailed, by such as live to spend all, and think
that whatsoever another man hath is more meet for them
and to be at their commandment than for the proper owner
that has sweat and laboured for it." In Queen Mary's
days the weather was too warm for any such course to be
taken in hand; but in the time of our gracious Queen
Elizabeth I hear that it was after a sort in talk the third
time, but without success, as moved also out of season; and
so I hope it shall continue for ever. For what comfort should
it be for any good man to see his country brought into the
estate of the old Goths and Vandals, who made laws against
learning, and would not suffer any skilful man to come
into their council-house: by means whereof those people
became savage tyrants and merciless hell-hounds, till they
restored learning again and thereby fell to civility.